ROBERT & GWEN MAYNE

Dedication

This small book is dedicated to the many thousands of winemakers and vine growers of Australia. Their energy is as truly impressive as the vigour of the other living thing that makes it all possible—*Vitis vinifera*.

Update information should be sent—by all means scribbled on photocopied pages—to PO Box 410, McLaren Vale SA 5171.

Reed Books Pty Ltd
3/470 Sydney Road, Balgowlah NSW Australia 2093
Telephone (02) 907 9966, Facsimile (02) 907 9664

First published 1987
Revised edition 1991

National Library of Australia
Cataloguing-in-Publication data

Mayne, Robert,
Pocket Australian wine companion,

ISBN 0 7301 0153 3.

1. Wine and winemaking—Australia. 2. Wineries—Australia. I. Mayne, Gwen. II. Title.

663'. 2'00994

This edition edited and designed by James Young
Typesetting processed by Everysize TypeArt
Printed in Singapore for
Imago Productions (F.E.) Pte. Ltd.

Contents

Introduction

Visiting the cellar door of a winery is one of life's gentler and more pleasant experiences. It gives the tourist an opportunity to slow down, see where the product comes from, to evaluate it (hopefully in relaxed circumstances), get a bit of local guidance or gossip and, more often than not, meet the winemaker.

In McLaren Vale, SA, where we live, the region has coined the rather irreverent slogan 'Meet your Maker in McLaren Vale'. And we often do! Chances are he (and increasingly, she) is dressed in old clothes with grape and wine stains on the shirt, and is often shod in gumboots. Writing this, in winter, hundreds of people near our area, and thousands in the many other wine areas of Australia, are pruning vines, braving the cold winds and rains of the season.

Winemaking (with, of course, its corollary, grape-growing) is an intensely agricultural pursuit. Many winemakers, particularly the smaller ones, are essentially farmers, albeit farmers with very special skills.

They are generally more outgoing than most other farmers. They usually have to be, because unlike *most* farmers, they have to sell their goods face to face, to their ultimate customers. At the cellar door they face the acid test: has all the work of preceding years produced something that people who walk through the door actually *like?* And like enough to part with their hard-earned dollars?

The wine industry is, on the whole, generous. The public is welcome to walk into just about any winery in Australia and taste the produce, often without charge. How many other industries encourage this?

This small book is about the people and the places who make up the Australian wine industry, and how and where to meet them at their front office, known as the cellar door. We believe it to be the most complete listing of Australian wineries ever put together. We also know from the research we have done that it lists many wineries, some in out-of-the-way places, not listed elsewhere. It is not really a guide to wine quality—others have done that very well and thoroughly. But we do touch on overall quality. In general terms a winery that makes one good wine usually makes other good wines.

This is the second edition of *The Pocket Australian*

Wine Companion and, three years after producing the first, we were amazed how many changes we had to make. There are now almost 600 wineries scattered across Australia, 50 more than three years ago. There is not a State nor a mainland Territory where one cannot visit a winery (admittedly the Northern Territory has only one!) to taste the wines. This is a glovebox guide to these wineries, something that is portable, straightforward and hopefully easy to use.

And the last three or four years have been times of considerable structural change in the Australian wine industry. Wine consumption has declined, particularly at the bulk end (casks), and prices have not increased much due to competition. Going through the wineries, we found a few without change, but not many. Most have undergone changes of some form—ownership, wines, mergers, takeovers, changed credit cards or have different people involved or new owners. Some have closed.

Some of the significant changes have involved small wineries from the Margaret River to the Hunter River. There have been many changes to big wineries—Penfolds acquired Lindemans, the French group Pernod Ricard took over Orlando, which in turn owns the Wyndham Estate, which in turns owns Montrose. Finally, SA Brewing Holdings Ltd bought Penfolds in late 1990, thereby stitching up 36 per cent of Australia's wine market.

Not everyone travels to a wine region, within or without his or her home State, for the express purpose of wine tasting and buying. More often it is a pleasurable aside to other activities. Most of the wineries welcome visitors to taste and try at their 'cellar door' (wine tasting and buying area) before deciding whether or not to buy. In the past year or two several larger wineries have started asking for a nominal payment, usually about a dollar or two.

Giving away wine can be an expensive business. Consider that every drop of the stuff had to pass up the stem of a grapevine somewhere; and that vine took four years before giving its owner a commercial crop. Some wineries estimate that they give away, as promotional stock, around 2 or 3 per cent of their total production. That is a considerable proportion in an industry with thin profits.

The winemaker, while happy to allow, even encourage, visitors to taste the wares, has certain expectations too. True, he'd *like* you to buy his wines; but he understands that you may genuinely not like the wine. His expectations relate mainly to your interest in what he is making; those who work at winery cellar doors can spot the freeloaders a mile off—and they will probably be shooed off as rapidly as possible.

The winemaker doesn't expect you to be a wine buff. In fact, you'll probably receive a warmer welcome if you say openly that you like wine, but you don't know much about it. There is a great deal of pleasure to be had with wine, not the least being its extraordinary variety.

The winemaker will also find it easier to help you at his cellar door if you give him some idea of what you are seeking. Walking into a library looking for 'a good book' gives the librarian pretty broad acres to plough; an indication of your interest in, say, biography will make life a lot easier. So it is with wine. Don't feel too embarrassed to say you're interested in sweet whites, dry whites, gutsy reds ... whatever. Larger wineries usually have a very considerable range of wines on hand, and you can save yourself time by indicating where your palate interests lie.

Rules about tasting at cellar door are—as they say—pretty fluid. And, without wishing to impose any unnecessary wine snobbery, you should be there to both learn and enjoy. But certain time-honoured habits, call them rules if you wish, might help guide you through the cellar door thicket with the minimum of fuss and the maximum enjoyment.

Taste sparking wines first, still white wines afterwards. Aromatic wines (for example rieslings) are better tasted before really dry whites (such as chardonnays), but keep the really sweet wines to either the end of the white wines—or the end of the tasting. With reds, again start with the lighter wines, such as pinot noir, and if you get enthusiastic enough to move on to the fortified wines, keep them to the very end, as they blunt the palate to other tastes.

It is easy to get carried away at the cellar door (if you see what I mean!). Wines always taste better where they are made, which is, I suppose, as obvious as saying candlelit dinners are more romantic than baked beans at home. It can be a trap for inexperienced tasters. Unless you are very sure of your needs and likes, buying more than a dozen bottles of any one wine at a cellar door situation may be a purchase you will later regret.

Think carefully, too, about carrying the stuff home yourself. Car boots can be hazardous places for cases of wine, particularly in summer, and of course carrying a few cases of wine (at around 18 kilograms a case) on top of your holiday needs will send petrol bills up and vehicle performance down. Most reputable wineries have an arrangement with transport companies to freight it home for you, and the costs, including insurance if you wish it (considered in the light of the above), are usually pretty reasonable.

There *is* a great deal of fun to be had by visiting wineries, meeting the maker, and tasting his or her wines. However subtly, the wines are always different from winery to winery; sometimes the products are dramatically different. That's what wine is all about.

It is nice to be able to retell the story of an individual wine, a story you may well hear from the maker at the winery. Every wine has a story to tell. Only the maker can tell it as it is, and this, of course, is the enduring charm of 'going around the wineries'.

The winemaker likes to hear that you appreciate his or her efforts, and he or she will usually respond reasonably to criticism too.

Most Australia's winemakers have tried their hardest to give their best to this business, and they offer us, their customers, a chance to taste before we decide to buy. If that seems a reasonable way to do business to you, the consumer, then respond by giving the winemaker an honest appraisal of what you think about the product, and respect the hospitality you'll almost certainly receive.

Your enjoyment of their products will give most winemakers enough reward to make them feel that giving a little of their product away is a worthwhile way to welcome you to their wineries, which we have tried to list here as completely and fairly as we can.

Finally, I would like to toast my wife, something I do too seldom! Gwen researched this book, as she did the first edition, by telephoning them all and visiting quite a few. She did it with her usual indefatigable tenacity, which is otherwise applied to keeping me in line. Thanks.

Robert Mayne

How to use this book

This book is designed to be the pocket companion to *The Great Australian Wine Book* (also published by Reed Books). That book was a compendium of some of the best wine writing and photography about Australian wine; this is the revised edition of the book that can accompany you when setting out to visit the wineries of Australia.

It is essentially a guide to going to wineries, a portable directory, if you like, to the cellar doors of Australia. Listed State by State and area by area, are the wineries, their locations, phone numbers, days and hours of opening, which credit cards they accept, whether they have tours of the winery, if they have picnic areas and BBQs, children's play areas and so on. We list the winemakers and, where possible, the owners, the main wine styles, comments and any other relevant information provided. Wineries were generally allocated to areas according to their own preferences (always a problem with wine books).

The maps are included as a very general location guide to most of the wineries mentioned. For more exact details we suggest you obtain the local tourist brochures that are always available.

For the large national marketing companies there is sometimes more than one outlet (not to mention State branches), and in some cases they have vineyard operations without attached cellar doors (for example, Lindemans' big vineyards at Padthaway, in south-eastern South Australia). This is indicated where possible.

Winemakers, companies and distributors are changing more rapidly than ever before as the wine business in this country undergoes profound change and, in some cases, much pain. The paradox is that we have never had better wines to enjoy, and they have never been such good value. You can certainly find some of the great wines of Australia at the cellar doors of our wineries; and you can find some bargains too. We hope this book helps you along that winding, but immensely pleasurable, path.

What they make it from

Winegrape varieties in use in Australia

(The more common winegrape varieties are in **bold.**)

Preferred name	Valid synonyms	Invalid synonyms
Aleatico		
Alicante couschet		
Alarelhao		
Barbera		
Bastardo	Trousseau	Cabernet gros (SA), touriga (NSW)
Biancone		White grenache (WA, SA), green doradillo
Bonvedro		False carignan (SA)
Cabernet franc		
Cabernet sauvignon		
Canocazo		False pedro (SA), common palomino (Vic.)
Carignan	Carignane	
Chardonnay	Pinot chardonnay	
Çhasselas	Chasselas doré, golden chasselas	
Chenin blanc		Albillo, stein, sherry
Cinsaut	Blue imperial	Ulliade, oeillade, black prince (Great Western)
Clairette	Blanquette (Hunter Valley)	
Colombard		French colombard
Cornifesto		
Crouchen		Clare riesling
Dolcetto		Malbec (Great Western)
Doradillo		Blanquette (SA)
Dourado		Rutherglen pedro
Durif		Petite sirah and serine (California)
Emerald riesling		

Preferred name	**Valid synonyms**	**Invalid synonyms**
Farana	Planta pedralba	False trebbiano (SA)
Gouais		
Graciano	Morrastel (France)	Xeres (California)
Grenache		
Grey grenache		White grenache (Vic., NSW)
Malbec	Cot	
Malvasia bianca		
Mammolo		
Marsanne		
Mataro	Balzac, esparte, mourvèdre	Morrastel (SA)
Melon	Muscadet	Pinot blanc (California)
Merlot		
Meunier	Pinot meunier	Miller's burgundy
Monbadon		Burger (California)
Mondeuse	Refosco	
Montils		
Müller thurgau		
Muscadelle		Tokay (Australia), Sauvignon vert (California)
Muscat à petits grains blanc	White frontignac	
Muscat à petits grains rosé	Red frontignac	Frontignan (for Europe)
Muscat à petits grains rouge	Brown muscat, brown frontignac	
Muscat gordo blanco	Gordo, muscat of Alexandria	
Nebbiolo		
Ondenc		**Sercial, Irvine's white**
Orange muscat	Muscat fleur d'oranger	
Palomino	Listan	
Pedro ximinez		
Peloursin		Durif (Vic. part), gros manseng (California)
Pinot gris	Rulander	
Pinot noir		Gamay beaujolais (California)
Riesling	Rhine riesling	Johannisburg riesling
Rkaziteli		
Ruby cabernet		
Saint macaire	Moustère	Saint macaire (for Europe)

Preferred name	Valid synonyms	Invalid synonyms
Sangiovese		Canaiolo (NSW)
Sauvignon blanc		Savignin musqué (California)
Semillon		Hunter River Riesling (NSW), madeira (SA)
Shiraz	Syrah	Caracosa, xeres (Vic.), hermitage, petite syrah
Sultana	Sultanina, Thompson seedless	
Sylvaner		
Tempranillo		Valdepenas (California)
Terret noir		Auldana No. 2, claret
Tinta amarella		Malbec (Wilksch), Portugal
Tinta cao		Mourisco preto (Calif.)
Tinta madeira		
Touriga		Alvarelhao (California)
Traminer	Gewürztraminer	
Trebbiano	Ugni blanc	St Emilion, white hermitage, white shiraz
Trousseau gris		Grey riesling (Calif.)
Valdiguié		Gamay (California)
Veltliner green		
Veltliner red		
Verdelho		Madeira (NSW)
Waltham cross	Rosaki	Malaga (SA)
Zinfandel		
Hybrids		
Jacquez		**Troya (MIA)**
Royalty		
Rubired		

What they put in it

Wine is surely one of the most pure foods (or drinks) available to the Australian public today.

However, in quite recent times, new food and drug laws—which vary from State to State but which for the most part have national ramifications, because most wine marketers sell their products in every State—have meant that wine additives are now being displayed on labels.

Ingredient labelling for all foods was first listed in

1981 by the Public Health Advisory Committee and, despite resistance from the wine and brandy industries, compliance to the listing of additives (preservatives, colourings, flavourings and anti-oxidants) was required from 1 January 1987. (Obviously, older vintages do not have to meet these requirements.)

While there are variations from State to State, the law is in general terms national in its scope.

One of the most common of all wine additives, being a preservative, is sulphur. However, if sulphur is evident in a wine because too much has been used, it is a wine fault, but it can largely dissipate when a bottle containing the additive is opened.

In future, labels or back labels, on wine will have to list either the type of additive, or its corresponding code number. For example, sulphur dioxide, or SO_2, would either be listed as that, or more likely by its code, namely 'Preservative (220) added'.

Other key preservatives include chemicals which will be labelled as 221, 222, 223 or 224. These include such things as hydrogen peroxide and sorbic acid.

Colourings are unusual in wines, but one in common use (mainly for fortified wines and brandy) is caramel, which is labelled 150.

In some cases, for example, wine coolers and vermouth, flavourings added to the drink will have to be listed. Chemicals added to stop fresh grapes spoiling or oxidising between vineyard and winery will not have to be listed, as they are not considered to be added as part of the winemaking process.

The full bottle

Weights and measures

A standard bottle of wine in Australia today should, by law, contain 750 millilitres of wine. This is, of course, the approximate equivalent of the old 26 fluid ounce bottle. The uniform legislation that governs this relates to metric measures and stipulates that wine (and spirits) should be packaged in containers that equate to rounded-off volumes, such as 200 millilitres, 375 millilitres (half bottle), 750 millilitres, 1 litre, 1.5 litres, 2 litres and so on.

Flagons which in the pre-metric days held half a

gallon (hence 'flagon'), now hold somewhat less than 2.25 litres (the half-gallon equivalent), namely 2 litres.

Cardboard 'casks' normally hold 4 litres (down from the full gallon, or 4.54 litres). However in recent years these bulk containers have been offered in other sizes: 2 litres, 5 litres, 6 litres and even larger—mainly restaurant-destined—packs of 10, 13 and 20 litres.

While the standard 750 millilitre bottle is the norm, others are appearing, particularly those with 'punted' bottoms. They are the bottles with the thumb-sized indent at the base. In using these more expensive bottles, wine companies are trying to signify that there is something special about the wine in the containers. However, they should still hold 750 millilitres of fluid. In fact, any bottle holding 750 millilitres will normally be over-filled, perhaps to 755 or 760 millilitres, by its makers, to ensure they comply with the law.

Common measures used in the wine industry are:

750 millilitres = 1.32 imperial pints = 1.58 US pints.
1 litre = 35.19 imperial fluid ounces = 33.78 US fluid ounces.
1 dozen 750-millilitre bottles = 1.98 imperial gallons = 9 litres = (approximately) 18 kilograms gross weight.

Casks

Octave = 95 litres = 21 imperial gallons.
Quarter cask = 160 litres = 35 imperial gallons.
Australian hogshead = 295 litres = 65 imperial gallons.
French hogshead = 225 litres = 50 imperial gallons.
Puncheon = 495 litres = 109 imperial gallons.

Alcohol strength in Australia

Brandy and other spirits	Minimum 37 per cent alcohol by volume
Table wine	Minimum 8 per cent; in practice usually between 10 and 13 per cent alcohol by volume.
Fortified wine	Minimum 18 per cent
Boiling point of alcohol	78.5°C (173.3°F)
1 litre of alcohol (lal or spirit designation)	3.6 x 750 millilitre bottles of brandy at 37 per cent alcohol by volume
1 litre of alcohol	0.386 imperial proof gallon 0.5283 US proof gallon
100° US proof	50 per cent alcohol by volume
100° Imperial proof	57 per cent alcohol by volume

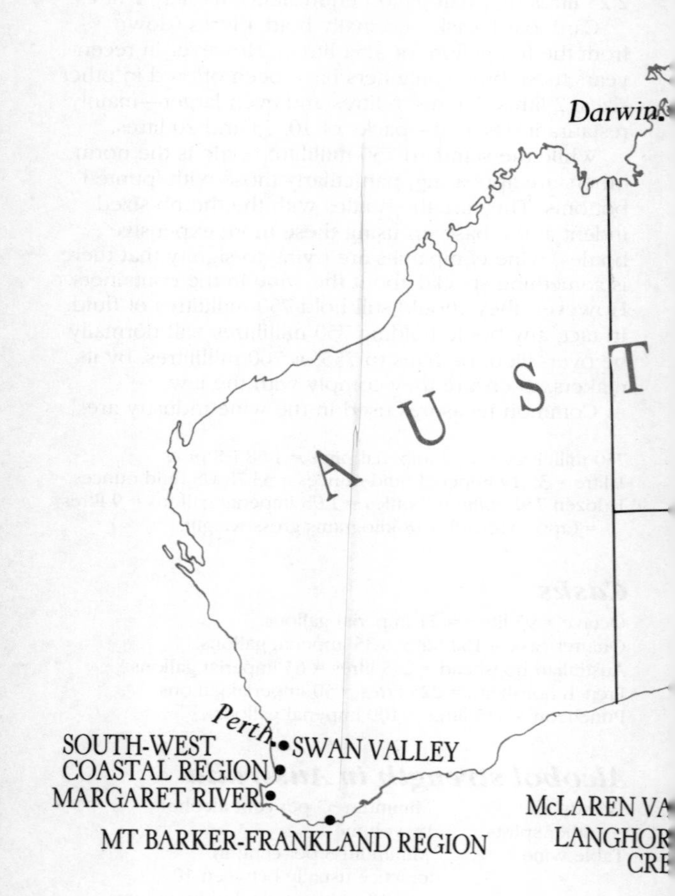
Darwin
Perth
SOUTH-WEST
COASTAL REGION
SWAN VALLEY
MARGARET RIVER
MT BARKER-FRANKLAND REGION

A L I A
ROMA
Brisbane
STANTHORPE
BAROSSA VALLEY
CLARE
RIVERLAND
MUDGEE
UPPER HUNTER
LOWER HUNTER
Sydney
MILDURA
GRIFFITH/LEETON M.I.A.
SWAN HILL
RUTHERGLEN
GLENROWAN/MILAWA
Melbourne
YARRA VALLEY
GEELONG
LAUNCESTON
HOBART

New South Wales

The most populous State of Australia is the largest consumer of wine, but not the largest maker or producer. In fact it produces less than a quarter of our wine, yet consumes roughly 40 per cent. Surprisingly, the next most populous State, Victoria, also consumes a lot, produces less, yet drinks more cask (bag-in-box) wine than New South Wales.

Wine in Australia began in Sydney in 1788, with cuttings that arrived with the First Fleet and later with others, and which were planted at places such as Camden, by the Macarthurs, and in outer suburbs of Sydney such as Vineyard and Minchinbury.

Sydney, capital of the State, now grows grapes only for pleasure, yet has some of Australia's best restaurants and bottle shops—the Berowra Waters Inn, Oasis Seros, the Restaurant, Doyle's several seafood restaurants, Pitts, Barrenjoey, Perry's and the Blue Water Grill, to name but a few. Not to mention a host of excellent Chinese, Vietnamese, Japanese, Korean, French and Italian restaurants scattered throughout this vibrant city of more than 3.5 million people.

All wine drinkers are parochial—the wines from next door are usually considered better than those from across the road or across the world. Residents of New South Wales are particularly parochial, their fidelity usually being directed to the Hunter Valley. The wines of the Upper Hunter, Griffith and perhaps Mudgee are increasingly recognised but are still something of an unknown quantity to many. There is also no doubt that there are other, undiscovered wine areas which have been rather slower in coming forward than their interstate counterparts.

New South Wales winemakers make some excellent wines from certain varieties in specific areas (Hunter semillons, Upper Hunter chardonnays)—but look elsewhere for top rieslings and cabernets.

Hunter Valley

The Hunter Valley, centred to the south of the Hunter River, which enters the Pacific Ocean near the industrial city of Newcastle, is one of Australia's two best known wine areas (the other being the Barossa Valley in South Australia). Paradoxically, however, the Hunter's production of wine has little to do with its high profile in the public eye. There are now some 3200 hectares of vineyards in the Valley, with about 60 per cent in the lower Hunter region, around Pokolbin. Depending on seasonal conditions, the entire Hunter Valley produces only up to some 4 per cent of the nation's wine.

Still, the Valley has much going for it apart from bulk production. It is a beautiful area, is relatively close to Australia's largest population centre (160 kilometres north of Sydney) and has a number of wineries, most of them producing quality table wines in an attractive environment. There are plenty of restaurants, parks, picnic areas and spots, and other forms of entertainment.

It is a historic area, being one of the first areas pioneered to the north of Sydney, and a drive along the Wollombi Road, emerging at Cessnock on the lip of the Lower Hunter Valley, takes you through mountainous, heavily wooded areas, with birds singing—an uplifting experience!

The wines of the Hunter have changed emphasis in recent times, though the two classics, semillon and hermitage (shiraz), are still, in my view, the underpinning strength of the district. More recently of course, cabernet and chardonnay have made a dash for the front, and all four styles can show great virtues after an appropriate amount of bottle ageing. At its worst, the Hunter makes (and often imports) mediocre or superficial wines for the gullible and unwary drinker; at its best it makes great dry white and red wines of world class.

Eating out

Eating out (or in) along the Hunter Valley is complicated by a wide range of options. Many of the wineries listed below have either restaurants of their own on the premises, some of them excellent, or else they have BBQs or picnic areas where you can either take your own or, in some cases, buy meat and cook on the spot, washing it down with the wineries' products. There is also a number of hotels scattered around the area—in the towns of Cessnock, Wollombi and Maitland, for example, and in other smaller

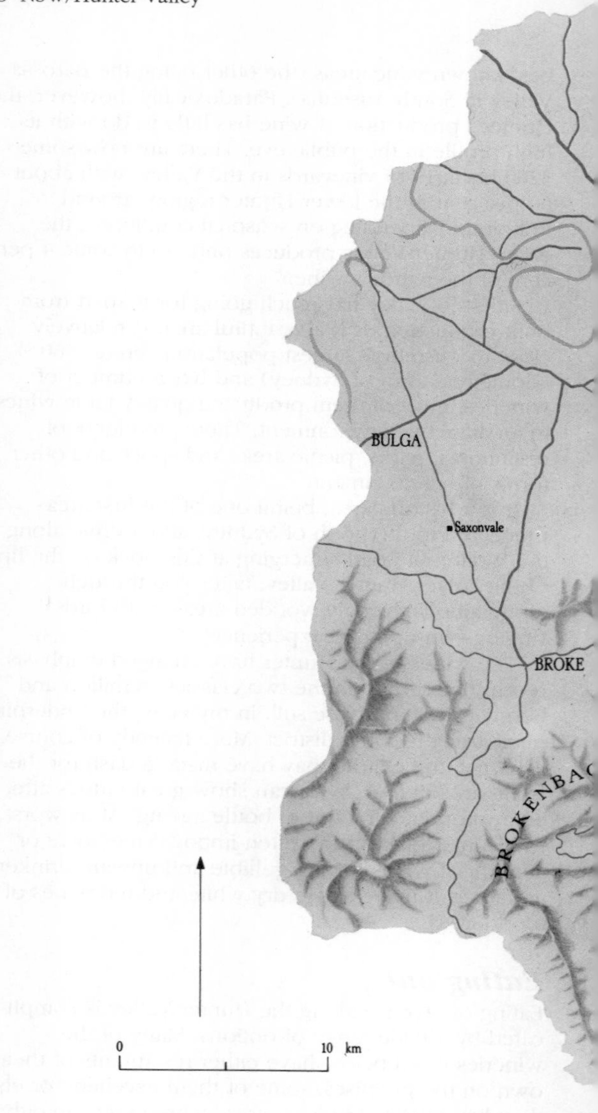

The Hunter Valley

INGLETON
HUNTER RIVER
BRANXTON
Wyndham Estate
Molly Morgan
Belbourie
Hermitage Hunter Estate
Marsh Estate
Sutherlands Wines
Millstone
Richmond Grove
Terrace Vale
Fraser
Casuarina
Allanmere
Littles Wines
Kindred Lochleven
Elliotts
Calais Estate
Wollundry
Murray Robson
Oakvale
Hungerford Hill
The Rothbury Estate
Lake's Folly
Tyrrells
Verona
Allandale
Brokenwood
Tamburlaine
Dawsons
Chateau Francois
McDougalls
Audrey Wilkinson
Tullochs
Lindemans Hunter Valley Winery
W. Drayton
Happy Valley
McWilliam's Mt Pleasant
KURRI KURRI
Mount View
Petersons
Robsons
Briar Ridge
CESSNOCK

centres as well. The Bellbird (049) 90 1094 is good value for meals and accommodation.

In Cessnock itself, the Cottage Restaurant (Wollombi Road) is excellent (049) 90 3062. Casuarina Restaurant and Country Inn, run by Peter Meier (049) 98 7888 is superb. Pokolbin Cellar (049) 98 7584 in Hungerford Hill's Village is also first rate. Somewhat more economic, yet still very good is the Blaxland's Restaurant, opposite the Rothbury Estate (049) 98 7550. Pepper's Motel and Restaurant is particularly highly recommended (049) 98 7596.

There is a complete list of tourist facilities in a very good Cessnock City Tourist Board *Gateway to the Hunter Valley Vineyards* brochure, and the Cessnock Information Centre is at the corner of Mt View and Wollombi Roads, Cessnock (049) 90 4477.

When the weather is fine the Hunter Valley is a great place for a picnic, washed down with a cool bottle of good Hunter semillon, and there are (outside the wineries listed here) plenty of good spots, with and without picnic facilities, to stop at along the roadside.

Allandale *Lovedale Road, Pokolbin, via Maitland NSW 2321. (049) 90 4526.*

Cellar door: Monday–Saturday and holidays 9–5, Sunday 10–5. Picnic area and two BBQs available. Tours by appointment. Amex, Bankcard, Diner's Club, Mastercard, Visa.
Winemaker: Bill Sneddon.

Privately owned; founded 1978. High-quality small maker. Wines two-thirds white, one-third red and include semillon, chardonnay, traminer, pinot noir, shiraz and cabernet sauvignon. Champagne made from pinot noir, chardonnay and sauvignon blanc. Distributed at cellar door and through Specialist Wine Company, Sydney.

Allanmere Winery *Lovedale Road, Allandale SA 2321. (049) 30 7387.*

Cellar door: Monday, Tuesday, Thursday, Friday 11–4 and weekends 9.30–5. All major credit cards.
Winemakers: Dr Newton Potter and Geoff Broadfield.

Owned by Newton and Virginia Potter, who had their first vintage in 1984. The Newton's lease vineyards in the Hunter Valley but make their wine in the winery at Allanmere. Best known for their Trinity White, a blend of chardonnay, semillon and sauvignon blanc, and their Trinity Red, a blend of cabernet, merlot and shiraz. Available through cellar door and mail order (PO Box 327, Maitland NSW 2320).

Audrey Wilkinson Wines (Oakdale Vineyards) *De Beyers Road, Pokolbin NSW 2321. (02) 498 3578.*

Cellar door: Open at weekends only 10–5. BBQ and picnic areas. No credit cards.
Winemakers: Consultants.

Owned by Mr and Mrs A. J. C. Carruthers; founded 1866. Wines include dry and sweet whites, dry reds plus a tawny port and vintage port. Distribution by cellar door and some Sydney and Hunter Valley restaurants, and by a wine club (membership enquiries to phone number above).

Belbourie *Branxton Road, Rothbury NSW 2321. (049) 38 1556.*

Cellar door: Open weekends and public holidays 10–5. All cards except Diner's Club. Tours by arrangement but no picnic area.
Winemaker: John Roberts.

Family owned; founded 1964. Wines include reds and whites, fortified wines, champagne—some unusual products. Distribution through cellar door and mailing list.

Bellevue (Drayton's) *Oakey Creek Road, Pokolbin NSW 2321. (049) 98 7513.*

Cellar door: Monday–Friday 8–5, Saturday and holidays 9–5, Sunday 10–5. Bankcard, Mastercard. Picnic areas and BBQs. Kiosk at weekends with hot food and drinks.
Winemaker: Trevor Drayton.

Long-established family company (founded 1860). Trevor's father Max heads the family business. Drayton's draws material from various family vineyards and some others, for a large range of traditional and general wines. Very large cellar door area in winery with (as the name implies) spectacular valley and mountain views.

Briar Ridge Vineyard *Mount View Road, Mount View NSW 2325. (049) 90 3670.*

Cellar door: Monday–Friday 9–5; Saturday and Sunday 10–5. The Squire Cottage is a delightful holiday cottage, with three bedrooms. Picnic areas. Bankcard, Mastercard, Visa, Amex
Winemaker: Kees van de Scheur.

This is one of the most charming and individualistic wineries in Australia, nestled in the southern end of the Valley, with roses at the end of the vine rows. Originally the Squire Vineyard, then the Robson Vineyard, it has been owned by a small group of wine-oriented people since 1987. Products include traminer, semillon, chardonnay, sauvignon blanc, champagne, hermitage, cabernet sauvignon, cabernet/merlot, pinot noir, muscats. Distribution through cellar door and mailing list.

Brokenwood *McDonalds Road, Pokolbin NSW 2321. (049) 98 7559.*

Cellar door: Monday–Sunday and holidays 9–5. No tours. Amex, Bankcard, Mastercard, Visa.
Winemaker: Iain Riggs.

High-quality small maker owned by a syndicate of shareholders (Brokenwood Wines Pty Ltd) who work at the chalet-like winery at weekends. Wines include dry whites, dry reds, semillon (wood-aged), chardonnay, shiraz, cabernet sauvignon and pinot noir. Distributed in Sydney by Tucker and Co.; in Victoria by Rutherglen Wine Co.; in South Australia by Chase Agencies; and in Tasmania by Fine Wine Distributors.

Calais Estate *Palmers Lane, Pokolbin NSW 2321. (049) 98 7654.*

Cellar door: Monday to Friday 9–5, Saturday and Sunday 10–5. Group tours by appointment only. Gas BBQs available. Bankcard, Master, Visa.
Winemaker: Colin Peterson

Owned by Colin Peterson. Founded 1971. This is a well-established, small Hunter winery which makes wines 'combining traditional techniques with modern technology'. Wines include traditional Hunter dry and sweet whites, and dry reds. Distribution through cellar door and retail outlets in Sydney, Brisbane and Melbourne. Also selected restaurants.

Cassegrain Vineyards Pty Ltd *Fernbank Road, Port Macquarie NSW 2444. (065) 83 7777.*

Cellar door: Open seven days 9–5. All major credit cards.
Winemaker: John Cassegrain.

Owned by Cassegrain family. Established 1985. Produces quality wines, including chardonnay, pinot noir, semillon, merlot, shiraz and chambourcin (a red hybrid, one of the better ones, also planted in the Loire Valley in France, among other places). Most of Cassegrain's fruit comes from the Hastings Valley, with shiraz from McLaren Vale and Pokolbin in the nearby Hunter Valley. Distribution through cellar door, and selected outlets in Sydney, Brisbane and Melbourne. Tastings can also be held at Pokolbin Estate (q.v.).

Casuarina Wines *Hermitage Road, Pokolbin NSW 2325. (049) 98 7562.*

Cellar door: Daily 9–5. Most cards.
Winemaker: Richmond Grove's Ian Scarborough.

A small vineyard owned by restaurateur Peter Meier (wines also available through Casuarina Restaurant in the Valley, [049] 98 7888). Wines include semillon, chardonnay and a cabernet/merlot. Distribution through mailing list, PO Box 218, Cessnock NSW 2325.

Chateau Francois *Broke Road, Pokolbin NSW 2321. (049) 98 7548*

Cellar door: Weekends 10–5 or by appointment. Cheques but no credit cards.
Winemaker: Dr Don Francois.

Founded 1970 by Canadian-born Dr Francois, a former NSW Director of Fisheries. Key products include semillon, chardonnay and shiraz/pinot noir—all well made. Distributed through cellar door only, but it's a cellar door with one of the finest views in the Valley!

Chato Pato *Thompsons Road, Pokolbin NSW 2321. (049) 98 7634.*

Cellar door: By appointment.
Winemaker: David Paterson.

This is claimed to be the Valley's smallest vineyard and wine cellar. Broadcaster David Paterson (Chato Pato—get it?) makes only two wines per vintage—a hermitage and a gewürztraminer, using no additives.

Dawson Estate *Londons Road, Nulkaba NSW 2325. (049) 90 2904.*

Cellar door: Daily 9–5. No winery (wines made elsewhere from Dawson Estate vineyards). All major credit cards.
Winemaker: Consultant Ian Scarborough, from Richmond Grove.

Owned by the Dawson family; founded 1979. Dawson Estate has 8 hectares of vines plus another 14 hectares of chardonnay recently planted. Specialises in a very good chardonnay; also produces a small amount of traminer. Distribution mainly through cellar door and mail order or through Fesq & Co. in Sydney and Victorian Wine Consultants in Victoria.

Evans Family *Palmers Lane, Pokolbin NSW 2321. Enquiries (049) 98 7555.*

This is the label in front of wines (made at Rothbury) grown in vineyards owned by Len Evans and his family, not far from the Rothbury Estate. Chardonnay is grown here, and sweet (botrytised) riesling comes from Coonawarra and is made at Petaluma in the Adelaide Hills. Distribution is through some selected restaurants, or through the Evans family itself, who live near the Rothbury Estate.

Fraser Winery *5 Wilderness Road, Rothbury NSW 2321. (049) 30 7594.*

Cellar door: Daily 10–5. Most major credit cards. Small art gallery.
Winemaker: Peter Fraser.

Owned by Peter and Beverley Fraser. First vintage 1987.

Varieties include chardonnay, sauvignon blanc, semillon, cabernet sauvignon, shiraz and malbec. Sales mainly through cellar door; also through several major Sydney hotels.

Gateway Estate *Corner Broke and Branxton Roads, Pokolbin NSW 2321. (049) 98 7844.*

Cellar door: Friday–Monday 10–4.30. Mastercard and Visa. Wood BBQs
Winemaker: Gary Reed.

Owned by Colin Peterson (who also owns Peterson's and Calais, q.v.). First vintage 1989. Wine is chardonnay only, made at Calais from fruit grown here and at Gateway vineyards. Available through cellar door at present.

Golden Grape Estate *Oakey Creek Road, Pokolbin NSW 2321. (049) 98 7588.*

Cellar door: Daily 10–5. Eight wood BBQs, tables and chairs. Wine museum. Gift shop. Inspections welcomed. Amex, Bankcard, Mastercard, Visa.
Winemaker: Bernd Mussler.

Established late last century and re-established 1920. Now owned by Wine International. Wines include dry and sweet whites and dry and sweet reds, Golden Grape Estate Anniversary Tawny Port and Golden Tango Cream (brandy-based liqueur). Distributed under Golden Grape Estate label through cellar door and mailing list (VIP Club).

Honeytree Vineyard *Gillards Road, Pokolbin NSW 2321. (049) 98 7693.*

Cellar door: Open weekends only 10–4. Mastercard, Bankcard and Visa. Very attractive setting, craft shop and picnic area with tables and chairs provided.
Winemaker: Ian Little.

This winery is owned by a partnership of eight. Vines planted in 1970. Wines include semillon, clairette (white sweet wine with dry finish), shiraz and pinot/shiraz, plus vintage port in half bottles. Distributed through cellar door and mailing list.

Hungerford Hill Wines *Corner Broke and McDonalds Road, Pokolbin NSW 2321. (049) 98 7519.*

Cellar door: Monday–Saturday and holidays 9–5, Sunday 10–5. Guided tours on weekends and public holidays (adults $2, children free) includes tasting. Unguided inspection on other days. The Hungerford Hill winery is adjacent to a large and well-done tourist complex, which includes extensive picnic and play areas; excellent children's playground, food kiosk for takeaway meals and a Farmer's Market selling potted jams, etc. There is also a pottery, and souvenir and gift shops. The Cellar Restaurant is available for à la carte meals (open

daily for lunch and Wednesday–Saturday dinners). Convention/function rooms. Large motel adjacent. All major credit cards.
Winemaker: Adrian Sheridan.

Like many of the larger, and some smaller, Hunter wineries, the Hungry Hill (as the locals call it), right in the centre of the Lower Hunter, has been through some troubled times. It was a bold venture which expanded rapidly, partly because of its placement at the key intersection in the Pokolbin district, partly because many good wines have emerged in various guises and under various labels and ownership, and partly because the Hunter Valley is a difficult place to grow good grapes consistently.

It was founded in 1967, and re-established 1970. Seppelts bought the company in mid-1990 and it will be interesting to see where it goes now. The wines are good, and include some excellent reds from their own Coonawarra (SA) vineyards.

Hunter Estate *Hermitage Road, Pokolbin NSW 2321. (049) 98 7577.*

Cellar door: Monday–Sunday and public holidays 10–5. Picnic area. Privately owned restaurant, Pino's Trattoria (affordable Italian cuisine). Licensed but advertise BYO. Open for lunch and dinner every day except Monday. Nearby Hunter Resort ([049] 98 7777) offers good accommodation. Bankcard, Mastercard, Visa.
Winemaker: Neil McGuigan.

Owned by Wyndham Estate group. Founded 1972. Formerly Hermitage Estate. Good range, including most Hunter types—chardonnay, semillon, gewürztraminer, sauvignon blanc, traminer/riesling, shiraz, pinot noir, cabernet sauvignon, vintage and tawny ports. Distributed by Wyndham Estate.

James Hunter Estate *Wilderness Road, Pokolbin NSW 2321. (049) 30 7582.*

Cellar door: Weekends and holidays 10–5. Most credit cards.
Winemaker: Newton Potter.

Vineyard established late 1960s by Oliver Shaul, well-known Sydney restaurateur, and known as the George Hunter Estate. Now owned by Greg and Robyn Hansen, who grow chardonnay, semillon, chenin blanc and shiraz Available through cellar door only.

Kindred's Lochlevan Estate *Palmers Lane, Pokolbin NSW 2321. (049) 98 7686.*

Cellar door: Some Sundays 10–4.
Winemakers: Various local consultants.

Wines include semillon, traminer and cabernet sauvignon. Small producer distributing only through cellar door with limited availability.

Lake's Folly *Broke Road, Pokolbin NSW 2321. (049) 98 7507.*

Cellar door: Monday–Friday 10–4. Closed weekends. Bankcard, Mastercard, Visa.
Winemaker: Stephen Lake. Consultant: Dr Max Lake.

Family-owned; founded 1963. Dr Lake, a Sydney surgeon, claims to have been the first person to establish a Hunter vineyard this century and this home-cum-winery overlooks Cessnock Airport. Cabernets a speciality.

Lesnik Family *Branxton Road (opposite Broke turn-off), Pokolbin NSW 2321. (049) 98 7755.*

Cellar door: Daily 9–5. Picnic facilities. All major credit cards.
Winemaker: Josef Lesnik.

Family owned. Wines include dry and sweet whites, cabernet sauvignon and shiraz reds, port and liqueur muscat. Distribution as 'Lesnik Family Wines, Wilderness Vineyard' through cellar door only.

Lindemans Hunter River *McDonalds Road, Pokolbin NSW 2321. (049) 98 7501.*

Cellar door: Monday–Friday 8.30–4.30, weekends and holidays 10–4.30 Picnic areas; historic wine museum. Amex, Bankcard, Mastercard.
Winemaker: Patrick Auld.

Company founded 1843. This winery (formerly Ben Ean winery) established 1886. Now owned by the SA Brewing group. The winery, set in front of an attractive lake, is a Hunter institution in the midst of continuing change in the Valley. A wide range of excellent Lindemans wines is available for tasting. This division of Lindemans specialises, of course, in semillon and shiraz wines, plus sweet whites (Hunter River Porphry). Distribution nationally

Little's Family Winery *Palmers Lane, Pokolbin NSW 2321. (049) 98 7626.*

Cellar door: Daily 10–5. Visitors welcome to inspect winery. Bankcard, Mastercard, Visa.
Winemaker: Ian Little.

Family owned; founded 1984. Wines include chardonnay, semillon, traminer, pinot noir, shiraz, cabernet sauvignon and vintage port. Distributed through cellar door and mail order.

McWilliam's Mount Pleasant *Marrowbone Road, Pokolbin NSW 2321. (049) 98 7505. Head office in Sydney (02) 707 1266.*

Cellar door: Monday–Friday 9–4.30, weekends 10–4.30. Daily tours (at 11 and 2). Coach tours by appointment only. Bankcard, Mastercard, Visa.
Winemaker: Phillip Ryan.

Owned by the McWilliam family. Founded 1877, McWilliam's acquired this property in 1932. This is a large company—the second-largest family-owned winemaker in Australia (after Hardy's) and most of its production comes from the Murrumbidgee Irrigation Area. The Hunter winery, however, is the home of the company's big selling Elizabeth, which is made from semillon from the Hunter Valley. A variety of other wines are offered from here—shiraz, semillon and other varieties under the Mount Pleasant label. The Homestead range of reds and whites is available from cellar door only. All other wines are distributed by McWilliam's

Marsh Estate *Deaseys Road, Pokolbin NSW 2321. (049) 98 7587.*

Cellar door: Monday–Friday 10–4, Saturdays and holidays 10–5, Sundays 12–5. Tours by appointment. BBQ facilities. All major credit cards.
Winemaker: Peter Marsh.

Family owned. Vines planted 1971, acquired by Marsh family 1978. Wines include semillon, traminer, chardonnay, hermitage and cabernet sauvignon, plus vintage and tawny ports. Distribution through cellar door only.

Millstone Vineyard *Talga Road, Allandale NSW 2321. (049) 30 7317.*

Cellar door: Weekdays 10–4 except Wednesday. Weekends and public holidays 10–5. Pottery for sale. Picnickers welcome. Children's corner. All major credit cards.
Winemaker: Rae Tait.

Family owned; founded 1972. Wines include cabernet sauvignon, ruby cabernet, shiraz, chardonnay, sauvignon blanc, pinot noir and *méthode champenoise*. Distribution through cellar door, selected restaurants and liquor retail outlets.

Molly Morgan Vineyard *Talga Road, Allandale NSW 2321. (049) 30 7695.*

Cellar door: Weekends and holidays 9–5.
Winemaker: Neil Sutherland.

First vintage 1984. Owned by Geoff Petty and Danlex Pty Ltd. Wines include semillon, hermitage, chardonnay and some riesling, totalling 10 hectares. Available mainly through cellar door and mailing list (PO Box 15, Willoughby NSW 2067).

Mount View Estate *Mount View Road, Mount View NSW 2325. (049) 90 3307.*

Cellar door: Friday and Monday 9–5, Tuesday, Wednesday, Thursday by appointment only.
Winemaker: Harold Tulloch.

Small family-owned winery founded in 1971 and operated by

skilled viticulturist Harry Tulloch. Wines include dry and sweet whites, dry reds and fortifieds, with its main feature, verdelho, in both dry and sweet fortified varieties. Distribution through cellar door and mail order.

Murray Robson Wines *Halls Road, Pokolbin NSW 2321. (049) 98 7539.*

Cellar door: Monday–Sunday and public holidays 9–5. Winery and sales area; restaurant and accommodation. Picnic and BBQ area. Bankcard, Mastercard, Visa, Amex, Diner's Club
Winemaker: Murray Robson.

Wines include semillon, chardonnay, traminer, late harvest semillon, hermitage, cabernet, malbec, pinot noir/merlot, ports and muscats. Robson is a colourful character who has been in various winemaking enterprises in the Valley for a number of years, beginning at what was originally called the Squire Vineyard (now in other hands as Briar Ridge, q.v.).

Oakvale *Broke Road, Pokolbin NSW 2311. (049) 98 7520.*

Cellar door: Monday–Saturday and long weekends 9–5, Sunday 9–1. Picnic facilities. Tours by appointment. Amex, Bankcard, Mastercard, Visa.
Winemaker: Barry Shields.
Family owned; founded 1893. Wines include traditional Hunter whites (semillons and chardonnay) and reds (shiraz and cabernet) and some fortifieds. Distributed through Carol Ann Martin Classic Wines Pty Ltd in Sydney and through cellar door and mailing list.

Peacock Hill *Pokolbin NSW 2321. (049) 30 0233.*

Winemaker: David Lowe.
Small winery run by former Rothbury Estate winemaker David Lowe. Wines available through Peacock Hill Winery (q.v.).

Pepper's Creek Winery *Broke Road, Pokolbin NSW 2321. (049) 98 7532.*

Cellar door: Wednesday–Sunday 10–5. Antique shop on site, offering jewellery, engravings, china and furniture.
Winemaker: Peter Ireland.

Owned by Peter and Pam Ireland; first vintage 1987. Wines mainly available through cellar door and include semillon/chardonnay, semillon, shiraz and merlot.

Petersons *Mount View Road, Mount View NSW 2325. (049) 90 1704.*

Cellar door: Monday–Saturday and holidays 9–5; Sunday 10–5. Tours welcome. BBQ and picnic areas. Visa, Bankcard, Mastercard.
Winemaker: Ian Peterson.

Family owned (see also Gateway and Calais). Wines include chardonnay, semillon, traminer, malbec, shiraz, cabernet, hermitage and pinot noir. Distribution through cellar door only.

Pokolbin Estate *McDonald Road, Pokolbin NSW 2321. (049) 98 7524.*

Cellar door: Monday–Sunday 10–6. Two BBQs, tables, and swings for children. Buses by appointment (no winery here). All major credit cards.
Winemaker: Made at Drayton's Winery.

Pothana Vineyard *Carramar, Belford NSW 2335. (065) 74 7164.*

Cellar door: By appointment only.
Winemaker: David Hook.

Owned by the Hook family; established 1985. Wines include chardonnay and pinot noir. Available through cellar door and can be tasted at Pokolbin Estate.

Richmond Grove's Brandon Manor *Hermitage Road, Pokolbin NSW 2321. (049) 98 7800.*

Cellar door: Open seven days 9.30–4.30. All major credit cards. Fully seated tasting room with damper and cheese platters served. Bus and small groups by appointment. Tours 11 and 2 during the week and at midday at weekends.
Winemaker: Ian Scarborough.

This is part of the Wyndham Estate empire now owned by Pernod and Ricard (Orlando); established in 1987. Wines include French Cask Chardonnay, chablis, white bordeaux, white burgundy, Black Marlin (semillon/chardonnay/sauvignon blanc), fumé blanc, Black Opal (Rhine riesling/traminer), champagne, Winter Vine, Nouvelle (cabernet/merlot), cabernet/merlot and cabernet sauvignon. Premium range includes semillon, chardonnay and cabernet sauvignon. All distributed nationally and through cellar door.

Rothbury Estate *Broke Road, Pokolbin NSW 2321. (049) 98 7555.*

Cellar door: Daily 9.30–4.30. Picnic and BBQ area. Tours by arrangement. Amex, Bankcard, Diner's Club, Mastercard, Visa.
Winemaker: Peter Hall.

Owned by Rothbury Vineyards Pty Ltd; founded 1968. Rothbury is among the most spectacular wineries in the country, sitting in the middle of sprawling vineyards beside lakes. It consistently makes some of the best Hunter white wines, while reds have been constantly improving. Len Evans, who is chairman of the company, lives nearby, and his smiling Welsh countenance can often be seen around the winery and at the spectacular members' lunches and dinners, which are worth attending. Wines include semillon, chardonnays from the Hunter Valley and Cowra, hermitage, cabernet sauvignon, pinot noir and sweet whites, plus a wide range of other wines, ports and muscats. The main range of wines is available to members of the Rothbury Estate Society (membership entails buying a case or two of wine annually and receiving the Society's excellent newsletters); also available from cellar door and in selected restaurants in some cities. Another limited range of Rothbury reds and whites (including the Cowra chardonnay) is available nationally through the Hardy Wine Company in all capital cities. Also available overseas in Sweden, Finland, the US, the UK, New Zealand and Asian countries.

Saxonvale *Fordwich Estate, via Broke NSW 2330. (065) 79 1009.*

Cellar door: Monday–Friday 10–4, Saturday, Sunday and public holidays 10–5. Gas and wood BBQs in grounds; steaks available, group lunches by appointment. Amex, Bankcard, Diner's Club, Mastercard, Visa.
Winemaker: John Baruzzi.

Saxonvale, a winery with a chequered history, founded in 1969, is now owned by the Wyndham Estate group. Wines include a range of traditional Hunter whites and red varietals. Distribution through Fesq & Co. in Sydney and cellar door.

Simon Whitlam *Wollombi Brook Vineyard, Broke Road, Broke NSW 2330. (02) 51 5735.*

Cellar door: Open at weekends by appointment.

Vineyard only. Wines made at Mountarrow Winery (which is involved with the same owners). Semillon (dry and sweet), chardonnay and cabernet sauvignon.

Nicholas Whitlam, son of Gough, and a prominent Sydney businessman and merchant banker, runs this company and is involved in Mountarrow (formerly Arrowfield) in partnership with Andrew Simon. Quality wines in small amounts available at cellar door. Tastings also at Verona Vineyard.

Sobels *McDonalds Road, Pokolbin NSW 2321. (049) 98 7585.*

Cellar door: Daily 10–5. BBQ and picnic areas. Restaurant and viewing tower. Affordable family restaurant open daily for lunches and dinners at the weekends. Caters for tours by appointment. All major credit cards.
Winemaker: Kevin Sobels.

Privately owned by Sobels Wines Pty Ltd. Winery founded 1974. Kevin Sobels used to run his winery in the Upper Hunter near Muswellbrook, and took over these Lower Hunter premises in mid-1986. The winery was formerly Pokolbin Co-operative/McPherson's/Tamalee Vineyard. Wines include range of dry whites and dry reds, plus port. Distribution via winery. Own wholesalers; distribute to Sydney retail outlets.

Sutherland Wines *Deaseys Road, Pokolbin NSW 2321. (049) 98 7650.*

Cellar door: Daily 10–5. Tours. All major credit cards.
Winemaker: Neil Sutherland.

Family owned; founded 1979. Wines include chardonnay, semillon, chenin blanc, shiraz, pinot noir and cabernet sauvignon. Distribution through Oak Barrel, Sydney, and cellar door sales.

Tamburlaine *McDonalds Road, Pokolbin NSW 2321. (049) 98 7570.*

Cellar door: Daily 10–5. Tours by appointment. BBQ and picnic area. All major credit cards.
Winemakers: Mark Davidson and Greg Silkman.

Owned by a private company. Wines include semillon, chardonnay, syrah (shiraz), cabernet sauvignon, blends such as sauvignon blanc, merlot and verdelho. Also vintage port, muscat and botrytised semillons. Available through cellar door and mailing list.

Terrace Vale *Deaseys Road, Pokolbin NSW 2321. (049) 98 7517.*

Cellar door: Daily 10–4. Tours invited. Bankcard, Mastercard, Visa.
Winemaker: Alain le Prince.

Owned by Terrace Vale Wines Pty Ltd; founded 1976. Wines include semillon/chardonnay, traminer, sauvignon blanc (sweet), pinot noir, shiraz, cabernet sauvignon and limited quantities of port. Distribution through cellar door.

Thalgara Estate *De Beyers Road, Pokolbin NSW 2321. (049) 98 7717.*

Cellar door: Daily 10–5. Mastercard, Bankcard, Visa. Self-contained accommodation for up to eighteen guests.
Winemaker: Steve Lamb.

First vintage 1988. Owned by Steve Lamb. Wines include semillon, chardonnay, shiraz, cabernet sauvignon and merlot. Wines mainly available through cellar door and selected restaurants.

J. Y. Tulloch *Glen Elgin, de Beyers Road, Pokolbin NSW 2321. (049) 98 7503.*

Cellar door: Monday–Friday 9–4.30, Saturday, Sunday and public holidays 10–4.30. Picnic and BBQ areas. No tours. Amex, Bankcard, Diner's Club, Mastercard.
Winemaker: Jay Tulloch

Tulloch is one of the long-established Hunter companies (founded 1893), and though it has passed through several hands and now belongs to Penfolds (part of the big SA Brewing group), it still has the family connection, with Jay Tulloch running the winery. High-quality traditional Hunter maker. Wines include Hunter varietal red and white wines (semillon, chardonnay, hermitage, cabernet, etc.), ports and champagnes. National distribution through Penfolds.

Tyrrells Vineyards ('Ashman's') *Broke Road, Pokolbin NSW 2321. (049) 98 7509.*

Cellar door: Monday–Saturday, and holidays 8–5; closed Sunday. BBQ and picnic areas. Tours by arrangement. All major credit cards.
Winemaker: Murray Tyrrell.

Family owned; founded 1858. Tyrrells are perhaps the best known Hunter winemakers, partly as a result of their family history, partly because of the quality of most of their wines and also because of their aggressive marketing and promotional activities.

Murray Tyrrell pioneered chardonnay in the Valley and the wines made by him, by son Bruce and others are, at their best, full of character—like the Tyrrells.

The winery is in a spectacular position on a hilltop looking towards the Hunter River and the mountains in the distance; and the various tasting rooms are homely and welcoming. Tyrrells produce a wide range of dry, sweet, sparkling and fortified wines, including fruit-based wines. Traditional Hunter semillons, chardonnay (such as Vat 47), hermitage and cabernet in various ranges, reliable reds and whites under the Long Flat labels and good sparkling wines. Distribution through cellar door and mail order, widely available in New South Wales restaurants and elsewhere.

Verona Vineyard *McDonalds Road, Pokolbin NSW 2321. (049) 98 7668.*

Cellar door: Monday–Sunday and public holidays 10–5. BBQ facilities available. Smorgasbord lunches for coaches, by appointment. Harry's Picnic Shop caters for light picnic lunches (Sunday brunches by appointment). Café Max (light lunches to full meals), open every day, BYO. Small Winemakers' Centre where you can taste wines from Dawson Estate, Simon Whitlam, Mountarrow and Horderns Wybong Estate. All major credit cards.
Winemaker: Keith Yore.

Owned by the Yore family, founded 1971. This is another winery (like Sobels) with its original roots in the Upper Hunter, but which has presumably spread to the Lower Hunter to find the tourist trade. Wines, especially whites, have traditionally been good. Products include Rhine riesling, semillon, chardonnay, gewürztraminer, sauvignon blanc, cabernet sauvignon and shiraz. Vintage and tawny ports. Distribution through cellar door.

Wyndham Estate *Dalwood, via Branxton NSW 2321. (049) 38 1311, Sydney (02) 373 1355.*

Cellar door: Daily 9–5. Restaurant for lunches. Function rooms available for weddings, small conventions. BBQ and picnic areas near Hunter River.
Winemaker: Brian McGuigan.

Owned by Pernod and Ricard (Orlando). Winery founded 1828. Markets good wines aggressively and persistently. Wines include a very wide range of traditional Hunter dry and sweet whites and dry reds (Bin 777 is always good), plus almost every other type of wine product from champagne to port. Distributed throughout Australia and overseas. A winery some twenty minutes' drive removed from the rest of the Hunter Valley, deliberately aiming their wares to the broadest public taste, but a winery which is successful because Brian McGuigan, Managing Director, knows what people like and want. Worth a visit.

Upper Hunter Valley

The upper Hunter, loosely based around the town of Muswellbrook, offers an entirely different image to its downriver Lower Hunter big brother. It is less touristy, if you like, more rural in appearance, the wineries are spread out and it is, in many ways, a 'new' area still striving to find its strengths. White wines certainly seem to be one strength, and they are dominated by one major producer, Rosemount Estate.

While many visitors go to the Pokolbin area with the express purpose of 'doing' the Lower Hunter Valley, very few do this for the upper part of the Valley, which is a pity, as it is a lovely drive and there are some interesting wineries to visit. It is also a good district to picnic or BBQ—you are unlikely to be crowded out by other picnickers in most areas, and the views to be had are spectacular. Other visitors to the area are those passing through Muswellbrook along the New England Highway; the town and its nearby wineries are worth a pause on the trip north or south.

Significant volumes of grapes and wine flow to the

Lower district, and it's good to report that in the early 1990s the Upper Hunter seems at last to be gaining some of the recognition it deserves.

Eating out

While there is not as much variety in restaurants in this district as there is an hour or so to the east around Pokolbin, there are quite a few recommended eating spots. They include:

The Belltrees Country House, Scone—a historic property with seven luxury bedrooms, country-style cooking, picnics, BYO (065) 46 1155; Country Cottage, 101 Liverpool Street, Scone (065) 45 1140, BYO, open Friday–Saturday for dinner—special lunches and dinners by arrangement; Governor's Retreat, in John Hunter Motel, New England Highway, Muswellbrook (065) 43 2277, open seven nights;

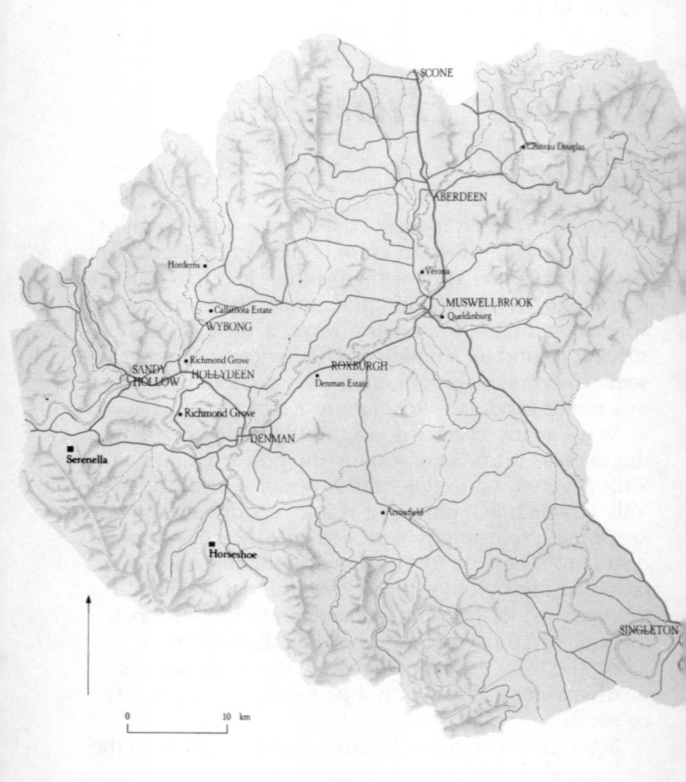

Hillside, New England Highway, Muswellbrook (065) 43 2945, Tuesday–Sunday dinners; Rosemount Vineyard Bistro (see winery entry for Rosemount) (065) 47 2467, Friday–Sunday 12–4, or by arrangement.

Callatoota Estate *Wybong Road, Wybong, NSW 2333. (065) 47 8149.*

Cellar door: Daily 9–5 (winter); 9–6 (summer).Tours welcomed. BBQs and children's playground. All major credit cards.
Winemaker: Andrew Cruickshank.

Owned by John Cruickshank. Founded 1974, the winery was built in 1981, nestled underground beside the Wybong Creek. Wines revolve around cabernet sauvignon, including dry reds and a rosé. Marketed as Cruickshank Callatoota Estate, distribution through cellar door and mail order.

Denman Estate *Denman Road, Muswellbrook NSW 2333. (065) 47 2473.*

Cellar door: No cellar door sales.

This winery was been taken over by Rothbury Estate. All wine is made at Rothbury Estate under the Denman Estate label. Enquiries should be directed to Rothbury Estate on (049) 98 7555.

Hollydene

The Hollydene label (owned by the Wyndham Estate) is dead, though the odd bottle can still be found here and there.

Horseshoe Vineyard *Horseshoe Road, Horseshoe Valley, Denman NSW 2328. (065) 47 3528 or (065) 47 3510.*

Cellar door: Visitors welcome, by appointment.
Winemaker: John Hordern.

The Hordern family, long involved in the Upper Hunter Valley, produced the first commercial wines under this label in 1987. Wines revolve mainly around semillon, chardonnay and shiraz.

Mountarrow Wines *Denman Road, Jerrys Plains NSW 2330. (065) 76 4041.*

Cellar door: Monday–Sunday and holidays 10–4. BBQ and picnic areas. Tours only by appointment. All major credit cards.
Winemaker: Simon Gilbert.

This was originally a large and daring enterprise called Arrowfield. The property was first established in 1824 by George Bowman. The winery is now owned by Mountarrow Wines Pty Ltd, with a component of Japanese ownership.

The Arrowfield Vineyard and Winery, sunk into the side of a hill outside Jerrys Plains, became the renamed Mountarrow Wines. They make premium varietal red and white table wines. Mountarrow processes grapes from various locations in the Lower and Upper Hunter Valley.

Additional parcels are selected from the best fruit available from other areas in Australia, including the Goulburn Valley, Coonawarra, McLaren Vale and the Barossa Valley. Oak fermentation and maturation are used extensively to produce full bodied and flavoursome varietals. *Méthode champenoise* and a selection of late harvest wines are also specialties. National distribution.

Reynolds' Yarraman *Yarraman Road, Wybong, via Muswellbrook NSW 2333. (065) 47 8127.*

Cellar door: Monday–Saturday 10–4; Sunday and public holidays 11–4. BBQs available seven days a week. Lunch available at the weekend—bookings advised. Set up in the old wine cellar among the oak barrels. Group tours by appointment only ($3 head). Bankcard, Visa, Mastercard, Amex.
Winemaker: Jon Reynolds.

Winery (as Horderns Wybong Estate) founded 1969. Jon and Jane Reynolds took over in October 1989 and are now running this spectacular winery (constructed from an old stone jail, built c. 1837). Jon spent three years winemaking at Chateau Reynella, moved to Houghton in Western Australia, where he made some outstanding wines.

More recently he made wine for the Wyndham Estate. Present products include cabernet sauvignon, cabernet/merlot, chardonnay and semillon, under the Reynolds label. Distribution through cellar door, Top 500 Club mailing list and through Fesq & Co in Sydney.

Richmond Grove *Due south of Sandy Hollow, off Rylstone Road, via Muswellbrook NSW 2333.*

Winemaker: Ian Scarborough

Founded in the early 1970s, Richmond Grove is another tentacle of the Wyndham Estate empire now owned by Pernod and Ricard (Orlando). All wines made from this vineyard are available for tasting at Richmond Grove's Brandon Manor (see Hunter Valley entry).

Rosemount Estate *Rosemount Road, Denman NSW 2328. (065) 47 2467.*

Cellar door: Monday–Saturday and holidays 10–4; Sunday 12–4. Bistro Friday and Sunday lunch. Beautiful landscaped rose gardens and large picnic areas, children's playground. BBQ packs available daily. Amex, Bankcard, Diner's Club,

Mastercard. Tours only by appointment.
Winemaker: Phillip Shaw.

Owned by Bob Oatley and family, now with a lot of input from son Sandy Oatley. Founded 1968, first vintage 1974. Rosemount also has vineyards and wineries elsewhere (although the only cellar door is at this winery, a lovely spot overlooking the upper reaches of the Hunter River).

A very high-quality winery for whites, especially the company's famous chardonnays, to which former New South Wales Premier Neville Wran was so publicly addicted. Managing Director Chris Hancock is a talented winemaker himself (he was with Penfolds at one stage of his career) and Phillip Shaw is a former Lindemans winemaker. A company committed to quality, and to exports. Wines include broad range of white and red varietals, notably chardonnay, riesling, cabernet, pinot noir, tawny port and champagne. National distribution through Rosemount; head office, Sydney (02) 439 3222.

Serenella Estate *Mudgee Road, via Denman, Baerami Creek NSW 2333. (065) 47 5168.*

Cellar door: Monday to Saturday 10–4, Sunday and public holidays 11–3. Bankcard.
Winemaker: Tish Cecchini.

Located 20 kilometres south-west of Denman on the scenic Mudgee Road near Widden Valley, Serenella is a family-owned business. Hereford cattle and Thoroughbred horses form part of the 1000-plus hectare property. Some 25 hectares of vineyards were planted in 1975. The Serenella label was created in 1987 by the Cecchini family. Wines include white burgundy, chardonnay, chablis, semillon, shiraz, hermitage and cabernet sauvignon. Available at cellar door and in New South Wales, Queensland and Western Australia.

Verona Vineyard *New England Highway, Muswellbrook NSW 2333. (065) 43 1055.*

Cellar door: Monday–Friday and holidays 10–4; weekends 12–4. BBQs available, children's playgrounds. All major credit cards. There is a large pecan nut plantation and nuts and pecan pie are available. This vineyard is also the local tourist information centre.
Winemaker: Consultants.

Owned by the Yore family; founded 1971; first vintage 1974. The Yore family had a family business selling farm machinery, and started making wines in their 'round-house' winery on the northern outskirts of Muswellbrook as a diversion. In more recent years they have started another outlet, under the same name, in the Lower Hunter. Wines include chardonnay, traminer, semillon, cabernet sauvignon and shiraz. Distributed through cellar door.

Mudgee

Mudgee's undoubted attraction for wine-drinking tourists revolves around the scenery, the nature of the band of small winemakers who toil in this nest in the hills, its historic buildings and other activities, such as honey production.

Wine was made in Mudgee over 100 years ago, but like many other wine areas, its appeal has only been rediscovered in recent years. Today there are some eighteen wineries and meaderies in the general Mudgee area. The district population is around 12 500. Mudgee is 261 kilometres north-west of Sydney, and around 470–500 metres above sea level.

One of the notable features about the Mudgee district is the participation of its wineries in an area 'authentication' scheme. This locally operated scheme guarantees purchasers of Certified Mudgee Wines that these products are of a certain quality and that they are completely locally grown. There is an active tourist information centre at 64 Market Street, Mudgee (063) 72 5875.

Eating out

Several of the wineries (such as Craigmoor and Augustine) provide food but there are a few other quite good eating spots in both Mudgee and nearby Gulgong. A spot I have enjoyed is the Wineglass Bar and Grill (7 Perry Street, Mudgee [063] 72 3417) with local wines, BBQs, salads and bread, for lunch and dinner; simple but enjoyable.

A major motel in town, the Wanderlight (107 Market Street, Mudgee [063] 72 1088), has a licensed restaurant (the Eagle's Nest). The Mudgee Motel (Sydney Road, Mudgee [063] 72 1122) celebrates the life of former townsman, Henry Lawson, with a restaurant, named after the poet, which features local wines.

The Winning Post is another good, large motel (101 Church Street, Mudgee [063] 72 3333) which also has a licensed restaurant. There are also Chinese and Indian restaurants in Church Street, both BYO. The Inverness (18 Sydney Road, Mudgee [063] 72 1701) is a former Cobb & Co. inn, built in the 1800s, with open fires for winter and outdoor dining for summer.

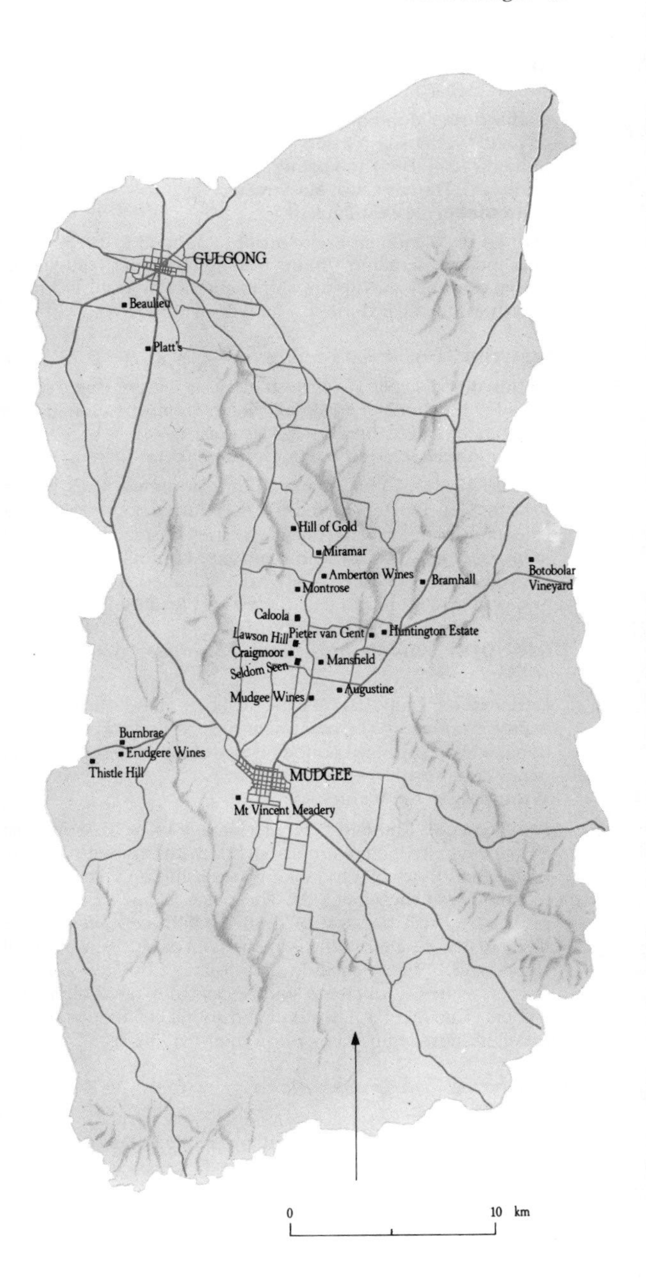
GULGONG
Beaulieu
Platt's
Hill of Gold
Miramar
Amberton Wines
Bramhall
Botobolar Vineyard
Montrose
Caloola
Lawson Hill
Pieter van Gent
Huntington Estate
Craigmoor
Mansfield
Seldom Seen
Augustine
Mudgee Wines
Burnbrae
Erudgere Wines
Thistle Hill
MUDGEE
Mt Vincent Meadery
0
10 km

Amberton *Henry Lawson Drive, Mudgee NSW 2850. (063) 73 3910.*

Cellar door: Monday, Thursday and Friday 8.30–4.30, Tuesday and Wednesday closed. Saturday and Sunday and public holidays 10–4. BBQ and picnic area. Tours welcomed. Amex, Bankcard, Diner's Club, Mastercard, Visa.
Winemaker: Robert Paul.

Owned by Wyndham Estate group. Founded in 1975, products include semillon, Rhine riesling, traminer, sauvignon blanc, cabernet sauvignon, shiraz and tawny port. Distribution through cellar door

Augustine *Airport Road, Mudgee NSW 2850. (063) 72 3880.*

Cellar door: Daily 10–4. Restaurant at winery open seven days for lunch 12–2; Saturday dinner by reservation. Tours welcomed. Amex, Bankcard, Mastercard, Visa.
Winemaker: Selected contract winemakers.

Owned by local business syndicate; founded 1915 by Dr Fiaschi, Surgeon General for Australia during both world wars (the statue of the wild pig outside Sydney hospital was erected in his memory). Specialise in chardonnay, traminer, pinot and dry reds. Also a unique variety called aleatico, a desert wine, and port. Sold through cellar door and mailing list.

Botobolar *Botobolar Lane, Mudgee NSW 2850. (063) 73 3840.*

Cellar door: Daily 10–5. Picnic facilities. Half-hour vineyard walk for groups, by appointment only, followed by instructional wine tasting and potted history of the Mudgee area. All major credit cards.
Winemaker: Gil Wahlquist.

Family owned; founded 1971; first vintage 1974. Gil Wahlquist is a former Sydney journalist who, with his wife Vincie, established Botobolar to make wines using organic growing techniques in the vineyards. The place is one of the more pleasant to visit because of the friendly reception you are likely to get (it's almost 20 kilometres out of Mudgee, but well signposted). Wines include chardonnay, Budgee Budgee (sweet white), crouchen, shiraz, cabernet, and blend (St Gilbert); Cooyal port. Distribution through cellar door and an excellent newsletter if you're on their mailing list.

Burnbrae *Hargraves Road, Mudgee NSW 2850. (063) 73 3504.*

Cellar door: Seven days, including public holidays , 9.30–5. Tours by appointment. All major credit cards except Amex.
Winemaker: Robert Mace.

Family owned; founded 1971; first vintage 1976. Wines include chablis-style semillon, chardonnay, semillon/chardonnay, grenache rosé, moselle, dry (Rhine riesling), shiraz, shiraz/cabernet sauvignon/malbec, liqueur muscat and vintage port. Distribution through cellar door and mail order and a few small outlets in Sydney.

Caloola Vineyard *Henry Lawson Drive, Mudgee NSW 2850. (063) 73 3954, after hours (063) 72 2115.*

Cellar door: Saturday 10–5, Sunday 11–3, holiday Mondays 10–5. Bankcard, Mastercard.
Winemaker: Hilton and Phillip Cross.

Founded 1977. Mainly fortified wines, rummy port, tawny port, liqueur muscat, gordo muscat, dry red, chablis, semillon moselle and sauvignon blanc. Available through cellar door and mail order (29 Burrundulla Avenue, Mudgee NSW 2850).

Craigmoor *Craigmoor Road, Mudgee NSW 2850. (063) 72 2208.*

Cellar door: Monday–Friday 9–5, Saturday 10–5, Sunday and public holidays 11–4. BBQ area. Group tours by appointment only. Licensed à la carte restaurant on site (bookings [063] 72 4320). Open seven days for lunch 12–2.30 and dinner on Friday and Saturday nights, from 6. All major credit cards.
Winemaker: Robert Paul

Historic winery; first vintage 1858; taken over in recent times by the Wyndham Estate group (in turn owned by Orlando). Wines include red and white table wines and fortifieds; well known for rummy port. Distribution nationally through Australian Vintners.

Huntington Estate *Cassilis Road, Mudgee NSW 2850. (063) 73 3825.*

Cellar door: Monday–Friday 9–5, Saturday and holidays 10–5, Sunday 11–3. No BBQ or picnic area. All major credit cards.
Winemaker: Bob Roberts.

Family owned. Founded 1969, first vintage 1972. High-quality local wines, with whites full of flavour and reds of distinction, usually on the fuller bodied side of the spectrum. Products include semillon, chardonnay, sauvignon blanc, shiraz, cabernet sauvignon, merlot (and blends) and rosé. Distribution through cellar door and mailing list.

Lawson Hill Estate *Henry Lawson Drive, Mudgee NSW 2850. (063) 73 3953*

Cellar door: Thursday–Monday 9.30–5. BBQ facilities. Mastercard, Bankcard, Visa.
Winemaker: José Grace

This little winery, situated next to Henry Lawson Drive, with impressive views over the Mudgee Valley, is owned by June and José Grace. They planted vines five years ago and opened the cellar door on 1 August 1990. Wines include semillon chardonnay, traminer/riesling, pinot noir and cabernet shiraz. Jose is also an accomplished pianist known well in Sydney and Mudgee. He was a member of the DJs who backed Johnny O'Keefe in the late 1950s and will play on request—both classical and modern. Wines available through cellar door.

Mansfield *Eurunderee Lane, Mudgee NSW 2850. (063) 73 3871.*

Cellar door: Monday–Saturday 9–6, Sunday 11–6. BBQ and picnic facilities. Inspections. Amex, Bankcard, Diner's Club, Mastercard.
Winemaker: Peter Mansfield.

Family owned; founded 1976. Full range of table and fortified wines. Distributed through cellar door.

Miramar Vineyards *Henry Lawson Drive, Eurunderee NSW 2850. (063) 73 3874.*

Cellar door: Daily 9–5. BBQs and picnics. Inspections. Bankcard, Mastercard, Visa.
Winemaker: Ian MacRae.

Founded 1974; first vintage 1977. Small winery, set in a lovely rural environment 15 kilometres out of Mudgee. Ian MacRae (the owner) is an excellent winemaker: he developed his skills working for some of Australia's biggest, and best, wine producers. Consequently his wines are usually very good. Products include chardonnay, semillon/chardonnay, semillon, sauvignon blanc, traminer/Rhine riesling, Rhine riesling, sauternes, rosé, shiraz, cabernet sauvignon and vintage port. Distribution mainly through cellar door and mailing list.

Montrose *Henry Lawson Drive, Mudgee NSW 2850. (063) 73 3853.*

Cellar door: Monday–Friday 8–4, weekends and holidays 11–4. Picnic areas. Tours by appointment. Amex, Bankcard, Mastercard, Visa.
Winemaker: Robert Paul

Founded 1974, Montrose is the largest winery in the region, a modern and high-tech winery founded by the Italian Transfield Corporation and then taken over in turn by Wyndham Estate, itself gobbled up by Orlando Wines The winery makes a range of good products, including a wide range of table and sparkling wines, semillon, chardonnay, Rhine riesling, traminer, shiraz and cabernet sauvignon. Distribution through Wyndham Estate, Sydney.

Mount Vincent Meadery *Common Road, Mudgee NSW 2850. (063) 72 3184.*

Cellar door: Monday–Friday 10–5, Sunday 10–4, public

holidays 9–4. BBQ facilities. Bankcard, Diner's Club, Mastercard, Visa, Amex.
Wine/meadmaker: Jane Nevell.

Founded 1976. Products include Rhine riesling, moselle, claret, liqueur muscat, dry and sweet mead (honey wine) and liqueur mead. Distribution through cellar door and some outlets in Sydney and country areas.

Mountilford *Mount Vincent Road, Ilford, via Mudgee NSW 2850. (063) 58 8544.*

Cellar door: Daily 10–4. No picnics. Tours welcomed. Bankcard and Mastercard.
Winemaker: Don Cumming.

This small winery, 50 kilometres south of Mudgee, was founded in 1982. Wines include Rhine riesling, riesling/sylvaner, riesling/traminer, chardonnay; shiraz, pinot noir and tawny port. Distribution through cellar door and mail order.

Mudgee Wines *Henry Lawson Drive, Mudgee NSW 2850. (063) 72 2258.*

Cellar door: Monday–Saturday and holidays 10–5; Sunday 12–4. Tours welcomed. Amex, Bankcard, Diner's Club.
Winemaker: Jennifer Meek.

Owned by Jennifer Meek and partners; founded 1963. A tiny winery, 5 kilometres out of town, run by a charming winemaker. Wines include a small range of varietal table wines. No pesticides have been used since 1977. Distribution through cellar door.

Pieter van Gent *Black Springs Road, Mudgee NSW 2850. (063) 73 3807.*

Cellar door: Monday–Saturday and holidays 9–5; Sunday 12–4. Picnics possible 'under the trees'. Group tours by appointment only. Bankcard, Visa.
Winemaker: Pieter van Gent.

Family owned; founded 1979. Pieter van Gent is a well-known Mudgee winemaker, having worked for Craigmoor Wines before launching his own winery. All wines are made and bottled on the premises and include chardonnay, frontignan, 'Angelic' sweet white, shiraz, white port, muscat and vermouth. Distribution mainly through cellar door.

Platt's *Mudgee Road, Gulgong NSW 2852. (063) 74 1700.*

Cellar door: Daily 9–5. Tours by appointment only. Bankcard, Mastercard and Visa.
Winemaker: Barry Platt.

Founded 1978. Small winery 20 kilometres north of Mudgee, making quality wines, including chardonnay, semillon, gewürztraminer and cabernet sauvignon. Distribution through cellar door and selected outlets in Sydney.

Seldom Seen *Craigmoor Road, Mudgee NSW 2850. (063) 72 4482.*

Cellar door: Daily 9–5.
Winemaker: Barry Platt (under contract).

Founded 1987 (vineyards 1975); owned by Harry Wood and Barry Platt. Semillon, chardonnay, chardonnay/semillon, some traminer and cabernet/shiraz. Distribution through cellar door and Haviland Wine Co. in Sydney.

Stein's Winery *Pipeclay Lane, Mudgee NSW 2850. (063) 73 3991.*

Cellar door: 10–4 daily. Visa, Bankcard and Mastercard. Tours by appointment. BBQ facilities.
Winemaker: Robert Stein.

Founded 1976. Wines include chardonnay, semillon/riesling, shiraz, cabernet sauvignon, Quarry Port (vintage style), rum cask port, old tawny port and liqueur muscat. Available through cellar door.

Thistle Hill Vineyard *McDonalds Road, Mudgee NSW 2850. (063) 73 3546.*

Cellar door: Seven days 9–5. Tours and coaches by appointment only. Bankcard, Mastercard, Visa.
Winemaker: David Robertson.

Founded 1976, a small winery, 10 kilometres from Mudgee, owned by David and Lesley Robertson. Wines include Rhine riesling, chardonnay, pinot noir, cabernet sauvignon and port. Distribution through cellar door and mailing list.

Murrumbidgee Irrigation Area (Griffith)

Griffith is usually not an area people think of as a tourist destination in the wine sense. Its sprawling, lush vineyards are over 600 kilometres west from Sydney and 450 kilometres north of Melbourne. In terms of accommodation, food and scenery, it offers little that cannot be found elsewhere in inland Australia. Just about the only unique tourist attraction

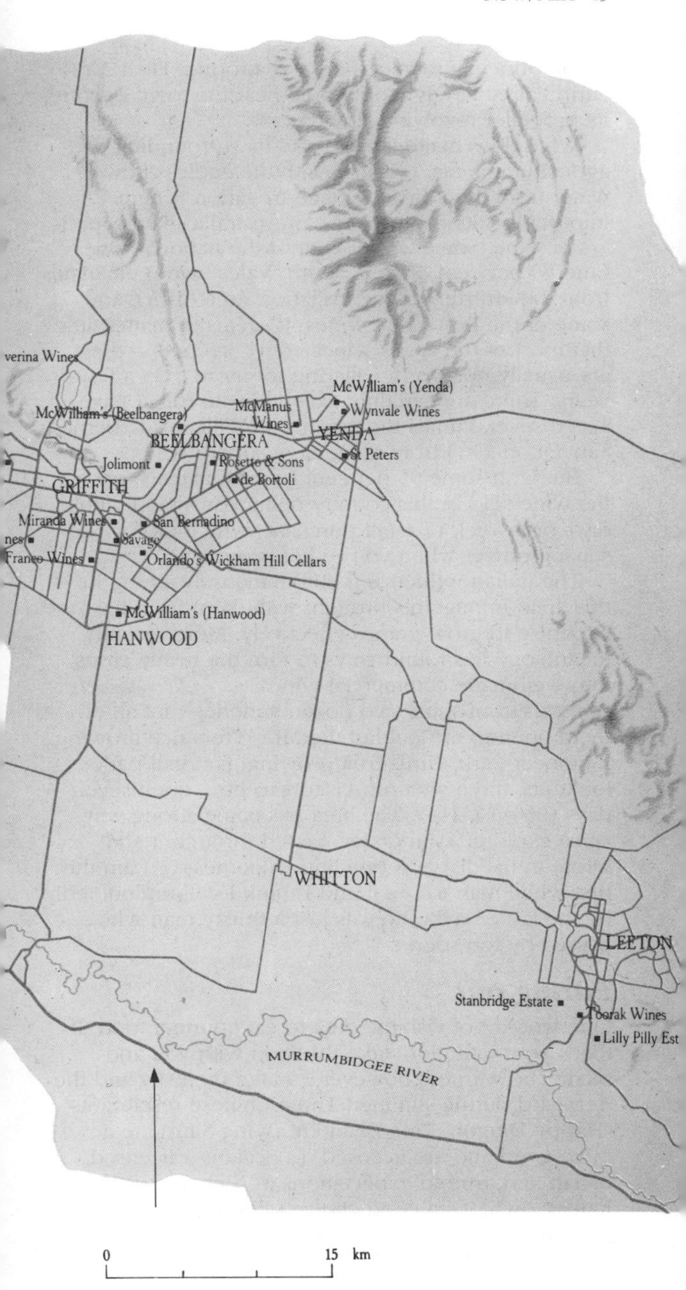
verina Wines
McWilliam's (Yenda)
McManus Wines
Wynvale Wines
McWilliam's (Beelbangera)
YENDA
BEELBANGERA
St Peters
Jolimont
Rosetto & Sons
de Bortoli
GRIFFITH
Miranda Wines
San Bernadino
Savage
Franco Wines
Orlando's Wickham Hill Cellars
McWilliam's (Hanwood)
HANWOOD
WHITTON
LEETON
Stanbridge Estate
Toorak Wines
Lilly Pilly Est
MURRUMBIDGEE RIVER
0
15 km

in the principal town, Griffith, is a former Fleet Air Farm Fairey Firefly atop a pole near the town's centre, its propeller revolving slowly.

What does make Griffith and its surrounding agricultural areas, irrigated with the endless flow of water from the Murrumbidgee Irrigation Scheme, important is its place as one of Australia's key suppliers of wine. Some 20 per cent of the nation's wine (and 80 per cent of New South Wales' wine) emanates from the Murrumbidgee Irrigation Area (MIA), and some of the best value wines. It seems to matter little that most of the area's wines aren't 'keepers'—they are usually not worth cellaring for more than a few years. There are certainly exceptions to this: I have tasted several times the famous McWilliam's Cabernet Sauvignon 1963 from the area; a superb wine.

But with some 95 per cent (guesstimates vary) of the wine sold in this country being consumed within days or a week of retail purchase, why look for staying power when you've got economy?

The Italian influence is still immensely strong in this area. Immigrants brought with them from Italy the expertise to grow grapes effectively. More recently technology has found ways to turn the heavy crops into well-made commercial wines.

Apart from some two dozen wineries (not all of them open to the public) the MIA offers rice growing, a Pioneer Park, citrus fruit growing, national parks, lookouts and a well-run visitors' centre, open seven days (060) 62 4145. The area has come a long way since explorer John Oxley passed through it and wrote in his diary: 'A howling wilderness ... I am the first white man to see it and I think I will undoubtedly be the last'. Maybe he was just a thirsty man who passed by too soon.

Eating out

One would not visit the area to eat gourmet food. If that's your intention, take the food with you and picnic; be warned, however, to take the Esky and the Aerogard during summer! Three Chinese restaurants (Happy Dragon, Cafe Beautiful, Wing Sing) are all quite good and are licensed. La Scala is a licensed Italian and, true to expectations in such a strongly Italian town, it's a good choice (455 Banna Avenue, Griffith [069] 62 4322); the Belvedere Bistro is somewhat simpler but also Italian (494 Banna Avenue,

Griffith [069] 62 1431). One of the best-known eateries in town is the Winewheel Restaurant in the Gemini Hotel (Banna Avenue, Griffith [069] 62 3833) where smorgasbords and local wines are featured. And there are restaurants in a number of other Griffith motels of the usual motel quality (the town has eight motels, three hotels and two caravan parks).

Baratto's *Farm 678, Hanwood, via Griffith NSW 2680. (069) 62 3946.*

Not open to public—maker of bulk wine for others.

Casella's *Farm 1471, Yenda NSW 2681. (069) 68 1346.*

Cellar door: Monday–Saturday 9–5, Sunday 9–12. Cheques and cash.
Winemaker: John Casella.

Family owned; founded 1965. Wines include dry and white wines, spumante, port and sherry. Distribution through cellar door and sells wine in containers to the public (up to 45 litre containers). Spumante is the only labelled product.

Cinzano *Walla Avenue, Griffith NSW 2680. (069) 62 4133.*

Cellar door: Monday–Friday 8.30–4, closed weekends and holidays. BBQ and picnic areas. No tours. Bankcard.
Winemaker: Andrew Schulz.

Owned by the Cinzano Family (Italy) 50 per cent, International Distillers and Vintners 25 per cent, Fiat 25 per cent. Founded (in Australia) 1931. Originally owned by Francesco Cinzano Cia (Australia) Pty Ltd. Wines include Rosso, Bianco and Dry, flavoured wines, coffee liqueur, sparkling wines, red and white table wines, bitters and port. Distributed nationally by Swift & Moore, Sydney.

de Bortoli's *de Bortolis Road, Bilbul, via Griffith NSW 2680. (069) 63 5344.*

Cellar door: Monday–Saturday 8–5.30, closed Sunday. Picnic area. Bus tours by appointment. Bankcard, Mastercard Visa.
Winemaker: Darren de Bortoli.

Family owned; founded 1928. One of the highest quality makers in the area, with an exceptionally large range of wines, plus Jean Pierre Australian champagne. The company's best known entrant in the quality stakes is an outstanding sauternes, a sweet white of French standard, made from semillon, for which a price of between $30 and $40 a bottle is asked. De Bortoli's also has one of the largest and most impressive cellar door operations in the area. Wines include a broad range of dry red and dry white table wines, sweet whites, fortified wines and champagne. National distribution, much of it direct, plus cellar door sales. Exports.

Franco's *Irrigation Way, Hanwood, via Griffith NSW 2680. (069) 62 1675.*

Cellar door: Monday–Saturday 8–6, closed Sunday. Tours invited. No credit cards.
Winemaker: Salvadore Francis.

Family owned; founded 1959. Wines include red and white dry and sweet table wines, and fortified wines. Distribution through cellar door.

Lillypilly Estate *Farm 16, Lillypilly Road, Leeton NSW 2705. (069) 53 4069.*

Cellar door: Monday–Saturday and holidays 9–5.30. Sundays only by appointment. Tours welcomed, buses by appointment. Amex, Bankcard.
Winemaker: Robert Fiumara.

Family owned; vineyard founded 1972, winery 1982. Wines include Rhine riesling, fumé blanc, chardonnay, tramillon (traminer/semillon blend), traminer, spätlese lexia, two botrytised sweet whites, cabernet sauvignon, hermitage, vintage port and Red Velvet (light red). Distribution through cellar door and mail order.

McManus *Farm 1347, Rodgers Road, Yenda NSW 2681. (069) 68 1064.*

Cellar door: Monday–Saturday and holidays 10–5.30, Sunday 1–5.30. No formal picnic area, but picnickers welcome. No credit cards; cheques accepted.
Winemaker: Dr David McManus.

Family owned; founded 1973. Wines include white burgundy, chardonnay, 'burgundy/port', cabernet sauvignon (17 per cent alcohol) and hermitage. Distribution through cellar door and mailing list.

McWilliam's Beelbangera *Winery Road, Beelbangera NSW 2686. (069) 63 5227.*

This winery, specialising in red products, is one of the three McWilliam wineries in the MIA. It is not open to the public—see below for the two that are.

McWilliam's Hanwood *Winery Road, Hanwood, via Griffith NSW 2680. (069) 62 1333.*

Cellar door: Monday–Saturday 9–4.30; Sunday and public holidays 10–4. Group tours weekdays, given notice. BBQ facilities, with tables and chairs seating sixty; large 'barrel' tasting room and walk-through giant 'bottle', which is a glass museum. Bankcard, Mastercard Visa.
Winemaker: Simon Crook.

Owned by the McWilliam family; company founded 1877,

winery 1917. For the visitor, this is McWilliam's largest visible presence, an imposing modern winery using high technology, yet matched with a feeling of the area's history dating back to World War I. There are some exceptional value-for-money wines to be had here, especially whites and fortified wines. A must for visitors to the MIA. Enormous range of every type of still table and bulk wine, sparkling wine and fortified wine, plus brandy. Hanwood range is the top-of-the-line range from this winery, but also offered are the Gold Selection range, the McWilliam range, the Mt Pleasant Charles King range, a fortified range, table wine in 2 litre flagons, 4 litre casks, 3 litre casks, and Max Brandy. Distributed nationally. Head office is in Sydney (02) 707 1266.

McWilliam's Yenda *Winery Road, Yenda NSW 2681. (069) 68 1001.*

Cellar door: Weekdays 9–4. Bankcard, Mastercard, Visa. Group tours not available.

This is another very large arm of the McWilliam's wine empire, 15 kilometres north-east of Griffith. You can taste and buy bulk wine here, for home bottling in any quantity; and you can buy bottled wines (see entry above for Hanwood), which can't be tasted.

Miranda *57 Jondaryan Avenue, Griffith NSW 2680. (069) 62 4033.*

Cellar door: Monday–Friday 9–6. Saturday 9–6, public holidays 10–6, Sunday 11–5. No BBQs. Tours by appointment. Bankcard, Visa.
Winemaker: Shane Cunningham

Owned by the Miranda family. Founded 1939. Large family maker producing huge range of wines, sold through supermarket-style operation in the town. These include full range of reds, whites, sparkling and fortifieds, marketed under Miranda and Golden Gate labels. Liqueurs include coffee marsala and cask wines. One of this company's products, Golden Gate Spumante, is one of the biggest sellers of its type in Australia. Sold nationally.

Orlando Wickham Hill *Harris Road, Griffith NSW 2680. (069) 62 2605.*

Winemaker: David Morris

A modern winery on outskirts of town, but no longer open to the public. A source of Orlando Coolabah cask wines. Owned by G. Gramp & Sons (a subsidiary of Pernod Ricard).

Penfolds *Mirool Avenue, Yenda NSW 2681. (069) 68 1184.*

A former Wynn winery (Wynvale), mainly for cask products, now operated by the Penfolds/Kaiser Stuhl/Wynn conglomerate; not open to the public.

Riverina *Hillston Road, Griffith NSW 2680. (069) 62 4122.*

Cellar door: Monday–Saturday and holidays 9–6; Sunday 10–3. Picnic area. Bankcard, Mastercard.
Winemaker: Andrew Vasiljuk.

Owned by Antonio Sergi; founded 1975. Wines include dry reds and sweet whites, fortifieds and spumante. Distribution under Riverina and Ballingal Estate labels, and in bulk, with containers provided for home bottling.

Rossetto & Sons *Farm 576, Beelbangera NSW 2686. (069) 63 5214.*

Cellar door: Monday–Saturday 8.30–5.30, closed Sunday. Lawn areas; BBQ facilities. Bankcard, Mastercard, Visa.
Winemaker: Ralph Graham.

Family owned; founded 1930. Wines include red and white table wines, fortifieds, liqueurs and sparkling wines. Distribution under own labels and in bulk, though cellar door.

Ruberto's *Moama Street, South Hay NSW 2711. (069) 93 1480.*

Cellar door: Daily 9–7 (summer), Monday–Saturday 9–6 and Sunday 10–12 and 1–6 (winter). BBQ and picnic area. Amex, Bankcard, Visa.
Winemaker: Frank Roberts.

Family owned; founded 1983. It's quite a surprise, after making the desolate crossing of the central south-western plains of New South Wales, heading west, to see thriving green vineyards some 2 kilometres on the Narrandera side of Hay. For those making the Sydney–Adelaide drive, Hay is a good midway stopover; and Ruberto's brings a touch of Italian viticulture to this flatland beside the Murrumbidgee. Wines include red and white table wines, port, brown muscat, lambrusco, sherries, spumante. Distribution through cellar door sales.

San Bernadino *Leeton Road, Griffith NSW 2680. (069) 62 4944.*

Cellar door: Monday–Friday 9–5, Saturday and holidays 10–5, closed Sunday. Bankcard, Mastercard and Visa.
Winemaker: No winemaker on premises.

A large winery founded 1973 by local chemist Stan Aliprandi and a colleague. Now owned by de Bortoli (q.v.). Wines include dry reds, dry whites, sweet whites, and sparkling, fortified and non-alcoholic wines.

Toorak *Farm 279, Toorak Road, Amesbury, Leeton NSW 2705. (069) 53 2523.*

Cellar door: Monday–Saturday 9–5.30 (winter), 9–6 (summer); closed Sunday. BBQ area. Bankcard, Mastercard, Visa.
Winemaker: Frank Bruno.

Owned by Frank and Vince Bruno; founded 1953. Colombard, fumé blanc, chardonnay, Rhine riesling, white frontignac, cabernet sauvignon, cabernet/shiraz, malbec, a fortified range, sparkling wines. Marketed through cellar door, locally and some distribution in New South Wales and Victoria.

West End *Braynes Road, Griffith NSW 2680. (069) 62 2868*

Cellar door: Monday–Saturday and holidays 9–5; Sunday 12–6. BBQ and grassed play area. Bankcard, Mastercard, Visa.
Winemaker: Bill Calabria.

Family owned; founded 1946. Wines include chablis, chardonnay, riesling, spumante, cabernet sauvignon, hermitage and fortified wines. Distribution through cellar door.

Wilton Estate (formerly St Peters Distillery) *Whitton Stock Road, 5 kilometres east of Yenda NSW 2681. (069) 68 1303.*

Cellar door: Not open to the public.
Winemaker: Kerrie Haydon

Opened in 1978 by an Italian company. Wines include selection of reds and whites. Will be making brandy and wines which will appear under the Wilton Estate label. No distribution as we went to press.

Hilltops Region

Being the tribal people we are, we tend to band together for the common good, and so it is with winemakers. Some regions—for example, Coonawarra or the Swan Valley of Western Australia—are clearly defined by physical geography. Others, such as the Hilltops Region, draw their own boundaries—they do not easily fit into other winegrowing districts.

Grapes and many other fruits (notably cherries) have been planted here since the nineteenth-century gold rush, with a resurgence of vine plantings in the 1970s. New plantings have increased by 50 per cent over the past ten years, and grapes from the area are now being sold to wineries from Canberra to Orange.

The Hilltops Winemakers' Association, formed in 1986, defines its area as being bounded by the towns of Young, Boorowa and Harden on the south-west slopes of the State. At time of press they had twelve vineyards and, though only a small area was involved, they have concentrated on premium grape varieties in the belief that the cooler ripening season of this higher area will give them quality wines.

They get good yields of grapes because of adequate rainfall, and well-structured soils also help quality and moisture retention. The long, cool ripening period, with harvesting usually starting in April and extending into May, holds promise for a reputation for quality wines and distinctive varietal flavours. One of the key vineyard areas nearby, just to the north, is Cowra, now producing excellent chardonnay fruit.

The district also operates a Certificate of Quality scheme. There are two distinct aspects of this scheme: the first offers a guarantee of local origin of grapes; the second, run by outside wine judges, guarantees that wines marked with their quality stamp are at least of bronze medal show standard.

Eating out

This is such a scattered region it is hard to recommend places to eat. However, there are a number of good country hotels and motels. In the pleasant town of Young there is the Doves Restaurant at the Services and Citizens' Club. The only BYO in town is Gabriella's, with very good Italian fare; there are also four Chinese restaurants. Harden has the excellent Terracotta Restaurant. Boorowa has one motel and a number of hotels with accommodation and meals.

Cartobe *Young Road, Boorowa NSW 2586. (063) 85 3128.*

Cellar door: Friday–Monday 9–5 (October–April). April–October by appointment only. Picnic tables available. Caters for groups of approximately twenty for evening meals by appointment only. Bankcard, Mastercard.
Winemaker: Geoffrey Carter.

Family owned; founded 1979. Rhine riesling, chardonnay, traminer, cabernet sauvignon, pinot noir. Own distribution.

Hercynia *Prunevale NSW 2587. (063) 84 4243.*

Cellar door: Open weekends by appointment only.

Owned by Mrs Shirley Doldissen. Wines include pinot noir, sauvignon blanc, Rhine riesling and muscat.

McWilliam's Barwang Vineyards *Barwang Road, Young NSW 2594. (063) 82 2689.*

Cellar door: Not open to the public. Vineyard only.

Originally Barwang Vineyards, this vineyard was taken over by McWilliam's in 1989 and is now being developed up to some 120 hectares. There are 14 hectares producing and 60 hectares have actually been planted. Vines are planted to chardonnay, pinot noir, sauvignon blanc, shiraz, cabernet sauvignon, semillon, Rhine riesling, merlot, cabernet franc. The wine is made at McWilliam's at Beelbangerra or Yenda.

Moppity Park *Moppity Road, Young NSW 2594. (063) 82 2869.*

Cellar door: Open by appointment only at this stage.
Winemaker: Geoff Carter

Owned by Pat and Leslie Wickham. Established in 1973. Wines include Rhine riesling, semillon, chardonnay, shiraz and cabernet sauvignon, with merlot vines being planted.

Nioka Ridge *Barwang Road, Young NSW 2594. (063) 82 2903.*

Cellar door: Open seven days. Attractively landscaped grounds with picnic and BBQ facilities and children's playground. Their '88 chardonnay was chosen in the Top 60 of the Australian Small Makers' wines in the May/June 1990 issue of Wine & Spirit Buying Guide. Bankcard, Mastercard, Visa.
Winemaker: Phillip Price.

Owned by Karl and Annette Robertson, Phillip Price and Karen Bisset. This small winery is at present making its wine through Charles Sturt University, Wagga. Wines include Rhine riesling, chardonnay, cabernet malbec, Rhine riesling kabinett and vintage port. Distributed at cellar door. Limited distribution in Canberra and Wagga.

Woodonga Hill *1 Cowra Road, outside Young NSW 2594. (063) 82 2972.*

Cellar door: Seven days a week 9–5 (winter), 9–6 (summer). Picnic area and BBQ facilities with magnificent panoramic views. Bankcard, Mastercard, Visa.
Winemaker: Jill Lindsay

Owned by Phil and Jill Lindsay; their first vintage was in 1986. Wines include Rhine riesling, auslese gewürztraminer, chardonnay, sauvignon blanc, soft shiraz, cabernet sauvignon and vintage port. Wines are sold from cellar door and at selected restaurants in Canberra.

Other areas

New South Wales seems to be following in the footsteps of Victoria as small wineries are established—or operate—in disparate areas all over the State. There is no doubt that there are some areas of viticultural promise in very varied areas of New South Wales, especially some cooler areas (such as Tumbarumba on the alpine slopes), areas of the central-northern coast and tablelands and around Orange in the central-west.

Many of them operate in isolation at this stage, though no doubt there will be others down the track, so we have listed them here under 'Other areas'. They are listed below by area, and the wineries themselves alphabetically in the following pages.

BEGA	Grevillea Estate
BERRY	Jasper Valley Wines
CAMDEN	Bridgefarm Wines
COBBITY	Cobbity (Cogno Bros)
HAY	Roberto's (listed under MIA area, above)
INVERELL	Gilgai
JASPERS BRUSH	The Silos
ORANGE	D'Aquino Winery Midas Tree
RICHMOND/	Richmond Estate
PENRITH	Vicary's
TUMBARUMBA	Tumbarumba Champagne Estate (not now operating)
WAGGA WAGGA	College Winery
WELLINGTON	Glenfinlass

Bridgefarm Wines *Lot 3, Macarthur Road, Camden NSW 2570. (046) 66 8337*

Cellar door: Friday, Saturday, Sunday and holidays 10–6. Tours by appointment only. Picnic areas along Nepean River (which runs through property). Cash payment preferred.
Winemaker: Dr Sue Hanckel.

Owned by N. P. Hanckel. Quality wines from a lovely vineyard just off the Nepean bridge outside historic Camden; nearby are the ruins of what is one of Australia's most historic wineries, John Macarthur's Camden Park Winery (see *Great Australian Wine Book*, p. 98). Wines include chardonnay, traminer and cabernet sauvignon, labelled under Bridgefarm and Le Docteur Hanckel (chardonnay). Distributed through cellar door and Carol Anne Classic Australian Wines, Sydney.

Charles Sturt University Winery *Charles Sturt University, Riverina, Barooma Street, Wagga Wagga NSW 2650. (069) 22 2435.*

Cellar door: Monday–Friday 10–4, Saturday, Sunday and holidays 11–4. Tours and buses by appointment. Picnic areas available. Amex, Bankcard, Mastercard.
Winemaker: Rodney Hooper

Public institution; founded 1977; formerly the Riverina College of Advanced Education Winery. Full-time and part-time students at Australia's second oenology school learn their skills by drawing on fruit from its own and various other Australian vineyard areas. The wines are generally good value—you can get some bargains. The sprawling college itself, containing the winery, is some 9 kilometres north of Wagga. Wines include full selection of red, white, fortified and sparkling wines, made, packaged and marketed commercially. Distribution: cellar door and Incredible Wine Co., Sydney.

Cobbity (Cogno Bros) *Cobbity Road, Cobbity NSW 2570. (046) 51 2281.*

Cellar door: Monday–Saturday 9–6, Sunday and holidays 12–6. No tours. BBQ and picnic areas. Cash or cheque only.
Winemaker: John Cogno.

Owned by Cogno Bros. Wines include wide range of red and white table wines, ports, sherries and vermouth; also lambrusco light, sparkling red. Marketed under Cobbity Wines and Mama Port. Distribution through cellar door only.

Cowra Vineyards *Boorowa Road, Cowra NSW 2794. (063) 42 1136.*

Cellar door: Tuesday–Sunday 10–4. Bankcard. Quarry Cellars restaurant, craft and home-made produce shop next to tasting area. Lunch from 10–4 Tuesday–Sunday; dinner from 7 p.m. Friday, Saturday. Bookings essential (063) 42 3630.
Winemaker: Simon Gilbert.
Vineyard Manager: Greg Johnston

Established 1973; owned by private shareholders. Vineyards planted to chardonnay, sauvignon blanc, riesling, gewürztraminer, pinot noir, cabernet sauvignon, cabernet franc and merlot. Distributed through cellar door and in New South Wales.

D'Aquino *129–131 Bathurst Road, Orange NSW 2800. (063) 62 7381.*

Cellar door: Monday–Saturday 9.30–8, closed Sunday. No tours, no BBQs. Bankcard only.
Winemaker: Rex D'Aquino.

Family owned; founded 1949. Wines include Rhine riesling, spätlese Rhine riesling, sauvignon blanc, moselle, chablis, burgundy, cabernet sauvignon, shiraz, claret, plus imported whisky, locally distilled gin, vodka, brandy. Labelled Garrallen for premium products, and D'Aquino. Own distribution.

Gilgai *Tingha Road, Gilgai NSW 2360. (067) 23 1204.*

Cellar door: Monday–Saturday 10–6, Sunday and holidays 12–6. Tours welcomed. Picnic tables. BBQs planned soon. Bankcard, Mastercard.
Winemaker: Dr Charles Whish.

Owned by Doctors Keith and Charles Whish; founded 1968. Wines include Rhine riesling, semillon, malbec, cabernet/shiraz, Chandelier (fortified white wine), port and liqueur muscat. Distributed through cellar door and mail order only.

Glenfinlass *Elysian Farm, Parkes Road, Wellington NSW 2820. (068) 45 2221, after hours (068) 45 2392.*

Cellar door: Saturday 9–5, other days by appointment. Tours by appointment. Picnic area nearby. Cash or cheque.
Winemaker: Brian Holmes.

Family owned; first vintage 1972. Wines include sauvignon blanc, shiraz, cabernet sauvignon and blend, and dry rosé. Labelled Glenfinlass, distribution through cellar door.

Grevillea Estate *Buckajo Road, via Bega NSW 2550. (064) 92 3006.*

Cellar door: Daily 9–5. Buses by arrangement. BBQs, light lunches. Bankcard, American Express, Mastercard, Visa.
Winemaker: Nicola Collins.

Owned by Nicola Collins; founded 1980. An interesting small winery in the Bega Valley, 3 kilometres west of Bega itself. Wines include Rhine riesling, chardonnay, traminer, traminer/riesling, cabernet sauvignon and merlot. Distribution through cellar door and some local restaurants.

Jasper Valley Wines *Croziers Road, Berry NSW 2535. (044) 64 1596.*

Cellar door: Monday–Saturday 9.30–5.30, Sunday and holidays 10–5.30. BBQs (buy steak and salad there and cook yourself) in scenic picnic ground. Pottery and giftware for sale. Bankcard, Mastercard, Visa.
Winemaker: Contract winemaker.

Owned by John and Pat Wyeth since October 1988, founded 1976. Wines include dry whites, moselle, sparkling wines, two dry reds (cabernet sauvignon and cabernet/shiraz). Labelled Jasper Valley Wine;, distribution cellar door and local outlets.

Lachlan Valley Wines *Wandary Lane, South Forbes NSW 2871. (068) 52 3983.*

Cellar door: Monday to Saturday 9–5.30; Sunday 1–5. BBQ area. Bankcard, Mastercard, Visa.
Winemakers: Frank and Les Chislett.

Owned by J. B. Reymonds & Son and leased by Frank and Les Chislett. First vintage 1965 with vines planted to cabernet sauvignon, shiraz, pinot noir, trebbiano, semillon, Rhine riesling, muscat and frontignac. Available cellar door only.

Midas Tree *Cargo Road, Lidster, via Orange NSW 2800.*

Small winery run by Swanston family.

Richmond Estate *Gadds Road, North Richmond NSW 2754. (045) 73 1048.*

Cellar door: Tuesday–Sunday 10–6 (closed Monday except public holidays). Mastercard, Bankcard, Visa.
Winemaker: Tony Radanovic.

This winery, founded in 1967, is now owned by Tony and Monica Radanovic, who bought it in July 1987. Wines include shiraz, cabernet sauvignon and malbec, with some whites to come. Sales are through cellar door.

The Silos *Princes Highway, Jaspers Brush NSW 2535. (044) 48 6082.*
Cellar door: Open seven days, owners live on premises. Adjacent restaurant open for lunches and dinners, with special vintage dinner from time to time. Area outside winery (a converted farmhouse) for drinking. All major credit cards.
Winemaker: Alan Bamfield

Owned by Alan and Marie Bamfield; founded 1985. Wines include chardonnay, sauvignon blanc, malbec, merlot, shiraz, cabernet/shiraz, semillon/crouchen, semillon and blended port. Distributed through cellar door. All-encompassing small winery some 10 kilometres north of Nowra, which even runs wine appreciation courses for beginners.

Vicary's *Northern Road, Luddenham NSW 2750. (047) 73 4161.*

Cellar door: Tuesday–Friday 9–6, Saturday and holidays 11.30–6, Sunday 12–6. Picnic areas. Amex, Bankcard, Mastercard.
Winemaker: Chris Niccol.

Owned by Ross Carbery; founded 1923. Wines include broad range of reds, whites, ports, liqueur muscat and frontignac. Cream and fino sherries also. Distribution cellar door only.

Canberra District

As with other cool-climate areas, winemakers and grape-growers are challenging the elements and trying to make better and more interesting wines. Land restrictions mean that, so far at least, all the district's vignerons are outside the Australian Capital Territory, in New South Wales, though not far from the national capital. All of the wineries are very small, making tiny volumes of wine. But, like some other districts—Tasmania and other parts of cool New South Wales—the wines show promise that should be delivered with experience, luck and skills.

Eating out

Canberra, of course, has a plethora of restaurants of most ethnic and cost hues, too numerous to list here. Several of the wineries listed below have places to eat your own food. There are also restaurants in Yass, plus the occasional hotel in places such as Collector. As with some other isolated wine areas, you might be well advised to take a picnic in the very scenic countryside or at one of the nominated wineries.

Affleck Vineyard *RMB 244, Millynn Road (off Gundaroo Road), Bungendore NSW 2621. (06) 236 9279.*

Cellar door: Open by appointment only.
Winemakers/owners: Ian and Susan Hendry.

Very small winery; founded 1975. Wines include semillon, chardonnay, Rhine riesling, sauvignon blanc, cabernet sauvignon and shiraz. Available through mail order.

Benfield Estate *Fairy Hole Road, off Wargeila Road, 8 kilometres south of Yass NSW 2582. (06) 22 62427.*

Cellar door: Weekends and holidays 10–5. BBQ facilities. Bankcard, Mastercard.
Winemaker: David Fetherston.

Owned by Benfield Wines Pty Ltd. Founded 1983, first crop 1986. Wines include semillon, dry and sweet riesling, chardonnay, shiraz, cabernet sauvignon, cabernet/merlot and merlot. Distribution through cellar door, limited retail outlets in Canberra and mail order (PO Box 336, Yass NSW 2582).

Brindabella Hills Winery *Woodgrove Close, via Walleroo Road, Hall ACT 2618. (06) 230 2583.*

Cellar door: Weekends and public holidays 10–5. Other times by appointment. Picnic and BBQ facilities available for wine club groups by arrangement.
Winemaker: Roger L. N. Harris.

Established in 1986, this small 2 hectare vineyard is owned by Roger and Faye Harris. Vineyard planted to cabernet sauvignon, cabernet franc, merlot, pinot noir, chardonnay, sauvignon blanc, semillon and Rhine riesling.

Brooks Creek *RMB 209, Brooks Road Bungendore NSW 2621. (06) 236 9221.*

Cellar door: Sales should be happening, no details available at time of publication.
Winemaker: Lawrence Brownbill.

This winery, founded in 1977 and formerly Shingle House, has recently been acquired by G. M. and M. J. Brownbill. Grape varieties: mataro, cabernet sauvignon, malbec, chardonnay.

Burra Winery *Badgery Road, via Williamsdale Road, Burra Creek NSW 2620. (06) 236 3216.*

Cellar door: Open weekends and public holidays 10–5.
Winemakers: Dr John Kirk and sons.

Clonakilla *Crisps Lane, off Gundaroo Road, Murrumbateman NSW 2582. (06) 246 5212, after hours (06) 251 1938.*

Cellar door: Weekends and holidays 11–5. Bankcard, Mastercard.

Founded 1971. Wines include Rhine riesling, semillon, pinot noir, cabernet sauvignon, cabernet/shiraz, muscat and vintage port. Distribution through cellar door and through Nick's Wine Merchants in Melbourne.

Doonkuna Estate *Barton Highway, Murrumbateman NSW 2582. (06) 227 5885.*

Cellar door: Monday–Friday 10–4. Weekends by appointment only.
Winemaker: Sir Brian Murray.

Owned by Sir Brian and Lady Murray. Founded 1973. Small winery (some 5.5 hectares of vines in various stages of development) owned by a former Governor of Victoria, who now makes the wines, with some outside help from Oenetech Pty Ltd and Garry Baldwin. Wines include Rhine riesling, chardonnay, fumé blanc, sauvignon blanc, pinor noir, shiraz and cabernet sauvignon. Direct mail order.

Helm's *Yass River Road, Murrumbateman NSW 2582. (06) 227 5953, after hours (06) 227 5536.*

Cellar door: Open every day 10–5 except Tuesday and Wednesday. Bankcard, Mastercard, Visa, Amex. Picnics.
Winemaker: Ken Helm.

Owned by the Helm Family; founded 1972. One of the larger wineries of the area, run by an ex-CSIRO scientist who is also very committed to supporting and promoting the entire district and its wine products. Wines include cabernet sauvignon, cabernet merlot, chardonnay, Rhine riesling, traminer/riesling, port and sherry, and Müller thurgau. Distribution through cellar door, selected Canberra restaurants and various outlets in Sydney.

Jeir Creek *Gooda Creek Road, Murrumbateman NSW 2582. (06) 227 5999, after hours (06) 258 8292.*

Cellar door: Weekends and public holidays 10–5. Bankcard, Mastercard, Visa. Picnic areas, BBQ, children's playground. Picturesque scenery.
Winemaker: Robert Howell (owner).

Winery founded 1987. Wines include sauvignon blanc, chardonnay, Rhine riesling, cabernet/merlot and champagne (50 per cent chardonnay and 50 per cent pinot). Distribution: cellar door, retail outlets in Canberra and some restaurants.

Kyeema Vineyard *Murrumbateman NSW 2582. (06) 254 7557.*

Cellar door: Open weekends by appointment.
Winemaker: Andrew McEwin.

New winery obtaining fruit from local vineyards. Shiraz, cabernet sauvignon, chardonnay and semillon. Available through cellar door, mail order (PO Box 282, Belconnen ACT 2616) and selected local restaurants and retail outlets.

Lake George Winery *Federal Highway, Collector NSW 2581. (048) 48 0039, after hours (06) 48 6302.*

Cellar door: No direct sales to the public.
Winemaker: Dr Edgar Riek.

Founded 1971. This winery, formerly Cullarin, was one of the pioneering vineyards in the Canberra district, and Dr Riek (the owner), a Canberra academic, is deeply involved in the annual Canberra National Wine Show. Wines include pinot noir, chardonnay, Bordeaux blend (merlot/cabernet franc/cabernet sauvignon) and semillon. Distribution in Canberra, and available at some Canberra clubs and restaurants.

Lark Hill *RMB 281, Gundaroo Road, Bungendore NSW 2621. (06) 238 1393.*

Cellar door: Weekends and holidays 10–5. Weekdays by appointment. Bankcard, Mastercard, Visa.
Winemakers: D. J. Carpenter and S. M. Carpenter (owners).

Founded 1978. Very high vineyards overlooking Lake George contribute some of the fruit for this label, other fruit coming from Young. By Canberra standards, a medium-sized winery producing good wines. Products include chardonnay, Rhine riesling (dry and sweet), semillon, cabernet/merlot and pinot noir. Distribution through cellar door, selected Canberra outlets and mail order. Distributed in Sydney through Greg Frazer & Associates and in Melbourne through Flinders Wine Merchants.

Madew Wines *Furlong Road, Queanbeyan NSW 2620. (06) 297 2742.*

Cellar door: Open weekends and public holidays 10–5 and by appointment. Bankcard and Mastercard.
Winemaker: Karen Leggat.

Owned by David and Barbara Madew and established in 1981. Wines include semillon, chardonnay, Rhine riesling, cabernet sauvignon, merlot and traminer.

Murrumbateman Winery *Barton Highway, Murrumbateman NSW 2582.*

Cellar door: Daily 10–5 except Monday. Tours, picnics and BBQs possible. Amex, Bankcard, Diner's Club, Mastercard.
Winemaker: Geoff Middleton (to late 1990).

Founded 1973. Geoff and Trish Middleton were selling this winery in late 1990 and its future was uncertain. Wines include Rhine riesling, traminer, chablis-style wine, shiraz/cabernet, port and mead (from honey). Distribution: cellar door only.

Pankhurst Wines *Old Woodgrove, Woodgrove Road, Hall NSW 2618. (06) 23 02592.*

Cellar door: Not open to the public.
Winemaker: Dr Roger Harris.

Owned by Christine and Alan Pankhurst; established in 1986. Wines include pinot noir, cabernet, merlot, chardonnay, semillon, sauvignon blanc. Mail order only: above address.

Ruker Wines *Barton Highway, near Hall NSW 2618. (06) 230 2310.*

Cellar door: Open every day except Monday 10–5. Mastercard, Bankcard, Visa.
Winemaker: Dr Richard A. Ruker (owner).

Small winery on 2 hectares, established in 1986. Planted to Rhine riesling and traminer. This winery, about halfway between Canberra and Yass, has a tasting area providing simple foods, morning and afternoon teas in a slab construction colonial-type room next to the winery. Distribution: cellar door and mail order (PO Box 421, Dickson ACT 2602).

Westering Vineyard *Federal Highway, Collector NSW 2581. (048) 48 0026, after hours (06) 295 8075.*

Cellar door: Open by appointment only
Winemaker: Captain Geoffrey Hood.

Owned by G. P. and A. R. Hood; founded 1973. Captain Hood, a retired naval officer, produces small quantities of wine, some 10 kilometres south of Collector. Mail order, 97 Jansz Crescent, Griffith ACT 2603. Wines include chardonnay, Rhine riesling, semillon, pinot noir, cabernet sauvignon, shiraz and sherry.

Yass Valley Wines *Crisps Lane, Murrumbateman NSW 2582. (06) 227 5592.*

Cellar door: Most weekends (ring first, preferably), and holidays 10–5. BBQ area. Bankcard, Mastercard, Visa.
Winemaker: Peter Griffiths (owner).

Founded 1978. Wines include semillon and Rhine riesling. Available at cellar door or through mail order (PO Box 18, Murrumbateman NSW 2582).

South Australia

South Australia is *the* wine State, as its proponents often suggest. Its Mediterranean climate makes it so. It is not surprising to find, in many of the winegrowing areas of the driest State on the driest continent, that olive trees and almonds thrive alongside the extensive vineyards.

It is easy to start arguments about this, but South Australia *does* produce many of the nation's best wines. Across the board the cabernets (such as those of Coonawarra), the Rhine rieslings (from the Barossa, Eden and Clare Valleys), the chardonnays of Padthaway, the brandies and the ports (such as those from the Riverland and the Southern Vales) are among the most outstanding wines Australia offers today.

The circle of wine districts stretches from the beautiful Clare Valley in the north, a couple of hours' drive from Adelaide, around through the relaxing Riverland to the best known wine area, the Barossa Valley, across the developing Adelaide Hills to McLaren Vale and through to the remote south-east, centred on Padthaway and Coonawarra.

South Australia is home to some of the largest winemakers, and many of the remaining family-owned wineries, and it is home to many of the big wine industry organisations, the major winemaking school (Roseworthy Agricultural College), the Australian Wine Research Institute and a lot of significant vine research activity. It is also, of course, a delightful State to visit and tour to taste the fruits of the half dozen wine-producing areas, most of which are within easy striking distance of Adelaide, the charming capital city of just over 1 million people.

There are also many delightful restaurants in Adelaide itself and scattered through most of the wine areas. While I would still argue that the handful of very best Australian eating places are around Sydney and Melbourne, South Australia has a large number of exceptional restaurants, by world standards.

A tour of three or four of the South Australian wine areas listed here can be a very enjoyable way to spend a few days or a week or so, particularly in the (southern hemisphere) autumn and spring.

'Whiskers' Blake was employed last century at Hardy's McLaren Vale vineyards to scare away birds with his muzzle-loading eight-gauge shotgun. He's being scolded by Tom Nottage, nephew of the company's founder, Thomas Hardy.

Adelaide

Adelaide, capital of Australia's largest wine State (about 60 per cent of Australia's wine production in 1990) is a fast-growing city. Its population is now around 1.1 million. People and their housing needs have taken precedence over wineries and vineyards. Over the decades, the vines which once grew close to the city centre have been pulled out, and today they are still disappearing. Sadly, but inevitably, this is occurring, just as it did in Sydney (Minchinbury, for example), Melbourne (the Yarra Valley) and even Perth (in the Swan Valley).

Nevertheless, vines are still growing vigorously to the north of Adelaide (the Adelaide Plains), to the south (Reynella at the northern fringe of the South Vales area) and not so far to the east in the lovely Adelaide Hills.

The enthusiasm for home-grown produce can be felt all over Adelaide, in the wineries, the restaurants, the bistros, wine bars and hotels. The head offices of a number of major Australian wine companies are still located in and around the city of Adelaide—Seppelt, Hardy's, Orlando, for example. Luncheon and dinner clubs flourish, as do dinner meetings which revolve around wine and food (the Bacchus Club, Beefsteak and Burgundy Clubs and the Wine and Food Society).

In recent times, the South Australian Government has been making strenuous efforts to promote wine and tourism to replace or enhance traditional industries such as cars and whitegoods. The Australian Grand Prix, the Adelaide Festival of the Arts and the various wine festivals—not to mention a virtually pollution-free environment—combine to make Adelaide a refreshing place to visit.

Anglesey Wine Estate *Heaslip Road, Angle Vale SA 5117. (085) 24 3157.*

Cellar door: Daily 10–5. Small groups only, tours by appointment. Bankcard, Visa.
Winemaker: Lindsay Stanley; consultant is Max Schubert.

Founded 1969. Dry reds and whites, including their QVS range.

Douglas A. Tolley *30 Barracks Road, Hope Valley SA 5090. (08) 264 2255.*

Cellar door: Monday–Friday 7.30–5, Saturday 9–5, closed

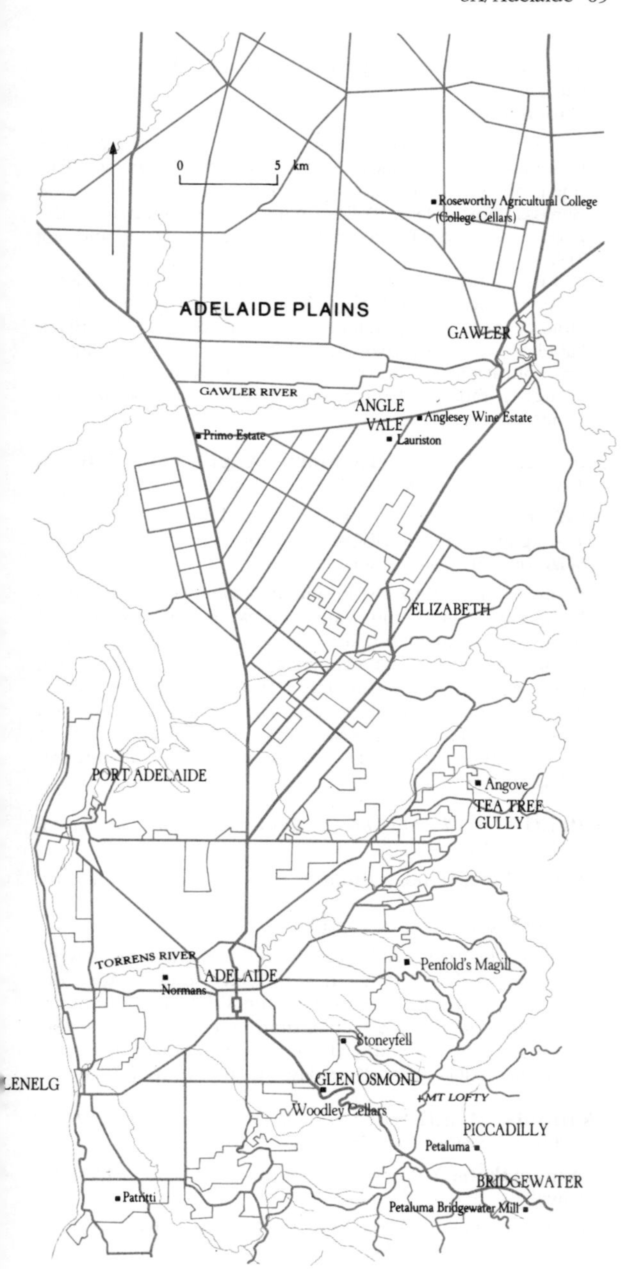
0
5 km
Roseworthy Agricultural College
(College Cellars)
ADELAIDE PLAINS
GAWLER
GAWLER RIVER
ANGLE
VALE
Anglesey Wine Estate
Primo Estate
Lauriston
ELIZABETH
PORT ADELAIDE
Angove
TEA TREE
GULLY
TORRENS RIVER
ADELAIDE
Penfold's Magill
Normans
Stoneyfell
LENELG
GLEN OSMOND
MT LOFTY
Woodley Cellars
PICCADILLY
Petaluma
BRIDGEWATER
Patritti
Petaluma Bridgewater Mill

Sunday. BBQ area, large oval for picnics. All major credit cards.
Winemaker: Christopher Tolley.

Founded in 1893. Like many other old-established family winemakers, D. A. Tolley has split into various branches. This one is not to be confused with Tolley, Scott and Tolley in the Barossa. Most of D. A. Tolley's wines are marketed under the Pedare label, which is a contraction of Peter, David and Reg Tolley.

Key brands are the Premium Wines (their best), Cellar Reserve and Hope Valley. The usual range of varietal table wines is supplemented by a ten-year-old Black Label Port, a five-year-old White Label Port, a vintage port sold at seven years of age, sherry and vermouth. In short, a large company of the middle rank, making some good wines.

Lauriston Winery (formerly Angle Vale Cellars) *Heaslip Road, Angle Vale SA 5117. (085) 24 3100.*

Cellar door: Monday–Friday 9–5, Saturday 11–5, Sunday 1–5. Tasting area, electric BBQs. All major credit cards.
Winemaker: Colin Glaetzer.

Founded in 1972. Lauriston Winery is jointly owned by Berri Renmano Limited and Valley Growers Co-operative Ltd (based in the Riverland), and the wines are well priced. Key brands are the Barossa Valley Estate range—Rhine riesling, chardonnay, semillon, sauvignon blanc, late-picked frontignan, hermitage and cabernet sauvignon; and the Lauriston range—chardonnay, cabernet/shiraz and *méthode champenoise* sparkling wines. Distributed nationally and through cellar door.

Patritti *13 Clacton Road, Dover Gardens SA 5048. (08) 296 8261.*

Cellar door: Monday–Saturday 8.30–6. Tastings. Bankcard, Visa, Mastercard.
Winemaker: Geoffrey Patritti.

Founded in 1926 in suburban Dover Gardens (Dover Wine Co.); vineyards at Aldinga, near the coast south of Adelaide, and Blewitt Springs, east of McLaren Vale. Makes semi-dry reds, burgundy and claret, plus grape juices. Wines available through cellar door and at Patritti's warehouse in Byards Road, Reynella—open Thursday, Friday, Saturday 10–6.

Penfolds' Magill *Penfold Road, Magill SA 5072. (08) 332 6099, head office (02) 559 1466.*

Winemakers: Various Penfolds makers, headed by John Duvall.

Grange Cottage is classified by the National Trust and is not open to the public. No sales are made from here and the remaining vineyards are now the source of a small amount of premium fruit for Penfolds. Another 'property' who should be classified by the National Trust is Max Schubert, who developed the famous Grange Hermitage. He still acts as a consultant to the company, and works here.

Primo Estate *Old Port Wakefield Road, Virginia SA 5120. (08) 380 9442.*

Cellar door: Closed during vintage (from Christmas to 1 June). Rest of year: Monday–Friday 9–5, Saturday 9–4.30, closed Sunday. BBQs, picnic area, pottery for sale. All major credit cards.
Winemaker: Joe Grilli.

First vintage 1979. This small company makes a range of quality varietal wines and experiments successfully with vineyard and winemaking techniques to improve and diversify wine quality. Sweet whites, dry whites (including sauvignon blanc) and colombard, double-pruned cabernet and shiraz. Agents in all States, plus cellar door.

Stonyfell Winery Complex *Stonyfell SA 5066. (08) 332 4033.*

Stonyfell Winery, on the slopes of the suburban hills fifteen minutes' drive east from Adelaide, was originally owned by Saltrams. It is one of South Australia's oldest wineries. Although wine is now not made on the premises, there is a cellar door open daily during restaurant hours, where wines from twenty different South Australian winemakers can be tasted and bought. There are three restaurants; Pickwicks which is open for a buffet lunch from Sunday to Friday and dinner on Wednesday, Friday and Saturday. It is also available for functions. The Dicken's Room, the Henry Martin Room and the Jack Kilgour Room are all for functions by appointment. You can also bottle, cork, capsule and label your own port.

Woodley Wines *181 Flinders Street, Adelaide SA 5000. (08) 236 3400.*

Woodley Wines was purchased by Seppelt (in turn controlled by the SA Brewing Company) in 1985, bringing to a close a long history which gave birth to some classic Australian wines. Seppelt sold the Woodley cellars in Blyth Street, in suburban Glen Osmond on the slopes of the Adelaide Hills. Woodley had been owned since 1971 by Industrial Equity Limited, and in latter days the quality of its big brand wines, such as Queen Adelaide Rhine Riesling had suffered; Seppelt lifted this game, and the Woodley range of wines includes an economical Queen Adelaide Chardonnay and a red.

Adelaide Hills

As wine fashions wax and wane, so too do areas. In the mid- to late 1980s there is no doubt that the Adelaide Hills, however that large area is delineated, is *the* 'in' area. Brian Croser and Petaluma led the rush to fashionability, but there had been others there, notably around Clarendon (at the Southern Vales end) and Eden Valley (at the Barossa Valley end), previously. The attraction for winemakers is the climate, considerably cooler than the Adelaide and Barossa plains. This produces wine grapes with more elegant flavours. They are also more costly, partly because growing is more expensive here, and yields are lower and more susceptible to cold weather damage.

For the tourist, this is an area well worth a day or so meandering along the hills and valleys, perhaps using nearby Adelaide as a base. The restaurants are varied and generally good, even the pubs (for example, at Stirling and Aldgate) have first-rate fare.

Bridgewater Mill, opened in 1986, is an offshoot of Petaluma and is thoroughly worth a visit. There are a number of good restaurants in Stirling and towns such as Hahndorf and the Mount Lofty areas. There are also many excellent and delightfully relaxing picnic and (out of the bushfire season) BBQ spots.

Influenced by the premium prices being paid for Adelaide Hills grapes—notably chardonnay, pinot noir and cabernet sauvignon—vineyards and wineries are springing up all over the Hills. Excellent as many of the resulting wines are, they *are* expensive!

One of the largest vineyards is at Gumeracha. Adelaide businessman Caj Amadio has over 50 hectares of premium varieties at his Gumeracha Vineyards, presently contracted to Penfolds.

In theory some of the other larger makers (Yalumba, Orlando, Wynn's Eden Valley) could be listed in this section, as the hills keep running north on the eastern side of the Barossa Valley. But for convenience they have been listed under 'Barossa Valley'.

Eating out

The Hills region has plenty of interesting eating places, plus of course an abundance of picnic sites both formal and informal. Two hotels in particular have good dining rooms: the Stirling Hotel (Mount Barker Road, Stirling [08] 339 2045) and the Aldgate Pump (Strathalbyn Road, Aldgate [08] 339 2015) offering good fare and extremely good wine lists, both in a welcoming atmosphere. Not far away, Mount Lofty House (74 Summit Road, Crafers [08] 339 6777) is an up-market restaurant and guest house with international cuisine.

The spectacular Bridgewater Mill (Mount Barker Road, Bridgewater [08] 339 3422) is a former mill with a giant water wheel, now the centre for the *méthode champenoise* production of sparkling wines for nearby Petaluma and some others. It also offers tastings and sales for the owners, Petaluma Wines, and their stable mate, Bridgewater Mill wines. The Granary (at Bridgewater Mill) is open seven days and offers fine à la carte lunches—highly recommended at the expensive end of the scale. The Petaluma Room is available for private functions and dinners for fifteen to thirty people.

Andrew Garrett Clarendon Estate

See Southern Vales.

Ashton Hills *Tregarthen Road, Ashton SA 5137. (08) 390 1243.*

Cellar door: Cellar door due to open in 1991.
Winemaker: Stephen George.

Established in 1982; owned by Peter van Rood. Three hectares planted to Rhine riesling, chardonnay, pinot noir and cabernet sauvignon/cabernet franc/merlot. Available in retail outlets in Adelaide and through mail order from PO Box 231, Ashton SA 5137.

Bridgewater Mill

Range of good wines available at the Mill, see Petaluma.

Craneford *Main Street, Springton SA 5235. (085) 68 2220.*

Cellar door: Seven days 11–5. All major credit cards except Diner's Club. Café C. is open for lunch Friday–Monday, dinner Friday and Saturday. Cuisine is modern Australian and the chef is Mardi Palmer.
Winemaker: Colin Forbes (owner)

Established 1978 as Holmes Springton Winery. Wines are generally very good, and include Rhine riesling, chardonnay, shiraz and cabernet sauvignon. Available through cellar door and national distribution.

Eden Springs Wine Estate *Boehms Springs Road, Springton SA 5235. (085) 64 1056.*

Cellar door: No cellar door. Wines from this Estate (established 1987) can be tasted at Eden Valley Wines (see Barossa entry). However, there is a restaurant complex for large groups by appointment. Restaurant can seat 200 people inside or 500 outside.
Winemaker: Peter Thompson (owner).

Wines available under the Eden Springs Wine Estate label at publication were a 1989 and a 1990 Rhine Riesling.

Grand Cru Estate *R. Dewells Road, Springton SA 5253. (085) 68 2378.*

Cellar door: Seven days 10–5.30. All major credit cards. The whole property is being redeveloped with an old dairy being restored and a tower being built as a cellar door outlet.
Winemaker: Karl Seppelt.

Wines sold privately under Grand Cru Estate label. First vintage 1985. Varieties include cabernet sauvignon, merlot and pinot meunier, with riesling and chardonnay being planted. Produce quality wines. Karl Seppelt was managing director of B. Seppelt & Sons when the company was taken over by the SA Brewing Company so, showing the true spirit of his Seppelt forebears, he decided to start again here in the Adelaide Hills. Distributed through Vintage Cellars, Adelaide and Nick's in Melbourne.

Holmes Springton Winery

See Craneford.

Moculta Wine Cove *Truro Road, Moculta SA 5353. (085) 63 9065.*

Cellar door: Monday–Saturday 10–4.30, Sunday 12–4.30. No formal tours but picnic area and scenic walk. Bankcard.
Winemaker: John Doughty.

Cottage-style winery which produces a range of Rhine riesling, white frontignac, shiraz/cabernet, and vintage and tawny ports. Ports under Parrot Hill label, others under Attunga Hill.

Mountadam Vineyard *High Eden Road, High Eden Ridge, Eden Valley SA 5253. (085) 64 1101.*

Cellar door: Open seven days a week 10–4. Bankcard, Mastercard, Amex, Diner's Club.
Winemakers: David and Adam Wynn.

This father and son team planted the vineyards in the Barossa Hills after their family sold Wynn's winery in the early 1970s. They built the technologically advanced Mountadam winery to make a range of premium varietal wines, including cabernet sauvignon, pinot noir, chardonnay and Rhine riesling. The wines are distributed nationally, widely available overseas and often found in better restaurants.

Norman's Chais Clarendon *Grants Gully Road, Clarendon SA 5157. (08) 383 6138.*

Cellar door: Monday–Saturday 10–5, Sunday 11–5. Visitors welcome, tours by appointment. All major credit cards. No BBQ. See McLaren Vale map.
Winemakers: Brian Light, with additional advice from Norman's James Irvine.

Chais Clarendon *(chais* meaning 'cellar above the ground') was formerly Coolawin Estate, and is now owned by Norman's. Atop the southern end of the Adelaide Hills, it is several minutes' drive from historic Clarendon. Wines mainly from Adelaide Hills, including Rhine riesling, chardonnay, gewürztraminer, frontignan, cabernet franc, pinot noir, merlot, cabernet sauvignon and shiraz. Available through cellar door and at Norman's bottle shop at Holbrook Road, Underdale.

Petulama *Spring Gully Road, Piccadilly, via Stirling SA 5151. (08) 339 3422.*

Cellar door: No cellar door sales or tastings at winery itself; tastings at the Bridgewater Mill (08) 339 3422, with restaurant.
Winemaker: Brian Croser.

Using the temperature control equipment evolved in the 1960s and 1970s, Petaluma produces (for itself and for a number of other makers) a high-quality range of premium table wines, especially Rhine riesling, chardonnay and cabernet. One-fifth of the company is owned by Bollinger of France, and Petaluma have produced their own champagne, 'Croser'.

While there is no cellar door outlet at the discreetly signposted Petaluma Winery behind Mount Lofty in the lush Adelaide Hills, wines can be tasted at the cellar door of the Petaluma Bridgewater Mill (see above), not far away near the hamlet of Bridgewater. Len Evans, Chairman of Petaluma, can be seen visiting the winery regularly. National distribution.

Robert Hamilton & Son *Springton Winery, Hamilton's Road, Springton SA 5235. (085) 68 2264.*

Cellar door: Seven days 10–4. Picnic areas. Bankcard, Diner's Club, Amex, Visa.
Winemaker: Robert Hamilton.

Owners Robert and Mark Hamilton are fifth and sixth generation Australian members of the famous Hamilton wine family. When Hamilton's Ewell Vineyards was sold in 1979 the family left the industry but started again, in a smaller way, two years later. Range of varietal wines and tawny port. Wines sold through mail order and retail outlets.

Stafford Ridge Wines *Lenswood SA 5240. (08) 272 2105.*

This small family concern, based in the Hills near Mount Lofty, is run by Geoff Weaver, who during daylight hours is the Chief Winemaker for the Hardy Wine Company. Seven hectares of vines are planted to riesling, cabernet, chardonnay, merlot and sauvignon blanc and all wine comes from grapes grown at Stafford Ridge. Winery not open to the public but the wines—which are very good indeed—can be purchased from the maker (2 Gilpin Lane, Mitcham SA 5062) and from agents in Victoria and New South Wales. Best vintages 1980, 1985, 1986 and 1988.

Temple Bruer *Milang Road (14 kilometres from Strathalbyn), Angas Plains SA 5070. (085) 37 0203.*

Cellar door: Cellar door and tastings are held in a special tasting room at the Wine Vat Restaurant, Wellington Road, Langhorne Creek SA 5255, (085) 37 3196. Open seven days 10.30–4.30. Bankcard, Visa, Amex, Mastercard.
Winemakers: David Bruer and David Haeusler

First vintage 1982 from a fifteen-year-old vineyard. Light dry reds, medium-bodied reds, sparkling burgundy, Eden Valley riesling, rosé and sauternes. Distributed almost nationally.

Wilson's *Woods Hill Road, Summertown SA 5141. (08) 390 3536.*

Cellar door: Operating in 1991.
Winemaker: Charles Hargrave.

Established in 1987. Owned by a syndicate of businessmen, the main shareholder being Ian Wilson. Vines planted to chardonnay and pinot noir, making only sparkling wines. Available nationally through retail outlets, restaurants and mail order (above address).

Lower Eyre Peninsula/ Kangaroo Island

Eyre Peninsula is one of Australia's newest wine areas. It is a large peninsula separated from Adelaide by 240 crow-flying kilometres and a lot more by road around the top of the Gulf of St Vincent and Spencer Gulf. There are several wineries and vineyards in the Boston Bay area, near Port Lincoln, a tourist delight which few Australian tourists have so far discovered.

Although they are separated by some 160 kilometres of water, Boston Bay and Kangaroo Island, at the mouth of the Gulf of St Vincent (St Vincent was the Patron Saint of winemakers!) share some maritime climatic similarities.

Kangaroo Island, the third largest island off the Australian mainland (the other two large islands being, of course, Tasmania and Melville Island) has had vineyards for some years, and will undoubtedly eventually have a winery or two. The major vineyard is at Emu Bay, not far from the biggest town, Kingscote, and it is owned by enterprising Adelaide builder, Caj Amadio. Results from the chalkstone soil are promising, with chardonnay, cabernet sauvignon and pinot noir planted there, and riesling on the way.

Boston Bay Wines *Lincoln Highway, Port Lincoln SA 5606. (086) 84 3600 or (086) 84 3521.*

Cellar door: Weekends, public holidays and school holidays 10–5. Bankcard, Mastercard and Visa. Closest vineyard to the sea and has a deer park within the vineyard.
Winemaker: Roger Harboard.

Owned by the Ford family; etablished in 1984. Wines include Rhine riesling, cabernet sauvignon and merlot, and quality, especially with the whites, is quite high.

Some guidance has been given to this new winery by Lehmann's in the Barossa Valley. Available through cellar door, retail outlets in Adelaide and mail order (PO Box 364, Port Lincoln SA 5606).

Delacolline Estate *Whillas Road, Port Lincoln SA 5606. (086) 82 5277.*

Cellar door: By appointment only.
Winemaker: Contract winemakers.

Owned by Durandel Pty Ltd, a syndicate of five businessmen. Established in 1984, with vineyards planted to cabernet sauvignon, merlot, shiraz, sauvignon blanc, semillon, chardonnay and Rhine riesling. Enquiries PO Box 1634, Port Lincoln SA 5606.

Barossa Valley

This is, perhaps, Australia's most famous wine area. The other contender would be the Hunter Valley of New South Wales. Out of interest, the Barossa produces some 10 per cent of Australia's wine, the

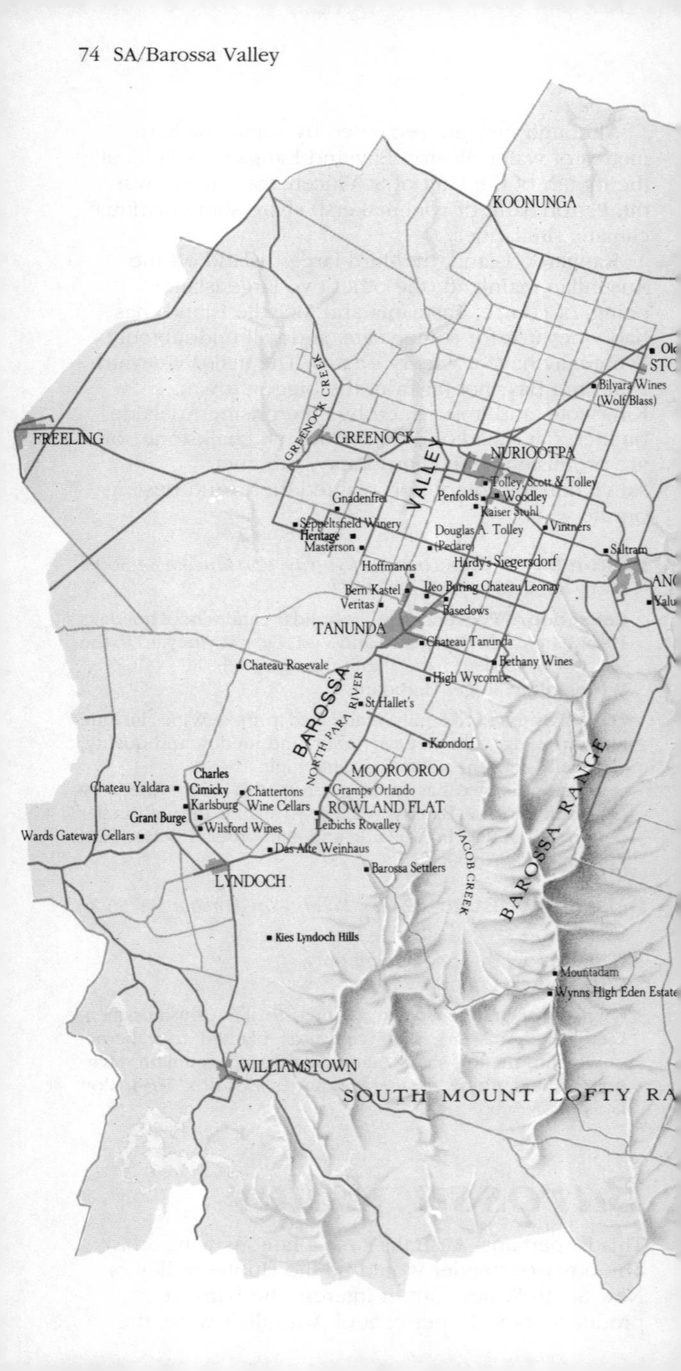

KOONUNGA
Bilyara Wines
(Wolf Blass)
FREELING
GREENOCK CREEK
GREENOCK
VALLEY
NURIOOTPA
Tolley, Scott & Tolley
Penfolds
Woodley
Kaiser Stuhl
Gnadenfrei
Seppeltsfield Winery
Heritage
Masterson
Douglas A. Tolley
(Pedare)
Vintners
Saltram
Hoffmanns
Hardy's Siegersdorf
Bern Kastel
Leo Buring Chateau Leonay
Veritas
Basedows
TANUNDA
Chateau Tanunda
Chateau Rosevale
Bethany Wines
High Wycombe
BAROSSA
NORTH PARA RIVER
St Hallet's
Krondorf
MOOROOROO
Charles
Cimicky
Chateau Yaldara
Chattertons
Wine Cellars
Karlsburg
Gramps Orlando
ROWLAND FLAT
Grant Burge
Wilsford Wines
Leibichs Rovalley
Wards Gateway Cellars
Das Alte Weinhaus
Barossa Settlers
LYNDOCH
JACOB CREEK
BAROSSA RANGE
Kies Lyndoch Hills
Mountadam
Wynns High Eden Estate
WILLIAMSTOWN
SOUTH MOUNT LOFTY RA

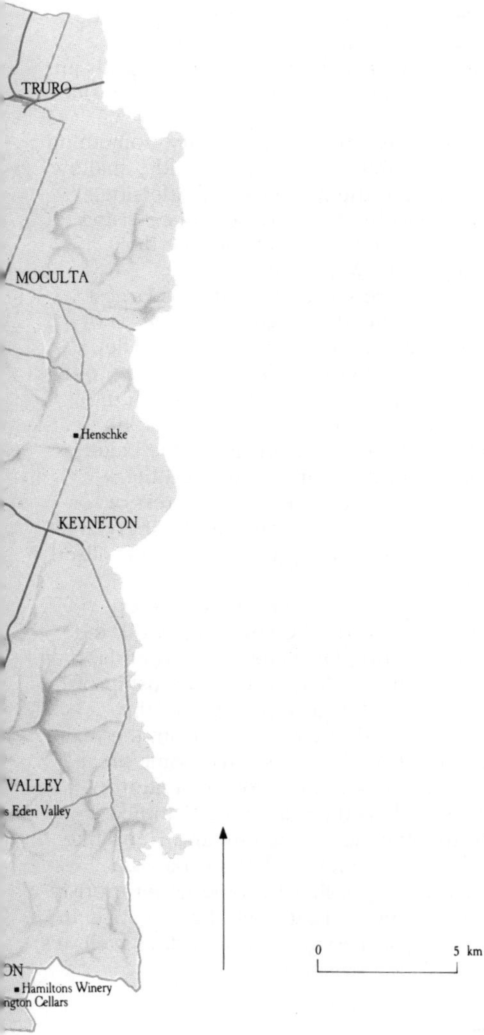

TRURO
MOCULTA
Henschke
KEYNETON
VALLEY
s Eden Valley
0
5 km
ON
Hamiltons Winery
ngton Cellars

Lower Hunter produces somewhere about 2 per cent.

Like the Hunter, the Barossa Valley is close to a large capital city, Adelaide, and shares its attractiveness and, traditionally, the quality of its wines. The German nature of the Valley, inherited from its German/Silesian settlers from the mid-1800s, adds an extra dimension of interest for the visitor. And visitors there are aplenty.

'Valley' is, as always in the Big Country, something of a misnomer. The Barossa Valley is a wide, shallow depression running to the north-east of Adelaide, bounded on the east by the Barossa Ranges, rising to over 400 metres. On the other side are the dry flatlands leading to the Murray River.

Inside the Valley are some of Australia's largest wineries, processing huge tonnages of grapes (not always, indeed often not, coming from the Valley's vineyards). Still, for the visitor, dropping by the towns of Nuriootpa, Tanunda and Angaston is worth the time—even a day or so—on the way to or from Adelaide. The pub food is usually good, the bakeries and butcher shops (with their wursts and other German fare) are the places to go for interest or for picnic fodder. There are some parks and winery areas where a lunchtime stop can be conducted in civilised style, flies permitting!

Restaurants include Die Weinstube (between Tanunda and Nuriootpa on the Sturt Highway), the excellent Pheasant Farm, Die Galerie in Tanunda, plus a few eateries at wineries. The historic township of Angaston, nestling on the eastern slopes of the Barossa Ranges, is worth the diversion from the main road into and out of Adelaide, as it has some great eating places and tourist nooks, not to mention nearby wineries such as the admirable Yalumba complex, and the wineries of Saltram and Henschke.

If a criticism could be levelled at the Barossa Valley, it is that the region has become rather touristy and 'on the beaten track'. That might be the price an area pays for being successful at what it does well. It's still a very nice place to visit.

Eating out

The Barossa has, as one would expect from Australia's best known wine area, plenty of places at which to eat out. There are also some delightful picnic spots—

as central as the 'train' park in Nuriootpa, or as informal as some rural spots along the highways and byways of the Barossa Hills to the eastern side of the valley.

Not surprisingly, many of the Valley's restaurants have a strong German influence. But there is also something for every palate and pocket. The Tanunda Hotel (Murray Street, Tanunda [085] 63 2030) has counter lunches every day. One of the best-known eateries is Die Weinstube (on the Barossa Valley Way, just south of Nuriootpa [095] 62 1416), a favourite haunt of local vignerons and, of course, big on sauerkraut and sausages.

Die Galerie (66 Murray Street, Tanunda [085] 63 2788) has mainly French cuisine and is in a pleasant, art gallery location. The Weingarten Restaurant in the Weintal Motel (Murray Street, Tanunda [085] 63 2303) is also central. In charming Angaston, a little off the beaten track for travellers passing through the Barossa (but well worth the slight diversion), there is Vintners' Restaurant (Nuriootpa Road [085] 64 2488).

Saving the best to last, there is the Pheasant Farm Restaurant, run by Colin and Maggie Beer, not far from the giant Seppeltsfield Winery, just west of Nuriootpa ([085] 62 1286). It is surely one of the most delightful eating spots in Australia, defying the old adage: 'Never eat in restaurants which float, revolve or have spectacular views!' The restaurant sits out over a large lake, stocked with ducks, trout and yabbies. The food is just superb and, perhaps best of all, you can take your own wine if you wish.

Barossa Settlers *Trial Hill Road, Lyndoch SA 5351. (085) 24 4017.*

Cellar door: Monday–Saturday 10–4, Sunday 1–4, closed Tuesday, except during school holidays. Bankcard, Visa, Amex, Mastercard.

Winemaker: Doug Lehmann and Howard Haese.

Small winery founded in 1983 making dry and sweet whites, cabernet sauvignon and shiraz. Available only through cellar door.

Basedow Wines *161–165 Murray Street, Tanunda SA 5352. (085) 63 2060.*

Cellar door: Monday–Friday 9–5, Saturday and public holidays 10–5. Sunday 12–4. Group tours by appointment only. BBQs and picnic areas. All major credit cards. Restaurants within walking distance.

Winemakers: Doug Lehmann and Roger Harbord.

Winery founded 1896; original building still stands. Basedow is a very old established Barossa name, now owned by Peter Lehmann wines which, in turn, is owned by M. S. McLeod. Quality is good and the key products are Barossa hermitage, an enjoyable white burgundy and an old tawny port.

Bernkastel Wines *Corner Para and Langmeil Roads, Tanunda SA 5352. (085) 63 2595.*

Cellar door: Daily 10–5. Bankcard, Mastercard, Visa, Diner's.
Winemaker: No resident winemaker as at going to press.

Rhine riesling, cabernet sauvignon and shiraz; also specialising in fortifieds. The winery is now owned by Liquor Corp. and is managed by Bruce and Louise Strachan. Wines appearing under the Bernkastel label are available through cellar door and Vintage Cellars, Adelaide. Wines marketed as Chateau Marbay can be purchased from 33 Oaklands Road, Somerton Park, Adelaide SA 5044, (08) 294 5000.

Bethany Wines *Bethany Road, Tanunda SA 5352. (085) 63 2086.*

Cellar door: Monday–Saturday 10–5, Sunday 1–5. Tours by appointment. Picnic facilities. Bankcard, Mastercard, Visa.
Winemakers: Robert and Geoff Schrapel.

This small winery, owned by the Schrapel family, was founded in an old quarry overlooking the Barossa Valley, in 1981. Wine styles include dry riesling, spätlese riesling, auslese riesling, chardonnay, semillon, cabernet/merlot, shiraz, Quarry port and white port.

Bilyara Vineyards

See Wolf Blass International.

Charles Cimicky Wines *Gomersal Road, Lyndoch SA 5351. (085) 24 4025.*

Cellar door: Open daily 10–4.30. All major credit cards.
Winemaker: Charles Cimicky.

Owned by the Cimicky family, established in 1972. Specialises in premium regional varietal wines. Available through cellar door only.

Chateau Dorrien *Corner Sturt Highway and Seppeltsfield Road, Dorrien SA 5352. (085) 62 2850.*

Cellar door: Daily 9.30–5.30. Old concrete fermentation tanks have been converted to shops and tasting area. Bistro with German-style meals in the $7–$10 range, with German wines, beer and spirits served. Morning and afternoon teas, popcorn (and twenty-four flavours of ice-cream!) Children's barnyard. Bankcard, Mastercard, Visa.

Winemaker: Fernando Martin.

This famous old Seppelt winery, owned by Fernando and Jeanette Martin, with its eighty-six concrete storage tanks, was started in 1913. Chateau Dorrien was launched in 1984. Wines include Rhine riesling, chablis, chenin blanc, traminer, cabernet sauvignon, cabernet/shiraz, tawny and vintage port, frontignac, spätlese, semillon, sauternes and four meads made from honey. Available only at cellar door.

Chateau Yaldara Estate *Gomersal Road, Lyndoch SA 5351. (085) 24 4200.*

Cellar door: Monday–Friday 8.30–5, Saturday and Sunday 9–5. Features of Chateau Yaldara are regular tours and films of winemaking. The film, winery tour and chateau tours are at 10.15, 10.45, 1.15 , 2.15 and 3.15. Picnic areas available. Bistro 10–4, with coffee and cakes, light lunches 12–2. Amex, Bankcard, Mastercard, Visa.
Winemaker: Dieter Thumm.

Owner Herman Thumm created this extraordinary edifice near the southern entrance to the Barossa Valley in 1947 after he arrived from Europe. The splendid stone chateau is full of works of art, there is a reception centre, and the Thumms also run the nearby Chateau Yaldara Motor Inn. Key products include Lakewood premium range of wines (there are two artificial lakes near the winery) and a range of premium white and red wines. Distribution: cellar door and nationally.

Eden Valley Wines *Main Street, Eden Valley SA 5235. (085) 64 1111.*

Cellar door: Daily 10–5. All major credit cards. Restaurant open seven days for lunch and dinner. Open until midnight for meals on Friday, Saturday and Sunday. Seats 300 inside and 400 outside. Group bookings by appointment.
Winemaker: Peter Thompson.

Owned by Peter and Karolina Thompson; established 1990. Wines include (under the Eden Valley Wines label—all from local fruit): Rhine riesling, traminer, spätlese frontignac, chardonnay, nouveau, pinot noir, shiraz, cabernet sauvignon and champagne. Under the Eden Springs Wine Estate label, made from grapes from the Estate, are a 1989 and 1990 Rhine riesling. Available through cellar door and in Brisbane, Sydney, Melbourne and Adelaide.

Elderton Wines *3 Tanunda Road, Nuriootpa SA 5355. (085) 62 1058.*

Cellar door: Monday–Friday 9–5, weekends and holidays 10–5. Landscaped lawn areas for picnics, park opposite. Vineyard tours. All major credit cards.
Winemaker: Neil Ashmead

Wines made from own vineyard fruit and other selected

Barossa growers. First vintage 1982. The company, run by Lorraine and Neil Ashmead, specialises in well-made dry red, white and sparkling wines with three major ranges: the Elderton Domain series, the Elderton Elegant series and the Elderton Command Performance series. All available nationally and through cellar door. Also exported.

Gnadenfrei Estate *Seppeltsfield Road, Marananga SA 5360. (085) 62 2522.*

Cellar door: Daily 10–5.30. No tours. BBQ area, indoor cellar. Restaurant serves light lunches (main course under $10). This winery also specialises in dinner parties and Barossa picnic baskets which can be taken away or eaten in winery grounds. Bankcard, Diner's Club, Visa, Mastercard.
Winemaker: Malcolm Seppelt.

This small winery, with views of the Barossa Valley, was founded by another breakaway group of the Seppelt family in 1979. Wines include dry reds and dry whites, plus late-picked whites and ports. Available only at cellar door and by mail order.

Grant Burge Wines *Jacobs Creek (on the main road between Lyndoch and Tanunda), Barossa Valley SA 5352.*

Cellar door: Open daily from 10–5. All major credit cards.
Winemaker: Grant Burge.

Owned by Grant and Helen Burge. Grant was one of the names behind Krondorf in the 1970s and 1980s. They bought this historic property in 1988 and restored it to a working wine centre, which features custom-built chandeliers, extensive use of jarrah wood and ornamental glass created for the new building. Grant makes his wine at Basedows, but a new winery is being built on the site. Premium wines include wood-matured semillon, Barossa frontignan, chardonnay, Rhine riesling and sauvignon blanc. Also available are amontillado sherry, a very old liqueur frontignan and a very old tawny port. Available through cellar door and mail order (PO Box 421, Tanunda SA 5352).

Hardy's Siegersdorf *Barossa Valley Way, Tanunda SA 5352. (085) 63 2071, head office (08) 381 2266.*

Cellar door: Monday–Friday 9–5, Saturday, Sunday and public holidays 10–4.30. No tours, as Siegersdorf is now not a major production centre for the Hardy Wine Company. Picnic area. Situated centrally in the Valley, near the railway crossing on the main road just outside Tanunda. All major credit cards.

The winery was named after a Silesian village used as a stopover by Napoleon on his way back from Moscow (the name Siegersdorf means 'Conqueror's Village'—not very accurate, when you think about what happened in Russia!).

The company's Siegersdorf Rhine Riesling and Chardonnay, together with a complete range of Hardy's admirable other products, can still be tasted here.

Henschke Cellars *Moculta Road (5 kilometres north of Keyneton), Keyneton SA 5353. (085) 64 8223.*

Cellar door: Monday–Friday 9–4.30, Saturday 9–12, closed Sunday, Christmas Day, New Year's Day and Good Friday; other holidays open only by appointment. Tours by arrangement. Bankcard, Mastercard, Visa.
Winemaker: Stephen Henschke.

The Henschke family is one of the longest established Barossa families and their winery dates from 1868. Specialises in dry varietal table wines, white and red. Best known brands include the excellent Hill of Grace and Mt Edelstone reds, both named after local vineyards. Distributed nationally.

Heritage Wines *Seppeltsfield Road, Marananga, via Tanunda SA 5362. (085) 62 2880.*

Cellar door: Daily 9–6.
Winemaker: Stephen Hoff.

A generally good small maker of semillon, chardonnay, riesling, shiraz, cabernet sauvignon and cabernet franc. Available through cellar door and mailing list (PO Box 129, Angaston SA 5353).

High Wycombe Wines *Bethany Road, Bethany SA 5352. (085) 63 2776.*

Cellar door: Most days 9–5. Nearby Bethany Reserve for picnics. Five cottages available on property for overnight accommodation, including light breakfast; serviced. Riding school with eighteen horses run by the winery. Trail rides, pleasure rides and lessons. Landhaus restaurant is three doors away. Mastercard, Bankcard, Visa.
Winemaker: Colin Davis.

Owned by Angela Davis, established in 1974. Wines include Bethany white frontignac and Rhine riesling, Bethany red shiraz and cabernet. Selection of ports and muscats. All wines made on the premises and sold only at cellar door.

Hoffman's North Para

See Peter Lehmann Wines.

Irvine's *Roeselers Road, Eden Valley SA 5235. (085) 64 1046.*

Winemaker: James Irvine.

Jim Irvine is a skilled winemaker who has worked for a number of large makers. He is now running his own show. Winery established to make sparkling wine (blanc de blanc). Merlot and chardonnay planted.

Kaesler Wines *Barossa Valley Way, Nuriootpa SA 5355. (085) 62 2711.*

Cellar door: Wednesday–Sunday and public holidays 10–5. Bankcard, Mastercard, Visa, Amex.
Winemaker: Made at Basedows.

Owned by Toby and Treena Hueppauff who have recently opened their cellar door. They specialise in semillon and shiraz, the shiraz vines being 100 years old. In fact, most of the vines planted are well over 30 years old. Wines include Rhine riesling, a late harvest Rhine riesling, semillon, late harvest semillon, shiraz, cabernet sauvignon, port, muscat and sherry. Available through cellar door.

Kaiser Stuhl Wines *Sturt Highway, Nuriootpa SA 5355. (085) 62 0290.*

See Penfolds Wines, this section.

Kellermeister Wines *Barossa Highway, Lyndoch SA 5351. (085) 24 4303.*

Cellar door: Daily 9–6. No tours. No BBQs. All major credit cards.
Winemaker: Trevor Jones.

Owned by the Jones family; established in April 1979. Wine styles include table whites and reds, and tawny and vintage ports. Sold only at cellar door; labelled as Kellermeister Wines and Das Alte Weinhous.

Kies Lyndoch Hills *Lyndoch–Williamstown Highway, Lyndoch SA 5351 (PO Box 4, Lyndoch SA 5351). (085) 24 4110.*

Cellar door: Daily 10–4. Picnic areas and BBQs. Bankcard, Visa.
Winemaker: James Irvine.

Owned by the Kies family; vineyards planted 1880; winery launched 1968 (formerly named Karrawirra). Wines include Rhine riesling, semillon, frontignac, fumé blanc, cabernet sauvignon and light reds.

Koala Ridge Vineyard *Main Road, Eden Valley SA 5235. (085) 64 1025.*

Not open to the public. (Vineyard for Mildara Wines—enquiries to them at [050] 25 2303. Export label.)

Kroemer Estate Wines *Barossa Valley Way, Tanunda SA 5352. (085) 63 3375.*

Cellar door: Open seven days 10–5. Mastercard, Bankcard, Visa, Diner's Club.
Winemaker: Consultants.

Owned by Michael Hislop, Robert Taplin and Trevor Cowling.

Wines include sylvaner, Rhine riesling, shiraz, cabernet sauvignon, champagne and tawny port. Available at cellar door.

Krondorf Wines *Krondorf Road, Tanunda SA 5352. (085) 63 2145.*

Cellar door: Monday–Sunday 10–5, closed Christmas Day, Good Friday. All major credit cards.
Winemaker: Nick Walker.

Krondorf's good range of table wines include dry whites (Rhine riesling, chardonnay, traminer and blends, plus a commercial chablis) and reds (cabernet, shiraz, cabernet franc and blends), plus fortified wines, often from the Barossa and/or McLaren Vale. The company was taken over by Victoria's Mildara in late 1985, but was originally founded in 1861. National distribution and some internatonal.

Leo Buring *Chateau Leonay, Para Road, just off the Sturt Highway on the northern outskirts of Tanunda SA 5352. (085) 63 2184.*

Cellar door: Monday–Friday 9–4.30, Saturday and public holidays 11–4.30, Sunday 12–4. All major credit cards.
Winemakers: John Vickery, Robert Ruediger, Tracey Low

The winery and vineyards date back to 1887 and were purchased by the late Leo Buring, who developed the winery and built the imposing three storey Flemish chateau. Some of Australia's greatest Rhine rieslings, made from fruit emanating from the Barossa, Eden and Clare (Watervale) areas, were produced here, and several of the greatest Australian rieslings I have tasted, including the splendid 1972 and 1973 DW wines, are (still) outstanding examples. Apart from current vintage white and red wines, the cellar door sales offer a selection of older Reserve Rhine rieslings. The company is a division of Lindeman, in turn now owned by Penfolds.

Old Stockwell Cellars *Duck Ponds Road (behind Stockwell Hotel), Stockwell SA 5355.*

Cellar door: 10–4 daily.
Winemaker: Made at Chateau Dorrien.

Wines include cabernet sauvignon, Rhine riesling, Rhine riesling spätlese, white burgundy, frontignac spätlese, frontignac blanc, port, sherry and old raisin liqueur. Available through cellar door.

Orlando Wines *Barossa Valley Highway, Rowland Flat SA 5352. (085) 24 4500. Head office: 33 Exeter Terrace, Devon Park SA 5008. (08) 208 2444.*
Cellar door: Monday–Friday 9.30–5, Saturday, Sunday and public holidays 10–4. BBQ, picnic and children's play areas. Delicatessen opposite. All major credit cards.
Chief Winemaker: Robin Day.

Founded by the Gramp family in 1847, Orlando is now owned by Pernod Ricard of France. The large range of wines, both table, sparkling and fortified, come from the very large Barossa winery at Rowland Flat (south of Tanunda), from Griffith in New South Wales and elsewhere. Wine styles include Jacob's Creek, Australia's largest selling bottled red wine, now accompanied by a Rhine riesling and chardonnay; the RF (for Rowland Flat) cabernet and pinot noir; a premium range including St Helga Rhine Riesling, St Helga Chardonnay, St Hugo Coonawarra Cabernet; plus the ubiquitous Coolabah cask range. There are many others, from Carrington champagnes through to fortified and imported wines, from this excellent maker, which in turn owns the Wyndham Estate group in New South Wales. Also a major exporter.

Penfold/Kaiser Stuhl Wines *Sturt Highway, Nuriootpa SA 5355. (085) 62 0290.*

Cellar door: Monday–Friday 9–5, Saturday and public holidays 10–5, Sunday 1–5. Tours 10, 11, 1.30 and 2.30 (except public holidays and weekends). No picnic or BBQ areas, but park nearby, plus a number of restaurants and hotels. All major credit cards.
Winemakers: Various (Senior Production Manager is John Duval).

There are two very big wineries here, side by side, at the heart of the Barossa Valley. This is the production home of Australia's largest wine group, with Penfolds at the centre of it, all owned by Adelaide-based Adsteam (controlled by John Spalvins) which owns other things, such as David Jones.

Kaiser Stuhl (the 'Seat of Kings')—the name of a nearby peak in the Barossa Ranges—was a large co-operative winery (once owned by grape-growers) established in 1912. The co-op was taken over by Penfolds in 1982. The spectacular cellars can't be missed, just on the southern outskirts of Nuriootpa. This has now been integrated with Penfolds, forming a huge winery. Kaiser Stuhl was noted for years for its excellent Barossa rieslings (dry and fruity/sweet) and some good reds; today it is harder to differentiate between Kaiser Stuhl wines and those of its parent/partner wineries, Penfolds and Wynn's.

Many of Penfolds' great reds, such as Grange Hermitage, St Henri, Bin 707 Cabernet Sauvignon, Bin 389 and Bin 128, come from this site. Many other excellent wines are available at the cellar, right across the tasting spectrum of Kaiser Stuhl, TST, Wynn's/Seaview and their other companies.

Peter Lehmann Wines *Para Road, Tanunda SA 5352. (085) 63 2500.*

Cellar door: Monday–Friday 9.30–5.30, Saturday, Sunday and public holidays 10.30–4.30 All major credit cards.
Winemakers: Peter Lehmann, Doug Lehmann, Andrew Wigan, Peter Scholz and Leonie Bain.

A large producer making wine under the Peter Lehmann labels, plus wine for a number of other makers. Now owned by the M. S. McLeod group. Peter and son Doug are among the Barossa's best known characters, and until Peter started his own business (with backing from others, including the Cerebos salt company) he was winemaker at Saltram in the Valley. A wide range of quality table and fortified wines, including Rhine riesling, wood-matured semillon, semillon sauternes, chenin blanc, shiraz, pinot noir, cabernet and ports. A Lehmann red wine won the 1990 Jimmy Watson Trophy at the Melbourne Wine Show and the Stoddart Trophy. Lehmann also owns Hoffman's North Para, founded 1847, but the label was discontinued several years ago. Mailing list and national distribution includes some premium aged wines and the appealing Clancy's red blend and the Cellar Collection range of wines.

Rockford Wines *Krondorf Road, Tanunda SA 5352. (085) 63 2720.*

Cellar door: Daily 11–5. No BBQs. All major credit cards.
Winemaker: Robert O'Callaghan.

Tanunda Vintners owns this small winery, which makes premium wines, including some unusual styles and varieties, notably a sparkling red wine which is delicious. Distribution through cellar door and some restaurants.

Roseworthy College Cellars *Roseworthy Agricultural College (4 kilometres from the small town of Roseworthy), Roseworthy SA 5371. (085) 24 8222. See Adelaide map.*

Cellar door: Monday–Friday 10–4.30, closed weekends unless for functions, by arrangement. BBQ areas, restaurants available at Gawler, ten minutes' drive away. Catering for functions is available by arrangement only. Use of student dining room by arrangement also. All major credit cards.
Winemaker: Tricia Jane.

Roseworthy is South Australia's major agricultural college, and also Australia's oldest winemaking (and now also wine-marketing) school, having trained some of the country's greatest winemakers. The college has been operating since last century, and its winery (which can be toured, by arrangement) was established in 1936. The college makes and markets wines, in all States, as a part of student training. Roseworthy is near the southern end of the Barossa Valley but, being just off the beaten track, is little appreciated by most visitors. Wide range of table, sparkling and fortified wines.

Rovalley Wine Hillside Vineyard *Sturt Highway, Rowland Flat SA 5352. (085) 24 4537.*

Cellar door: Monday–Friday 9–4.30, weekends, holidays 10.30–4.30; closed Christmas Day, Good Friday. Bankcard,

Mastercard, Visa. The Gingerbread Shop nearby sells coffee, snacks.
Winemakers: Christopher Schmidt and Karl Lambert.

Founded 1919, the key wines are red and white table wines, flagon wines, fortifieds and sparkling wines. Distributed through cellar door and retail outlets in most States.

St Hallett (Lindner McLean Vineyards and Cellars) *St Halletts Road, Tanunda SA 5352. (085) 63 2319.*

Cellar door: Monday–Saturday 10–5, Sunday 10–4. Picnic area around dam, lawn. All major credit cards except Diner's Club. Tours on request only.
Winemaker: Stuart Blackwell.

Founded in 1944, the winery is now run by Carl Lindner, Stuart Blackwell and Bob McLean, and between them they have revved the old place up in the last few years—worth a visit. Wines under the St Hallett/Lindner McLean Vineyards and Cellars label include some high-quality dry whites and reds with some lovely old fortifieds. Available through cellar door and interstate distribution.

Saltram Wine Estates *Angaston Road (just east of Angaston), Angaston SA 5353. (085) 64 2200.*

Cellar door: Monday–Friday 9–5, weekends 12–5., public holidays 10–5. No tours but lawns for picnics. All major credit cards.
Winemaker: Mark Turnbull.

Founded in 1859, owned by giant Canadian-based corporation, Continental Seagram Pty Ltd. A historic and attractive winery set in the Barossa hills just outside Angaston. Special cellar door range of varietal wines, plus older museum stocks. Range of commercial products—top range is Pinnacle Selection wines—available nationally. Large, high-quality maker featuring products such as Saltram varietals (and a good chardonnay), plus classics such as Mamre Brook, Mr Pickwick Port and Metala Claret. If you are a fortified enthusiast, a visit to this winery is a must!

Seppelt's Wines *Seppeltsfield (signposted to the north-east of Tanunda), via Tanunda SA 5352. (085) 63 2626. Head office: 181 Flinders Street, Adelaide SA 5000. (08) 236 3400.*

Cellar door: Monday–Friday 8.30–5, Saturday 10.30–4.30, Sunday 11–4, public holidays 10–5. Large BBQ area (twelve BBQs), picnic area with seating, two ovals. Kiosk. Tours daily. Seppeltsfield is now classified under the State Heritage Act as a historic village and is a major tourist attraction of South Australia. All major credit cards.
Winemaker: Various, but Brian Miller—who is both charming and erudite—runs this operation.

Seppeltsfield is one of the Barossa's larger and more significant wineries, with its characteristic boulevards of palm trees and mausoleum for the departed members of the family who launched this major—and very high-quality—winemaking dynasty in 1851. The company, based in Adelaide, along with other wineries (notably Great Western, in Victoria), was taken over by the SA Brewing Company in 1985; it subsequently took over Woodley Wines in July 1985. Seppelt's famous Para Ports (some over 100 years old), plus other great fortified wines and sherries are made here, together with wide range of sparkling (Great Western Champagne) and red and white table wines. A 'must' stop for the wine enthusiast, if not for every tourist in the Barossa. Very successful at major Australian wine shows in recent years, making an across-the-board range of good to exceptional wines. Wide national distribution.

Tarchalice Wines *Research Road, Vine Vale, via Tanunda SA 5352. (085) 63 3005.*

Cellar door: Monday–Saturday 10–5, Sunday 11–5. Tours welcomed, picnic area, restaurant 500 metres away. Bankcard, Mastercard, Visa.
Winemaker: Christopher Schmidt.

Wines include Rhine riesling, gewürtztraminer (experimenting with botrytis riesling), shiraz, cabernet sauvignon, merlot and ten-year-old tawny port. Distribution through cellar door.

Tollana Wines *Tolley, Scott and Tolley, Sturt Highway (on the outskirts of Nuriootpa on the Adelaide side), Nuriootpa SA 5355. (085) 62 0408. All wines can be obtained from Penfolds' cellar door, along with Penfolds and Kaiser Stuhl wines.*

Cellar door: Monday–Friday and holidays 9–5, Saturday 10–5, Sunday 1–5. Organised tours, weekends excepted
Winemakers: Various

The trio who gave their names to this large maker have, of course, long gone (they began in 1888, though the company dates back three decades from that). The winery is now owned by SA Brewing Holdings. Distillation has featured prominently in TST's history. First they were a major brandy maker, more recently they were the Australian subsidiary of a large Scotch company. Generally, very high-quality table wines and fine sparkling wines belied the factory-like front of TST.

Tolley's Pedare *Seppeltsfield Road, Nuriootpa SA 5355. (085) 62 1366.*

Cellar door: Open Friday, Saturday and public holidays 10–5, except during school holidays when they are open seven days. Bankcard, Diner's Club, Mastercard, Visa.

Cellar door outlet for Douglas A. Tolley (Pedare brands). See Adelaide section.

Twin Valley Estate *Red Gum Vineyards, Hoffnungsthal Road, Lyndoch SA 5351. (085) 24 4584.*

Cellar door: Seven days 10–5. Organised tours available. Large picnic, BBQ areas available. Bankcard, Mastercard, Visa.
Winemaker: Fernando Martin.

Owned by Fernando and Jeanette Martin (see also Chateau Dorrien, this section). Wines available are cabernet sauvignon, cabernet franc, semillon, sauvignon blanc, Rhine riesling and fortifieds. Available through cellar door.

Veritas Winery *94 Langmeil Road, Tanunda SA 5352. (085) 63 2330.*

Cellar door: Monday–Saturday, 9–5, weekends, holidays 11–5. Lunches by appointment. Bankcard, Mastercard, Visa.
Winemaker: Rolf Binder.

Hungary plays a special part in the food and wines of this small winery, owned by the Binder family. Leanyka (semi-sweet white), Bikavar ('Bull's Blood' red) and a full range of varietal red and white wines are available.

Ward's Gateway Cellar *Barossa Valley Highway, Lyndoch SA 5351. (085) 24 4138.*

Cellar door: Daily 9–5.30. No picnic or BBQ facilities.
Winemaker: Ray Ward.

Owned by the Ward family. Dry white and dry red wines, and fortified wines. Sold at cellar door and by mail order.

The Willows Vineyard *Light Pass Road, Light Pass SA 5355. (085) 62 1080.*

Cellar door: Open seven days 10.30–4.30. Mastercard, Bankcard, Visa.
Winemakers: Peter and Michael Scholz.

Owned by the Scholz family, this property was taken up in 1845 and was where the pioneer Willows Hospital stood. The vines are over half a century old, and wines include Rhine riesling, semillon, pinor noir, shiraz and cabernet sauvignon. Available through cellar door, restaurants and some outlets in Adelaide.

Wilsford Wines *Gomersal Road, Lyndoch SA 5351. (085) 24 4644.*

Cellar door: Monday–Saturday and public holidays 10–5, Sundays 11–4. Bankcard, Visa and Mastercard.
Winemaker: Noel and Rick Burge.

Established in 1928, owned by the Burge family. Local table and fortified/dessert wines, and sparkling wines.

Wolf Blass International *Sturt Highway, Nuriootpa SA 5355. (085) 62 1955, Adelaide head office (08) 232 0255.*

Cellar door: Monday–Friday 9.15–4.30, Saturday, Sunday and public holidays 12–4.30. Elaborate tasting rooms but no BBQ/picnic areas. There is a wine heritage museum—no entry charge. The winery is well out of the Barossa town of Nuriootpa, that is, on the way out of Adelaide on the main road, but there are plenty of picnic areas, parks, restaurants and hotels in and around 'Nuri' (as the town is locally known). All major credit cards.
Winemakers: Wolf Blass (owner), John Glaetzer, David Wardlaw, Stephen John, Chris Hatcher and Christa Binder.

Blass is an extraordinary immigrant success story. He based his expansion on the exceptional quality of his red wines (winning the Jimmy Watson Trophy three times running). His company now owns Tim Knappstein Wines, Eaglehawk Estate and various vineyards and production interests. Other major lines include Yellow Label Rhine Riesling (one of the biggest selling in Australia), frontignac, Classic Dry White, champagne and Yellow, Grey and Black Label reds with outstanding wine show records. His reds continue to impress for intensity of fruit, balance and excellent wood treatment. The garish winery itself is worth a visit because of the technical excellence of its products.

Yalumba Wines *Eden Valley Road (on the uphill, southern side of the town), Angaston SA 5353. (085) 64 2423 (PO Box 10, Angaston SA 5353). Adelaide office (08) 51 3963.*

Cellar door: Monday–Friday 8.30–5, Saturday and public holidays 10–5, Sunday 12–5. Lawns, gardens and pergola surrounded by horses, houses and family members of the proprietors, S. Smith & Sons. There is an excellent tasting centre and wine-buying area. Old buildings. Entertainment and meals in winery, by arrangement. All major credit cards.
Winemakers: Peter Wall, Brian Walsh, Allan Hoey, Geoff Linton, Simon Adams, David Zimmerman and Andrew Murphy.

This beautiful winery was founded in 1849 by the Smith family, who are still racing horses as keenly as they make fine wines. It is a little off the beaten Barossa track, but is thoroughly worth the ten-minute detour to Angaston.

Yalumba make some outstanding table and fortified wines, including brands such as Pewsey Vale Rhine Riesling and cabernet sauvignon, sweet whites, Heggie's Rhine Riesling, Hill Smith Estate wines (export). Their Oxford Landing series includes cabernet/shiraz, chardonnay and Rhine riesling (the vineyard [240 hectares] is at Oxford Landing on the River Murray), and there is a very wide range of other products, for example, Galway Tawny Port, and the Signature Series reds. Their champagnes are also very good.

Clare

The term 'valley' in the Australian wine industry generally means a broad, shallow area between low hills that may be scores or hundred of kilometres apart, a generalisation best illustrated by the example of the Murray Valley.

The Clare Valley is probably the best example of a clearly delineated valley, in the true geographical sense of the word, in Australia. Driving into the Clare Valley from the south (that is, from Adelaide or the Barossa) the road winds through rising hills, wooded areas, the towns of Watervale and Sevenhill and vineyards, until you reach the picturesque town of Clare.

The Clare region also abounds in paradoxes. While the Clare Valley itself is fairly clearly marked, offshoots have identities which they are determined to establish, for example, the Polish Hill River area—and there are others. While it is one of the most attractive tourist destinations (if you are into visiting wine areas), the Clare Valley is right off the beaten track: you are likely to be going to Central Australia or Broken Hill to go there on the way to somewhere else.

The area is producing some of the best wines to come from South Australia, from some of the most respected makers, such as Wolf Blass, Penfolds and Petaluma, to the locals, such as Tim Knappstein. The general drinking public are likely to know the area only because it is the spiritual home of one very large maker, Stanley, but this company has moved out of the area for its Leasingham cask operations.

Yet the quality of the white and red table wines from better makers in the Clare Valley can be extraordinarily high. The area is definitely worth visiting; there are fine restaurants and individualistic places to stay (for example, the splendid Mintaro Mews at Mintaro). There is an excellent wine and food weekend each year, perhaps the best in Australia.

There seems little doubt that Rhine riesling was, and is, the grape variety which has made Clare one of Australia's better wine areas but dry varieties, notably sauvignon blanc, and fine reds (cabernet, shiraz and blends including malbec) have been coming out of the area for a long time.

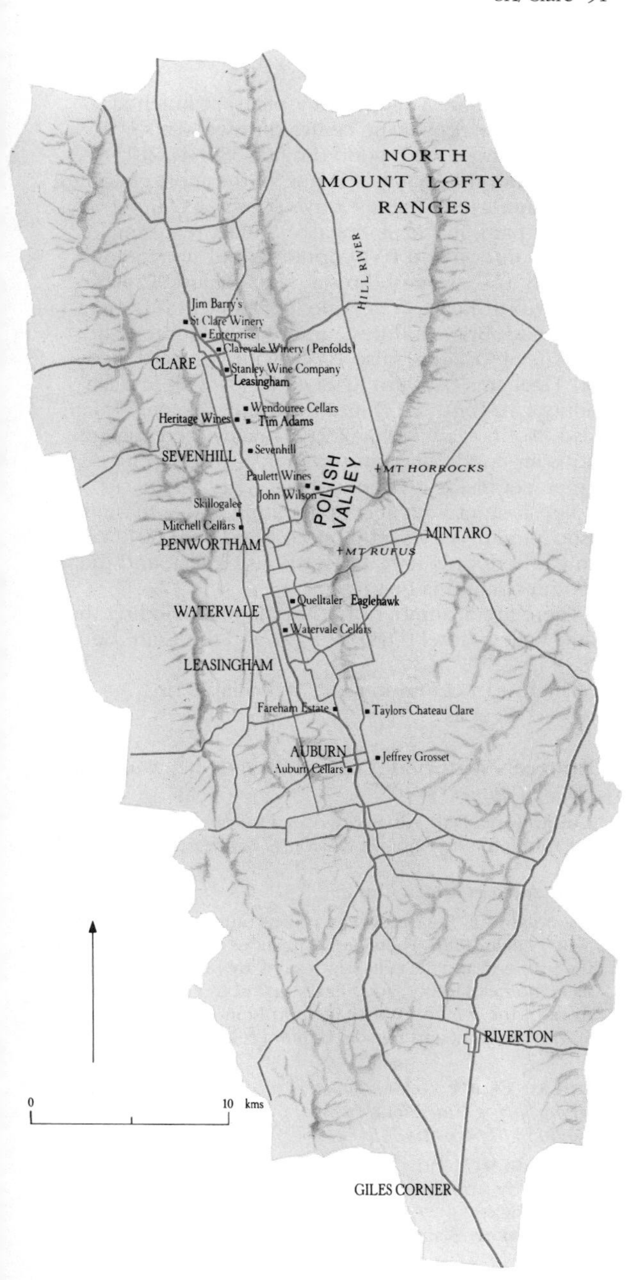
NORTH
MOUNT LOFTY
RANGES
HILL RIVER
Jim Barry's
St Clare Winery
Enterprise
Clarevale Winery (Penfolds)
CLARE
Stanley Wine Company
Leasingham
Wendouree Cellars
Heritage Wines
Tim Adams
SEVENHILL
Sevenhill
POLISH
VALLEY
+MT HORROCKS
Paulett Wines
John Wilson
Skillogalee
Mitchell Cellars
MINTARO
PENWORTHAM
+MT RUFUS
Quelltaler
Eaglehawk
WATERVALE
Watervale Cellars
LEASINGHAM
Fareham Estate
Taylors Chateau Clare
AUBURN
Jeffrey Grosset
Auburn Cellars
RIVERTON
0
10 kms
GILES CORNER

Eating out

Start in the Clare Valley with a pleasant lunch at Bentley's Hotel near the centre of town. This is a hotel and motel with good dining (088) 42 2815.

Kilikanoon Restaurant is one of the most charming in the area—ten minutes' drive south of Clare at Penwortham, in the Skillogalee Valley, featuring provincial food and BYO drinking, but no smoking (088) 43 4277. Licensed restaurants include Crawley's (Main North Road, Watervale [088] 43 0136) for à la carte food; Brice Hill Restaurant (Wendouree Road, Clare [088] 42 2786), also BYO, with vineyard views; and Tatehams (Auburn [088] 49 2030) with English county fare (both BYO and licensed); Treloars (Main Road, North Clare [088] 42 2277) has varied cuisine and is air-conditioned in summer, with open fires in winter, set inside a large motel.

A restaurant with accommodation is the charmingly rustic Mintaro Mews, at Mintaro (088) 43 9001. You can eat here only if you are a house guest, and the accommodation is first rate.

There are a number of good motels including the Clare Valley Motel (088) 42 2799 and the Clare Central (088) 42 2277.

The tourist centre in Clare is available on (088) 42 2131.

Crabtree's Watervale Cellars *North Terrace, Watervale SA 5452. (088) 43 0069.*

Cellar door: Daily 10–5. Lawn area for picnics. Winery tours by appointment. Families welcome. Bankcard, Diner's Club, Visa.

Winemaker: Robert Crabtree.

Founded in 1977. A new winery was built on the property at Watervale in 1986. There are 12 hectares of vineyards around the property and the cellar door sales are held at the heritage-listed home of Robert and Elizabeth Crabtree, which stands in front of the winery. Wines include Rhine riesling, semillon, shiraz/cabernet and muscat (limited release).

Duncan Estate *Three kilometres south of Clare, 300 metres along Spring Gully Road (west of Clare caravan park), Clare SA 5453. (088) 43 4335.*

Cellar door: Monday–Sunday 10–4, closed Good Friday. Bus groups by appointment. No BBQs. Bankcard, Mastercard, Visa, Amex .

Winemaker: Blair Duncan.

This family-owned property is twenty-two years old, but first vintage was in 1984. Wines include Rhine riesling, gewürztraminer, sauvignon blanc, müller thurgau, cabernet sauvignon, shiraz, merlot, malbec and pinot noir. Distribution through cellar door and mail order.

Eaglehawk Estate (Quelltaler Vineyard) *Off Main North Road Road, Watervale SA 5452. (088) 43 0003.*

Cellar door: Monday–Friday 9–5, Saturday 11–4, Sunday 12–4 (including public holidays). Museum open daily and picnic areas available. All major credit cards.
Winemaker: Stephen John.

First vines were planted 1853 and this impressive and historic large winery has been owned by Wolf Blass since 1987. Wines include Wolf Blass reds, Quelltaler Rhine riesling, fumé blanc, hock, noble Rhine riesling and Treloar's port. National distribution through Remy Blass.

Horrocks Vineyard *Mintaro Road, Watervale SA 5452. (088) 43 0005.*

Cellar door: Daily 10–5 (while stocks last), closed holidays. No tours, though large lawn area can be used for picnics. Bankcard, Mastercard, Visa.
Winemaker: Jeffrey Grosset.

Founded in 1982 by the present owners, three Ackland brothers, Trevor, Roger and Lyall. Quality wines in limited supply, sold through cellar door, plus limited selected stockists in each State. Key products include Rhine riesling, chardonnay, semillon, cordon cut (dessert wines), Rhine riesling and cabernet/merlot.

Jeffrey Grosset *King Street, Auburn SA 5451. (088) 49 2175.*

Cellar door: Wednesday–Sunday 10–5 (while stocks last, from availability of wines in September). Tours by appointment only. Bankcard, Mastercard, Visa.
Winemaker: Jeffrey Grosset.

Small high-quality winery established in 1981 and owned by Cate and Jeffrey Grosset. Wines include Watervale Rhine Riesling, Polish Hill Rhine Riesling, chardonnay, wood-matured semillon and cabernet sauvignon. Distribution through wholesalers in most States, and cellar door, plus mailing list.

Jim Barry Wines *Main North Road, Clare SA 5453. (088) 42 2261.*

Cellar door: Monday–Friday 9–5, Saturday, Sunday and public holidays 10–4. No tours, no BBQ or picnic areas. Bankcard, Mastercard, Visa.
Winemakers: Jim Barry and sons Mark and Peter Barry.

Jim Barry was a highly qualified Clare winemaker when he

started his own winery at the northern end of the Valley in the mid-1970s. His wines have flavour and character, as befits the character of their makers and the grape sources up and down the valley which they tap. The winery produces small quantities of premium varietal wines, including Rhine riesling, chardonnay, sauvignon blanc, cabernet sauvignon and merlot, also Sentimental Bloke Port (because C. J. Dennis was born at nearby Auburn). National distribution through different agents.

Leasingham *7 Dominic Street, Clare SA 5453. (088) 42 2555. Distribution through the Hardy Wine Company (08) 381 2266.*

Cellar door: Monday–Friday 9–5, weekends and holidays 9–4. BBQs and picnic areas available. All major credit cards.
Chief Winemaker: Chris Proud.

Founded 1893, bought by Hardy's in late 1987 from H. J. Heinz. Broad range of wine styles from this large producer, including Rhine rieslings in dry and spätlese variants, shiraz, cabernet sauvignon, cabernet/malbec. Chardonnay, fumé blanc, chablis, white burgundy and gewürztraminer, plus a wider range of other varietal and generic wines, including the value-for-money Domaine series, plus sparkling and fortified wines. Quality maker and the largest in the Clare Valley, though in recent times Stanley has been concentrating more of its production across the border near Mildura, where the Stanley Leasingham cask ranges come from. Wines distributed by Hardy's in all States.

Mintaro Cellars *Leasingham Road, Mintaro SA 5415. (088) 43 9046.*

Cellar door: Monday–Sunday 9–5.30. No BBQs, tours by appointment. Restaurant open seven nights—bookings essential. Accommodation available. Bankcard, Mastercard.
Winemaker: Jim Pearson.

A small winery with cellar door sales, plus several outlets in Sydney. Founded 1985. Wines include Rhine riesling, late-picked Rhine riesling, shiraz, cabernet sauvignon and Jack Hector port.

Mitchell Cellars *Hughes Park Road, Skillogalee Valley, via Sevenhill SA 5435. (088) 43 4258.*

Cellar door: Daily including holidays 10–4. Bankcard, Diner's Club, Mastercard, Visa, Amex. Picnic area, restaurant within walking distance.
Winemaker: Neil Pike.

Jane Mitchell is one of Clare's most energetic organisers (and it is terrific to see winemakers in an area working together so enthusiastically to support their district). Her winery is buried amid gums near Sevenhill, and high-quality dry table wines have emerged since 1975. Wines include Watervale Rhine Riesling, late-picked Rhine riesling, chardonnay, wood-aged semillon, cabernet sauvignon and Peppertree Vineyard shiraz. Distributed through cellar door and specialist distributors in several States.

Paulett's *Polish Hill River Road, Sevenhill SA 5453. (088) 43 4328.*

Cellar door: Daily 10–4.30. No BBQs. Bankcard, Mastercard.
Winemaker: Neil Paulett.

Small family-owned winery established in 1982. Quality wines, including Rhine riesling, late-picked Rhine riesling, chardonnay, sauvignon blanc, shiraz and cabernet/merlot. Distributed through cellar door. Agents in Adelaide, Melbourne and Sydney.

Penwortham Cellars *Government Road, Penwortham, via Clare, SA 5453. (088) 43 4345.*

Cellar door: Weekends and public holidays 10–4. Bankcard, Mastercard and Visa.
Winemaker: Richard Hughes.

Owned by Richard and Marilyn Ann Hughes since 1985. Opened cellar door at Easter 1990. Using their own grapes, they make their wine at Sevenhill Cellars. Wines include Rhine riesling, muscat and tawny port. Distribution through cellar door.

Pike's Polish Hill Estate *Polish Hill River Road, Sevenhill SA 5453. (088) 43 4249 or (088) 43 4258.*

Cellar door: Open every day from 1 September while stocks last. Otherwise open at weekends, school holidays and public holidays 10–5. Space for picnics. Bankcard, Mastercard, Visa.
Winemaker: Neil Pike.

Small family-owned winery; founded 1984. Cabernet sauvignon, Rhine riesling, chardonnay, sauvignon blanc and shiraz. Distribution through cellar door and through Caon Tucker in Adelaide.

Quelltaler

See Eaglehawk.

Sevenhill Cellars *College Road, Sevenhill, via Clare SA 5453. (088) 43 4222.*

Cellar door: Monday–Friday 9–4.30, Saturday 9–4, closed Sunday, Christmas Day, Good Friday andNew Year's Day. Formal tours by appointment only, but visitors free to walk around historic winery. Picnic tables. Bankcard, Mastercard, Visa.
Winemaker: Brother John May and John Monten.

One of the most historic wineries of the Valley (the property dates from 1851), if somewhat off the beaten track to the north-east of Sevenhill. Owned by Manresa Society Inc. and run by a Jesuit order. The splendid old winery is worth a visit, as is the church (with its crypt) on the property. Wines, especially reds, have notably improved since Brother John May took over as winemaker in 1972. Key products include Rhine riesling, traminer/frontignac, tokay, cabernet sauvignon, merlot, cabernet/franc, some fortified wines and sacramental wines. Available through cellar door, mailing list and specialist distributors in most capitals.

Skillogalee Wines *Skillogalee Valley Road, via Sevenhill SA 5453. (088) 43 4274.*

Cellar door: Daily 10–5. Vineyard lunches and afternoon and morning teas. Also picnic baskets. Buses only by appointment. Bankcard, Mastercard, Visa.
Winemaker: David Palmer.

Founded in 1976 and owned by David and Diana Palmer. Quality small winery, using only estate grown grapes, for products including dry Rhine riesling, spätlese riesling, gewürztraminer, shiraz, cabernet sauvignon, vintage and tawny ports, muscat and *méthode champenoise*. Distribution through cellar door, with outlets in State capitals.

Taylor's *Mintaro Road, Auburn SA 5451. (088) 49 2008.*

Cellar door: Monday–Friday 9–5, Saturday and holidays 10–5, Sunday 10–4. Lawn space for picnics. Tours by appointment. All major credit cards.
Winemaker: Andrew Tolley.

A significent winery; founded 1973 by present owners Bill and John Taylor. White burgundy, chardonnay, riesling, some good reds (which is what the winery was founded to make), hermitage, cabernet sauvignon, pinot noir, special bin wines and port. Distributed through cellar door and in all States.

Tim Adams Wines *Windouree Road, Clare SA 5453. (088) 42 2429.*

Cellar door: Open seven days 10–5 from 1 September, while stocks last. Bankcard, Mastercard, Visa.
Winemaker: Tim Adams.

Owned by Tim Adams since 4 January 1988. Wines include Rhine riesling, semillon, shiraz and tawny port. Distribution through wholesale outlets in Adelaide, Melbourne and Sydney and through cellar door.

Tim Knappstein *2 Pioneer Avenue, Clare SA 5453. 088) 42 2096.*

Cellar door: Monday–Friday 9–5, Saturday 10–5, Sunday and public holidays 11–4. Lunches and tours only by arrangement.

Park adjacent. Restaurant and hotels close by. All major cards.
Winemaker: Tim Knappstein.

This winery was founded in 1976 by Tim and his mother after Tim had been making wine for the largest local winery, Stanley Leasingham. The winery is established at the top end of the town of Clare in the old Enterprise Brewery and is a must for visitors. You can often meet the winemaker there—if he's not flying his plane. Wines include Rhine riesling, fumé (sauvignon) blanc, gewürztraminer, cabernet sauvignon and cabernet/merlot. Until recently they were marketed under Tim Knappstein's Enterprise Wines label. In late 1986 Wolf Blass Wines acquired a major financial interest in the company. Distribution through Wolf Blass.

Wendouree *Spring Farm Road, Clare SA 5453. (088) 42 2896.*

Cellar door: Monday–Saturday 10–4, closed Sunday (except long weekends). Bankcard, Mastercard.
Winemaker: Tony Brady.

Small but historic winery producing classic big Australian reds—cabernet sauvignon, shiraz and cabernet/malbec—from very old vines. The old winery buildings were established in 1895. A. P. Birks established it as a winery in 1892 and ran it until his son, Roly Birks, took over in 1917. Roly ran it for an astonishing sixty-five vintages. The winery was sold in 1970 and again in 1972. Its present owners have retained the powerful and long-living style of the wines. Distribution through cellar door, and several distributors in South Australia, New South Wales and Victoria.

Wilson Vineyard *Polish Hill River Road, Sevenhill SA 5453. (088) 43 4310.*

Cellar door: Saturday, Sunday and long weekends 10–4.30. From May 1991 open afternoons during the week. Bus tours by appointment. No BBQs, etc. No smoking in winery. Bankcard, Mastercard.
Winemaker: Dr John Wilson.

Owned by the Wilson family and run by an enthusiastic doctor of medicine. Wines include Rhine riesling, cabernet sauvignon, cabernet shiraz, pinot noir, chardonnay and zinfandel. Distributed in all States and through cellar door. There's a very good newsletter, scripted by the doctor himself.

Coonawarra

Of all Australia's vineyard areas, Coonawarra ('Place of the Wild Honeysuckle') is perhaps the least attractive to the visitor. Some 380 kilometres south-east of Adelaide, the approach to the Coonawarra is pretty uninteresting, whichever way one comes. And, once there, there isn't much to see except vineyards and the occasional winery building, most of them new and uninspiring and sited along the road running through the district. The paradox is that Coonawarra is viewed by many, including myself, as home of some of Australia's finest wines, particularly red wines, and notably cabernet sauvignon.

For the visitor passing through on the way to or from Melbourne or Adelaide, however, there are attractions not too far away which make it an interesting stop, aside from the wineries. Mt Gambier and the coast around Kingston offer splendid scenery, not to mention great seafood, including crayfish.

The two things that have combined to give Coonawarra the ability to produce grapes for wines of legendary quality are its terra rossa soil, a narrow strip of it, and the comparatively cool climate. Access to subterranean water helps produce large yields both here and in the similar Padthaway region not far to the north.

Eating out

In Coonawarra itself, there is little other than the restaurant in the Chardonnay Lodge (Penola Road, Coonawarra [087] 36 3309) which has an à la carte dining room as a part of the modern motel. Counter lunches are available a little further south in Penola at the Log Cabin Hotel (087) 37 2404 and Heyward's Royal Oak Hotel (087) 37 2322 offers food and accommodation. Coonawarra Motor Lodge (114 Church Street, Penola [087] 37 2364) also has an à la carte restaurant. The Penola Information Centre can help if you ring (087) 37 2855.

Bowen Estate *Penola–Naracoorte Road, Coonawarra SA 5263. (087) 37 2229.*

Cellar door: Open Monday–Saturday 9–5 only, except during school holidays and long weekends. All major credit cards.

Winemaker: Doug Bowen.

Founded 1975; owned by Doug and Joy Bowen. Small maker who has established a reputation for high-quality and consistent wines. These include Rhine riesling, chardonnay, cabernet sauvignon, shiraz and merlot. Distributed in major capital cities, mail order and through the cellar door.

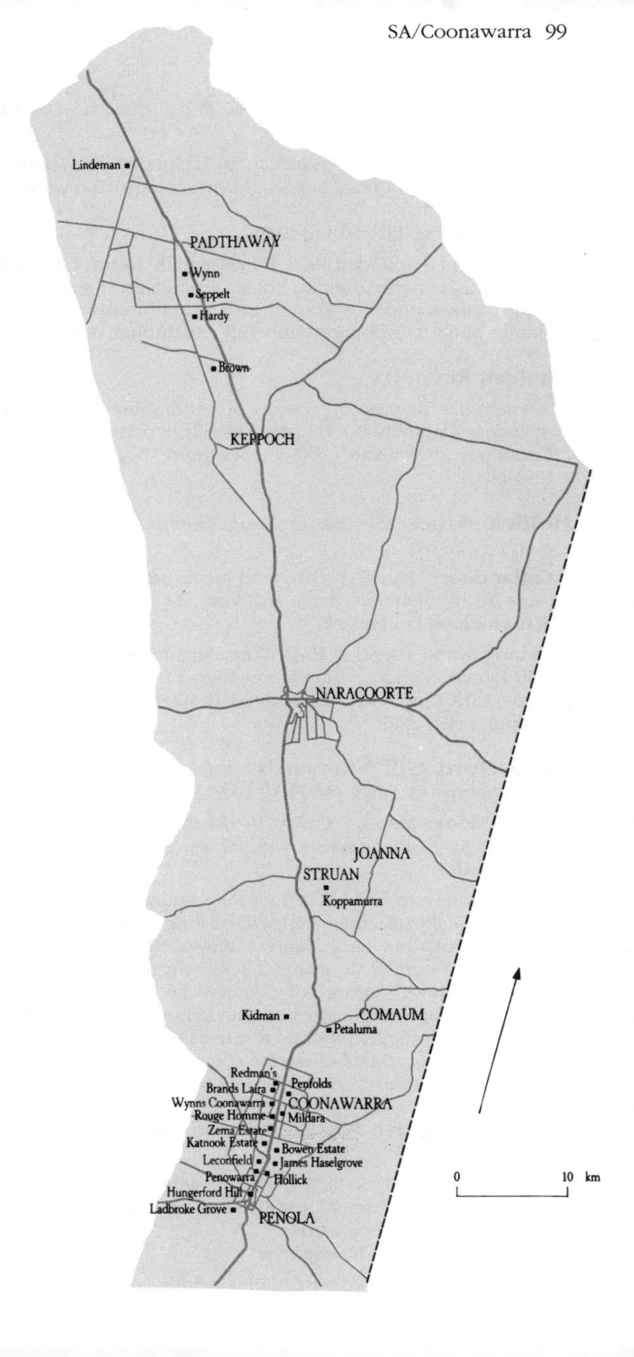
Lindeman
PADTHAWAY
Wynn
Seppelt
Hardy
Brown
KEPPOCH
NARACOORTE
JOANNA
STRUAN
Koppamurra
Kidman
COMAUM
Petaluma
Redman's
Brands Laira
Penfolds
Wynns Coonawarra
COONAWARRA
Rouge Homme
Mildara
Zema Estate
Katnook Estate
Bowen Estate
Leconfield
James Haselgrove
Penowarra
Hollick
Hungerford Hill
Ladbroke Grove
PENOLA
0
10 km

Brand's Laira *Penola–Naracoorte Road, Coonawarra SA 5263. (087) 36 3260.*

Cellar door: Monday–Saturday 9–5, Sunday and public holidays 10–4. BBQ facilities, visitors welcome to tour winery. All credit cards.
Winemakers: Bill and Jim Brand.

Family owned; founded 1966. Wines include shiraz, cabernet sauvignon, cabernet/merlot, Rhine riesling and chardonnay. Wines appear under two brand names, Brand's Laira and the Brand Family. Distribution nationally and through cellar door.

Chateau Reynella

Reynella has no physical presence here, but sources a number of its wines, notably its reds, either wholly or partially from the Coonawarra vineyards. (See Southern Vales—Chateau Reynella.)

Hollick Wines *Racecourse Road, Coonawarra SA 5263. (087) 37 2318.*

Cellar door: Daily 9–5. BBQ and picnic area planned. Bus tours by appointment. Bankcard, Visa.
Winemaker: Ian Hollick.

Family owned; founded 1983. Wines include Rhine riesling, chardonnay, cabernet sauvignon (two Jimmy Watson trophies) and pinot noir. Distributed in all major States and through cellar door.

Hungerford Hill Vineyards *Penola–Naracoorte Road, Coonawarra SA 5263. (087) 37 2613.*

Cellar door: Monday–Friday 9–5, Saturday, Sunday and holidays 10–5. Picnic areas with tables. Playground. Major credit cards.

This is a vineyard and cellar door sales outlet; the grapes are crushed locally and then shipped to Hungerford Hill's large winery at Pokolbin in the Hunter Valley of New South Wales. The attractive cellar door outlet sells only the Coonawarra products. Rhine riesling (dry, late–picked and botrytised versions), chardonnay, cabernet sauvignon, shiraz and pinot noir, plus sparkling wines and fortifieds. Distributed nationally by Seppelt, which bought the company in late 1990, and through cellar door.

James Haselgrove *Penola–Naracoorte Road, Coonawarra SA 5263. (087) 37 2734.*

Cellar door: Daily 9–5. No winery. Wine tasters' lunches available, two/three courses, with wines bought at cellar door prices. All major credit cards.
Winemaker: James Haselgrove.

Family owned; founded 1981. Wines include Coonawarra and

McLaren Vale products (also see McLaren Vale—James Haselgrove), with dry whites and dry reds from both areas, plus area and varietal blends. Also sweet whites, ports and champagne. Distributed at cellar door and mail order.

Katnook Estate *Off Penola–Naracoorte Road, Coonawarra SA 5263. (087) 37 2394.*

Cellar door: Monday–Friday 8–4.30, Saturday and public holidays 10–4.30, closed Sundays. No tours or picnics. All major credit cards.
Winemaker: Wayne Stehbens.

Owned by Rentiers Pty Ltd; founded 1979. Large but low-profile maker of high-quality, though rather expensive, wines. The Katnook sauvignon blanc whites were among the first to show the potential of this grape variety in Australia. Wines include Rhine riesling, sauvignon blanc, chardonnay, cabernet sauvignon and pinot noir (under the Katnook label); and Rhine riesling, sauvignon blanc, chardonnay and cabernet/shiraz (under Riddoch Estate label). Distributed nationally and through cellar door.

Kidman *Penola–Naracoorte Road, Coonawarra SA 5263. (087) 36 5094, after hours (087) 36 5071.*

No cellar door sales. Vineyard only, with riesling, cabernet sauvignon, shiraz and a small amount of chardonnay planted. The Kidman label is available through the bottle shops of the owner, Melbourne wine merchant Dan Murphy.

Ladbroke Grove *Care of: Coonawarra Motor Lodge, 114 Church Street, Penola SA 5277. (087) 37 2364.*

Cellar door: Daily 9–8 All major credit cards.
Winemaker: Peter McDonald.

Owned by Peter and Carol McDonald; founded 1982. Cellar door sales are conducted at the Bushman's Inn Restaurant in the Coonawarra Motor Lodge. Wines include Rhine riesling (dry and late-picked), cabernet sauvignon and hermitage.

Leconfield *Penola–Naracoorte Road, Coonawarra SA 5263. (087) 37 2326.*

Cellar door: Monday–Saturday 9–5, Sunday and holidays 11–4.30. Tours and picnics welcomed. All major credit cards except Diner's Club.
Winemaker: Ralph Fowler.

Founded 1974. Small winery under control of Hamilton family (see Southern Vales—Richard Hamilton Willunga Vineyards). Wines include cabernet sauvignon, cabernet/merlot, shiraz, chardonnay and Rhine riesling. Distributed in South Australia, Victoria, Australian Capital Territory, Queensland and Western Australia by National Wine Merchants and in New South Wales by Regional Wines Pty Ltd. Good wines.

Mildara *Penola–Naracoorte Road, Coonawarra SA 5263. (087) 36 3380.*

Cellar door: Monday–Friday 9–4.30, Saturday and holidays 10–4, Sunday 12–4. Self-guided tours. BBQ facilities. Film and video room. All major credit cards.
Winemaker: Gavin Hogg.

Mildara first planted vines in Coonawarra in 1955. A winery was built for the first vintage in 1963. Mildara won the Jimmy Watson Trophy twice in the 1980s (for 1981 and 1988 wines). Red wines produced are Alexander's Coonawarra Cabernet Sauvignon, Jamieson's Run and Coonawarra Hermitage. Whites are Jamieson's Run Chardonnay and Coonawarra Rhine Riesling. Distribution nationwide by Mildara Wines Ltd.

Penfolds

No cellar door outlet or winery (other than Wynn's, acquired in 1985 in Coonawarra, and Rouge Homme, q.v.). However their vineyards here are an important source of material for Australia's biggest wine group, perhaps more so since some of Penfolds' reds started lightening up in recent vintages, as with many other red producers. Coonawarra fruit has been present in many great Penfolds reds, most particularly in their Bin 128.

Penowarra *Penola–Naracoorte Road, Coonawarra SA 5277. (085) 37 2458.*

Cellar door: Monday–Saturday and holidays 9–5. Open most Sundays. No tours or picnics. Bankcard, Visa.
Winemaker: Ken Ward.

Owned by Raymond and Kay Messenger. Founded 1978. Wines include Rhine riesling, cabernet sauvignon, shiraz, cabernet/shiraz, cabernet/malbec, and tawny and vintage ports. Distribution by cellar door only.

Petaluma

Coonawarra is an important source of grapes for several Petaluma wines, but there is no winery/cellar door presence here. (See page 71.)

Redman *Penola–Naracoorte Road, Coonawarra SA 5263. (087) 367 3331.*

Cellar door: Open seven days a week 9–5. Tours by appointment. Bankcard, Diner's Club, Mastercard, Visa.
Winemaker: Bruce Redman.

Founded 1966. The Redman family were among the great pioneers of the Coonawarra region but sold their family business, Rouge Homme Wines, to Lindemans in 1965, then starting up again as themselves in 1966. Today Bruce and Malcolm Redman run the winery and vineyards at Coonawarra. Redman makes two wines only, a claret (shiraz) and a cabernet sauvignon, from their own vineyards. The only variation is in bottle size. The claret comes in 375 millilitre and 750 millilitre containers, the cabernet in 750 millilitre, 1.5 litre (magnum) and 6 litre (imperial) bottles. National distribution (except in the Northern Territory) through the Hardy Wine Company, and sold at cellar door.

The Ridge *Penola–Naracoorte Road (20 kilometres north of Penola, 28 kilometres south of Naracoorte), Coonawarra SA 5263. (087) 36 5071.*

Cellar door: Daily 9–5. Pickles and home-made jams in season. Bankcard, Mastercard, Visa.
Winemaker: Sidney Kidman.

Owned by Susan Kidman; founded 1984. Wines include Rhine riesling, cabernet sauvignon and shiraz. Available through cellar door.

Rosemount Estates

Again, as with several other major producers, Rosemount simply (as if it was ever a simple business!) grows grapes here, and ships the juice to their Hunter Valley winery for processing. Impressive wines. (See page 36.)

Rouge Homme *Penola–Naracoorte Road, Coonawarra SA 5263. (087) 36 3205.*

Cellar door: Open seven days from 10–4. No tours, no BBQs. Amex, Bankcard, Mastercard, Visa.
Winemaker: Greg Clayfield.

Winery founded 1908. Lindemans Wines (in turn now owned by Penfolds) bought this property from the Redman family in 1965 and an outstanding series of wines has resulted in many years since then, including two Jimmy Watson Trophies (with wines from the 1980 and 1985 vintages). The range of red table wines made here under the Rouge Homme label, including the Rouge Homme Claret and cabernet sauvignons, plus the vineyard range from Lindemans, such as St George, Limestone Ridge and Pyrus from Coonawarra, are all extremely high-quality products. Distribution nationally; now owned by SA Brewing Holdings.

Wynn's Coonawarra Estate *Memorial Drive, Coonawarra SA 5263. (087) 36 3266.*

Cellar door: Daily 10–4. Self-guided tours. Picnics possible in grounds. All major credit cards.
Winemaker: Peter Douglas.

Now owned by SA Brewing Holdings Ltd. This winery, founded in 1891, is the most spectacular in the region, with its old buildings, depicted on the Wynn's Coonawarra Estate labels. Now has the strength of the immense SA Brewing/ Penfolds group behind the company (Wynn's), which was already of considerable size, producing excellent products. Wines include wide range of premium dry whites (Rhine riesling, chardonnay, etc.), plus dry reds (notably cabernet sauvignon), and others. Distribution through Penfolds/Kaiser Stuhl/Wynn's in all States.

Zema Estate *Penola–Naracoorte Road, Coonawarra SA 5263. (087) 36 3219.*

Cellar door: Daily 9–5. No picnics or BBQs. Amex, Bankcard, Mastercard, Visa.
Winemaker: Ken Ward.

Family owned; founded 1982. Wines include Rhine riesling, shiraz and cabernet sauvignon. Distribution through cellar door.

Padthaway

This large grape-growing area (which was also known as Keppoch) is north of Coonawarra in south-east South Australia. It is dominated by three large makers: Lindemans, Seppelt and Hardy's. All grow and crush a wide variety of grapes here, but take them elsewhere to turn into wine, so there are no opportunities for cellar door sales from them. The only outlet is at the splendid Padthaway Estate, a stone mansion magnificently restored as an upmarket guest house, with top dining and other facilities. Padthaway Estate also grows pinot noir and chardonnay grapes for its own sparkling wines.

This big, open and rich grazing and farming country has adapted well to growing large volumes of premium table wine grapes since it was developed in the late 1960s by Karl Seppelt and others.

Hardy's

Big vineyards, visible from the main road between Naracoorte and Padthaway, which supply much of the premium fruit for Hardy's table wines. No cellar door outlet here, though some products available at Padthaway Estate. See Southern Vales—Hardy's Reynella Winery and Southern Vales—Hardy's Tintara for full entry on Thomas Hardy & Sons.

Lindemans

At the time Australia's largest wine company, Lindemans moved into Padthaway at the same time as Hardy's, in 1968.

They have been the most publicly known presence in the area, with their enormous vineyards and a large advertising campaign for their wines, principally (though not entirely) white wines. They also do not sell wines made here in the area itself, though some can be purchased at the Rouge Homme winery, just to the south in Coonawarra, where most of the fruit from these big vineyards is processed.

Padthaway Estate *Padthaway SA 5271. (087) 65 5039.*

Cellar door: Weekends 11–5. By appointment at all other times. All major credit cards.
Winemaker: Leigh Clarnette.

From 1990, Padthaway Estate has been hand-picking their own grapes from 45 hectares of vines, crushing and making their own wine. They have recently converted a woolshed to a winery, in which is housed a traditional French champagne press (said to be the only one in Australia). All wines are available for tasting and purchase at the cellar door, with complimentary winery tours and tastings with the winemaker. Wines include champagne, chardonnay and pinot noir. Distribution through cellar door and mail order.

Seppelt Wines

Karl Seppelt pioneered this area as an alternative to the limited area of Coonawarra, further south, because it had a similarly cool climate, good soils and underground water. Again, no cellar door sales though the vineyards are important contributors to some of Seppelt's premium lines.

Langhorne Creek

Langhorne Creek, alongside the River Bremer, is one of the least known of Australia's wine-producing areas. It lies some 70 kilometres to the south-east of Adelaide. The region is best known by discerning wine drinkers for the wine brought from the area over the decades by quality winemakers such as Stoneyfell, Wolf Blass and Lindemans, who appreciated the intensity of flavour which Langhorne Creek red wines have traditionally offered. The area is attractive (though subject to flooding in the rainy season). It forms part of an enjoyable drive to the south and south-east of Adelaide and the Adelaide Hills areas.

Bleasdale Vineyards *Wellington Road, Langhorne Creek SA 5255. (085) 37 3001.*

Cellar door: Monday–Saturday and holidays 9–5, Sunday

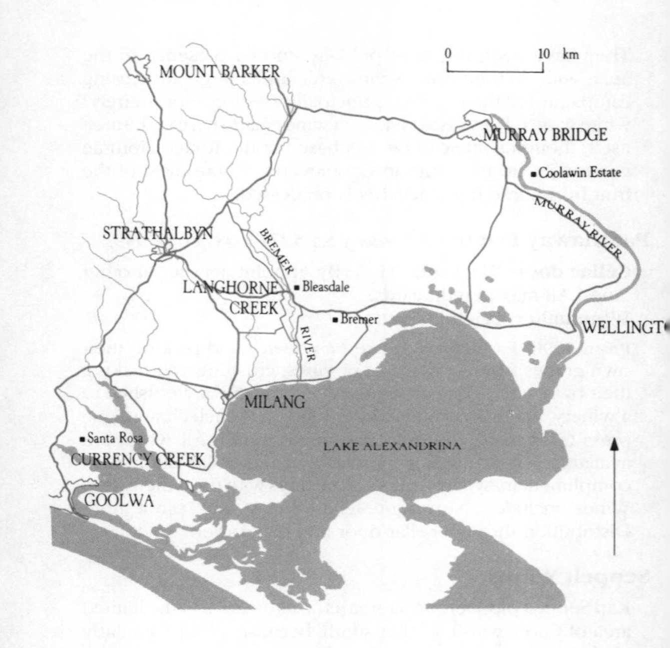

11–5. No conducted tours but visitors can see winery. Public reserve close by for picnics; restaurant 1 kilometre away at Langhorne Creek. Bankcard, Mastercard, Visa.
Winemaker: Michael Potts.

Owned by Bleasdale Vineyards Pty Ltd, this historic winery, founded in 1850, has been classified by the National Trust. The cellars and most of the equipment in it are worth seeing, being constructed from red gum and limestone. In particular the splendid red gum lever press, made in 1892, is worth a look. Wines span the normal commercial spectrum of table wines, plus several special old fortified wines (including verdelho); also ports, muscats and sparkling wines. National distribution and through cellar door

Santa Rosa

See entry in Southern Vales section.

Riverland

The South Australian side of the Murray-irrigated grape-growing areas, like the other side of the border in Victoria, produces very large quantities of wine, much of it destined for casks (bag-in-box) and flagons. But also, of course, as many are starting to realise, the area produces some very good table wines in 750 millilitre glass bottles. The only qualifier most would make about these premium wines is that they do not have the longevity of their cooler climate counterparts. But does this matter, as something like 95 per cent of bottled wine purchased in Australia is probably consumed within a week of purchasing?

Eating out

In Loxton, the Hotel Loxton serves good meals (East Terrace [085] 84 7266). In Berri, the Canton Palace (Sturt Highway [085] 82 2952) is recommended for 'country' Chinese meals (including takeaway); the Wine Barrel Restaurant (9 William Street [085] 82 1680) features local products. In Barmera, the Sunset Boulevard (Dean Drive [085] 88 2669) features Riverland wines.

Angove's *Bookmark Avenue, Renmark SA 5341. (085) 85 1311.*

Cellar door: Monday–Friday 9–5, closed weekends. Open some selected public holidays. No BBQs, picnics. Nearest restaurant 3 kilometres away in Renmark. Major credit cards.
Winemakers: Frank Newman and Ian Marchant.

Founded 1886. Often overlooked, large family-owned winery (Managing Director, John Angove), making wines of high quality. These include a very wide range of varietal and generic wines plus one of Australia's best known brandies, St Agnes, and several products made under licence, such as Stone's Green Ginger Wine. Also makers of large-selling Marko Vermouth. Worth a visit if passing near Renmark. Distribution through own State branches.

Berri Renmano Ltd *Sturt Highway (between Berri and Barmera), Glossop SA 5344. (085) 83 2303.*

Cellar door: Monday–Friday 9–5.30, Saturday 9–5, closed Sunday except during long weekends. Tours at 11 a.m. Monday–Friday. BBQ and children's play area. All major credit cards.
Winemaker: Reg Wilkinson.

Founded in 1912, Berri Renmano Ltd (originally Berri Estates, which became part of the Berri Renmano group in 1982) is probably Australia's largest single winery, situated in Australia's largest wine-producing area, the South Australian Riverland. It is a huge operation, marketing wines nationally and internationally. Big or not, it has striven in recent years to make high-quality table wines in 750 millilitre bottles, generally with considerable success. The winery's key products include Berri 5 litre and 3 litre casks (especially Fruity Gordo Moselle), Renmano Chairman's Selection label (Rhine riesling, sauvignon blanc, chardonnay and cabernet sauvignon) and Renmano bottle quality varietal 2 litre casks. National distribution and through cellar door.

Bonneyview *Sturt Highway, Barmera SA 5345. (085) 88 2279.*

Cellar door: Daily, including holidays 9–5.30. Tours welcome, BBQ available for visitors. Gallery and pottery shop. All major credit cards.
Winemaker: Robert Minns.

Founded in 1976, owned by Warwick Lumbers and Robert Minns. Wines include cabernet sauvignon blend, shiraz blend, chardonnay, frontignac blanc, traminer riesling and a

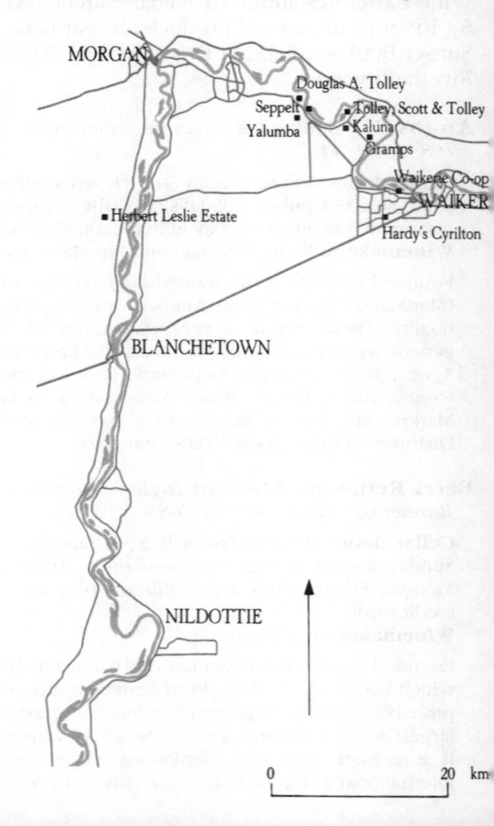

range of vintage ports. Labelled under Bonneyview Wines and Nookanka Vineyard. Distribution through cellar door only.

Cyrilton Winery *Via Waikerie SA 5330 (off Sturt Highway—signposted—about 2 kilometres west of the town). (085) 41 2277.*

Cellar door: Monday–Friday 9.30–5, holidays 10–4.30. Major credit cards. Picnic and entertainment areas. Near River Murray.

Hardy's Cyrilton was founded after World War I (and named after Robert Cyril Hardy, who was killed in France). Managed by Philip Neilson, it provided Hardy's with fruit from local irrigated areas for some table wine and brandy production. A feature is a cool, deep underground cellar. Range of Hardy's products available to taste, but sold by Hardy's to manager Neilson in mid-1987 to produce juice for a number of makers,

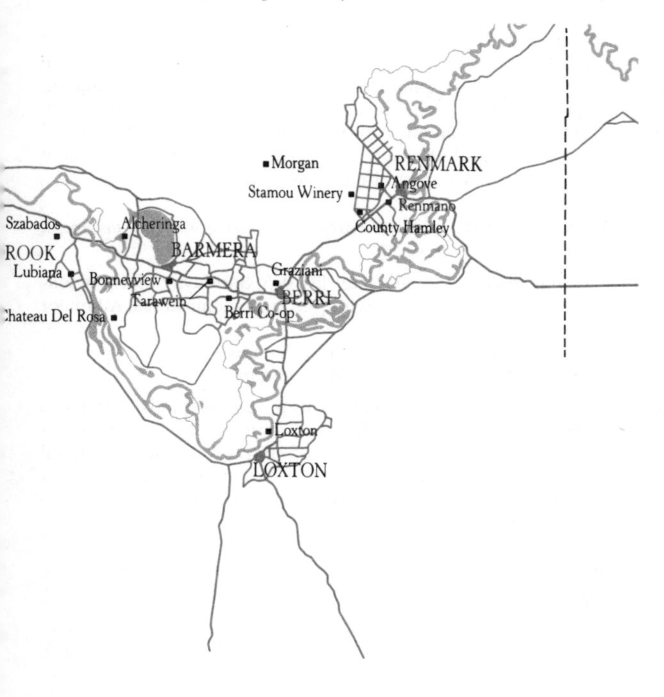

including Hardy's. As we went to press, it was up for sale again.

Kingston Estate *Corner East Terrace and Sturt Highway, Kingston-on-Murray SA 5331. (085) 83 0244.*

Cellar door: By arrangement. Tours by arrangement.
Winemaker: Bill Moularadellis.
New winery, first vintage in 1979 (formerly Apollo Winery). Wines made for bottle shops and restaurants. Bulk wholesalers.

Penfolds' Loxton Winery *Bookpurmonong Road, near Loxton SA 5333. (085) 84 7236.*

Cellar door: Monday–Saturday 9–5, closed most Sundays. Gifts and souvenirs. Tours by arrangement. Major credit cards.
Winemakers: Stuart Auld, Jon Ketley and Lyndon Crockett

Founded 1949, owned by area grape-growers until taken over by Penfolds in mid-1987. Wide range of wines from the Penfolds group, plus the Loxton Medea label (frontignan, spätlese Rhine riesling, cabernet shiraz and port). Also low-alcohol wine. Situated on banks of River Murray. Distributed nationally and through cellar door. (At time of press it appeared that it might be closed down.)

Renmano (Berri Renmano) *Renmark Avenue, Renmark SA 5341. (085) 86 6771.*

Cellar door: Monday–Saturday 9–5, Sundays of long weekends 10–4. Tasting area with play and picnic areas. All major credit cards.
Winemaker: David Hayman. (Manager)
Senior Winemaker: Paul Kassebaum

Now part of the Berri Renmano group (see Berri Renmano above); founded (by Chateau Tanunda) 1914. Key wines include Chairman's Selection of six premium table varietal wines, brandy, vintage varietal casks, altar wines and Vanessa non-alcoholic wine. National distribution through Berri Renmano Ltd.

Wein Valley Estate *Eastern Road (4 kilometres from Berri, formerly Monash Winery), Monash SA 5342. (085) 83 5365.*

Cellar door: Monday–Friday 9–4.30, Saturday 11–3, Sunday closed. Near famous Monash playground (100 metres away). All major credit cards.
Winemaker: Otto Konig and Doug Wilson

Founded 1964. Large producer, making small amount of bulk wine—4 litre and 2 litre casks. Full range of reds, whites and fortifieds with a new premium range. Distribution through cellar door and to major States.

Southern Vales

The Southern Vales, after much agonising over the years, is now promoted as the Wine Coast of Adelaide. I suspect, however, that most people will still call it by the name it has borne for many years, the Southern Vales.

It is one of Australia's most appealing regions for the wine-interested visitor. It is relatively compact, is close to Adelaide and has a large number of comparatively small wineries and a number of good restaurants within its limits.

It is, of course, centred on the town of McLaren Vale, 45 kilometres and about as many minutes south of the South Australian capital. Grape-growing, almonds, rose cultivation and other general agricultural pursuits are the region's livelihood—plus tourism. Many thousands of visitors, particularly Victorians, flock to the area each year to sample the local wares.

The area, sometimes described as McLaren Vale (or 'the Vales'), claims to be the home of small winemakers in Australia. Of the more than four dozen (a number that fluctuates according to fortunes) only a few can claim to be large—Thomas Hardy and Sons, Wynn's Seaview, Pirramimma and the Southern Vales Winery. Almost all the others vary between tiny and small to middling.

Most of the area's wineries produce wines of character, and the area is noted for its cabernet and shiraz red wines, plus ports. In more recent times some excellent whites have been made, with chardonnay booming in the area.

Forgive my parochialism (for I live here!) but the area is one of considerable beauty, with green vineyards and the brown backdrop of the southern Mount Lofty Ranges in summer, and green hills and brown vineyards in winter. If driving in or out of the State try looping around through the Adelaide Hills or Clarendon. There are spectacular beaches 10 minutes' drive from McLaren Vale, and many of them allow parking on the beach itself.

Eating out

There are some excellent restaurants in the Southern Vales area. The best known is perhaps the Barn (Main

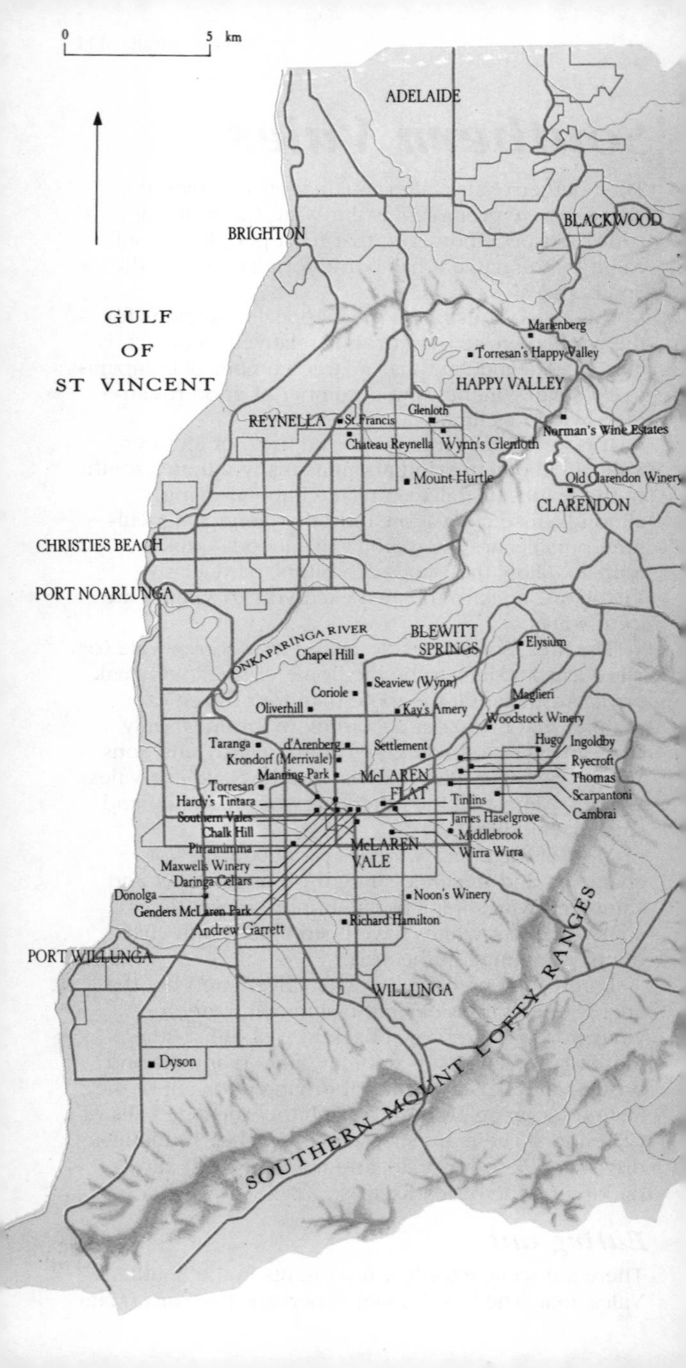
0
5 km
ADELAIDE
BLACKWOOD
BRIGHTON
GULF
OF
ST VINCENT
Marienberg
Torresan's Happy Valley
HAPPY VALLEY
REYNELLA
St Francis
Glenloth
Chateau Reynella
Wynn's Glenloth
Norman's Wine Estates
Mount Hurtle
Old Clarendon Winery
CLARENDON
CHRISTIES BEACH
PORT NOARLUNGA
ONKAPARINGA RIVER
BLEWITT
SPRINGS
Elysium
Chapel Hill
Seaview (Wynn)
Coriole
Oliverhill
Kay's Amery
Maglieri
Woodstock Winery
Taranga
d'Arenberg
Settlement
Hugo
Ingoldby
Krondorf (Merrivale)
Ryecroft
Manning Park
McLAREN
FLAT
Thomas
Torresan
Scarpantoni
Hardy's Tintara
Tinlins
Cambrai
Southern Vales
James Haselgrove
Chalk Hill
Middlebrook
Pirramimma
McLAREN
VALE
Wirra Wirra
Maxwells Winery
Daringa Cellars
Donolga
Noon's Winery
Genders McLaren Park
Richard Hamilton
Andrew Garrett
PORT WILLUNGA
WILLUNGA
Dyson
SOUTHERN MOUNT LOFTY RANGES

Road, McLaren Vale [08] 323 8618), a delightfully relaxed lunching and dining spot with a central garden courtyard, an art gallery and a choose-your-own-wine room. Further down the Main Road is the Hotel McLaren (08) 323 8208, which has a choice of simple pub food or à la carte restaurant menu in a relaxed dining room; the wine selection is also good. Almost opposite the hotel is Pipkins (08) 323 8707) a bistro-style restaurant with light but nicely presented food and the added advantage, in a wine-producing area, of BYO. At the southern end of the township on the Main Road to Willunga is the Salopian Inn (08) 323 8769, a simple but enjoyable eatery in a historic inn, featuring local wines and some unusual dishes.

A little further afield from the township is Middlebrook (Sand Road, McLaren Vale [08] 383 0004), a winery several kilometres from town which serves good and wholesome food in relaxing surroundings. McLarens on the Lake (Kangarilla Road, McLaren Vale [08] 323 8911) is a large and touristy restaurant/motel/conference centre which has changed hands several times in recent years. Driving in a circle back towards Adelaide, through the Scenic Hills, is the Old Clarendon Winery (Main Road, Clarendon [08] 383 6166), which has several restaurants in an open-plan, plus craft shops, art gallery and conference areas.

Nearby is a relatively new restaurant, the Stone Cottage (corner Potter Road and Main Street, Clarendon [08] 383 6038, after hours [08] 388 3298). It is a homely 150-year-old cottage with food just like that—home-made soups, quiches, pies and game, featuring Southern Vales wines. Relaxed, and worth a visit going to or from the Vales. Bric-à-brac sales too.

Closer to town is Carter's Restaurant (Old South Road, Reynella [08] 382 6963), which serves lunch Wednesday–Friday and dinner Wednesday–Saturday.

Nearly an hour further south, along the coast towards Cape Jervis (on the way around to Victor Harbor) is a charming restaurant and motel, Leonard's Mill (Main Road, Second Valley [085] 59 4184), also featuring Southern Vales wines. Well worth the drive.

Andrew Garrett Wines *Kangarilla Road, McLaren Vale SA 5171. (08) 323 8911.*

Cellar door: Daily 10–5. Restaurants, picnic areas, large lake. All major credit cards.

Winemaker: Andrew Garrett and Warren Randall.

Andrew Garrett took over the winemaking operations at this large and scenic winery in late 1986—formerly the Estate, now McLarens on the Lake. His cellar door operation runs alongside the extensive motel/restaurant/convention centre in beautiful grounds. The company makes a wide range of good wines, including Watervale Rhine riesling, chardonnay, fumé blanc, cabernet sauvignon, cabernet/merlot and shiraz. Andrew Garrett Wines is owned by Andrew Garrett and Suntory Australia Pty Ltd. Distribution through cellar door and mail order.

Babidge Burgundy Hill Coopers *Lot 24C, Seaview Road, McLaren Heights SA 5171. (08) 386 0770.*

Cellar door: Monday–Friday 7–4.

Strictly speaking, not a winery, but you may wish to drive past and see the fascinating world of the cooper as you head into McLaren Vale on the way to, or from, the Seaview winery. Owned by John and Christina Babidge, established in 1979. Makers of oak barrels. They also make port barrels, priced from $130 for a 6 litre barrel, $155 for a 14 litre barrel and $200 for a 20 litre container. Enquiries during the weekend can be made by telephoning for an appointment.

Beresford/Bosanquet Wines *Old Horndale Winery, Fraser Avenue, Happy Valley SA 4825 (08) 322 2344.*

Cellar door: Monday–Friday 8–5. BBQ and picnic area. All major credit cards.
Winemaker: R. J. Dundon.

Old Horndale Winery is approaching 100 years of age, nestled just below the western approaches to Clarendon. It is alleged to have its own ghost (which leads one to ask if they produce wines with hidden body!). This is one of a trilogy of historic wineries within coo-ee of each other, the others being Chateau Reynella and Mount Hurtle (all are worth visiting, and all are close to the city of Adelaide).

Horndale is said to be the last remaining local gravity-fed winery. Rob Dundon was for some years the red and fortified winemaker for Hardy's, and knows his business. Wines under the Beresford label include pinot noir, sauvignon blanc, chardonnay and cabernet sauvignon/cabernet franc. Under the Bosanquet Estate label wines include fumé blanc, Rhine riesling, semillon/chardonnay and cabernet/shiraz. Distributed at cellar door and retail outlets in all States.

Blewitt Springs Winery *Recreation Road, McLaren Vale SA 5171. (08) 323 8689.*

Cellar door: Weekdays 9–5 and by appointment. Mastercard, Bankcard, Visa.
Winemaker: Brett Howard.

Wines include cabernet sauvignon, shiraz, chardonnay and

semillon, bottled under the Blewitt Springs Winery label. Distribution through cellar door.

Cambrai Vineyards *Hamilton's Road, McLaren Flat SA 5171. (08) 383 0251.*

Cellar door: 9–5. No tours, no BBQ. All major credit cards.
Winemaker: Graham Stevens.

Family owned; founded 1975. The winery is near the centre of the hamlet of McLaren Flat. Wines include full range of reds and whites, including sweet white (frontignac), with vintage and tawny ports and *méthode champenoise*.

Chalk Hill *Brewery Hill Road, McLaren Vale SA 5171. (08) 267 2436.*

Cellar door: Daily 1–5. BBQ and picnic areas available. Cheques or cash.
Winemaker: Nancy Benko (owner).

Founded 1972. Wines include two cabernet sauvignons, shiraz, special (shiraz) rosé, Rhine riesling and four ports. Available only through cellar door.

Chapel Hill *Chapel Hill Road, McLaren Vale SA 5171. (08) 323 8429.*

Cellar door: Daily 11–5. Adjacent to the winery is Chapel Hill Park, with coin-operated BBQs, children's playground and the spectacular Onkaparinga Gorge bushwalk. Bi-monthly art exhibitions by well-known South Australian artists. All major credit cards.
Winemaker: Pamela Dunsford.

Family owned; founded 1979. Chapel Hill Winery (formerly Chapel Hill Cellars) is a tiny scenic winery, set in an old chapel atop the slopes of McLaren Vale to the north-east of the town. Wines include Rhine riesling, chardonnay, hermitage, cabernet sauvignon, botrytis sweet white and tawny port. Pam Dunsford is a skilled winemaker. Distribution through cellar door and retail outlets in Adelaide.

Chateau Reynella *Reynell Road, Reynella SA 5161. (08) 381 2511.*

Cellar door: Daily 10–4.30, tastings finish 4.15. Self-guided tours from cellar door; guided tours by arrangement. Sweeping grounds and botanic gardens, picnic areas nearby, delicatessen and takeaway food shops. Major credit cards.
Chief Winemaker: David O'Leary.

Owned by Thomas Hardy & Sons Pty Ltd; founded 1838. Chateau Reynella itself, and its surrounding historic buildings, is one of the great showpieces of the Australian wine industry, and the winery, some 23 kilometres south of Adelaide, just off the Main South Road on the way to McLaren Vale, is a must for visitors to the Southern Vales. The historic premises were begun in 1838 by Devonshireman, John Reynell; today the Reynell family has gone, but another great South Australian wine family, the Hardys, bought the winery and grounds in late 1982 and lavishly restored it.

Wines include Vintage Reserve Chablis (dry white), chardonnay, late-picked white, Vintage Reserve Claret, Reynella and Coonawarra cabernet sauvignons, cabernet/malbec/merlot, Alicante Flor Fino Sherry, Old Cave Tawny Port and superb vintage port. National distribution through Rhine Castle Wines.

Coriole *Chaffeys Road, McLaren Vale SA 5171. (08) 323 8305.*

Cellar door: Monday–Friday 9–5, weekends and holidays 11–5. Visitors invited to tour winery, and can picnic if desired. Major credit cards.
Winemaker: Mark Lloyd.

Family owned; founded 1968. Coriole is a high-quality small maker based in buildings dating from 1860. Tastings are conducted in a historic stone barn with an adjacent house/barn/lawn area where visitors can take a bite to eat. Wines including cabernet sauvignon, shiraz, pinot noir, sangiovese, chardonnay, chenin blanc and Rhine riesling. Distributed through cellar door and retail outlets in all States.

Curtis Wines *Foggo Road, McLaren Vale, SA 5171. (08) 323 8389.*

Cellar door: 11–5 weekends and holidays.
Winemaker: P. Curtis (proprietor).

A very small, new winery, first vintage 1988 with an Italian flavour, in the centre of the Vales. Grapevines up to seventy-five years old yield semillon, grenache and shiraz wines, plus both vintage and tawny ports.

d'Arenberg Wines *Osborn Road, McLaren Vale SA 5171. (08) 323 8206.*

Cellar door: Monday–Friday 9–5, Saturday and holidays 10–5, Sunday 12–4. Tree-lined scenic area for picnics. All major credit cards. Tours by arrangement.
Winemakers: Chester Osborn and d'Arry Osborn.

Family owned; founded 1928. The winery is on top of a hill overlooking the district. The d'Arenberg label and d'Arry Osborn's face are well known in the McLaren Vale area, and his distinctively flavoured reds (burgundies and clarets) reflect much of the history of the area. Wines include broad range of reds, whites, ports and muscats. Distribution in all States and through cellar door.

Dennis of Daringa Cellars *Kangarilla Road, McLaren Vale SA 5171. (08) 323 8665.*

Cellar door: Daily, including holidays 11–5. Area available for picnics. All major credit cards.
Winemaker: Peter Dennis.

Family owned; founded 1972. Key wines produced under the Dennis McLaren Vale/Daringa label include Rhine riesling, chardonnay, sauvignon blanc, shiraz/cabernet, cabernet sauvignon, 25-year-old tawny port and mead. National distribution and through cellar door.

Donolga *Main South Road, Aldinga SA 5173. (085) 56 3179.*

Cellar door: Daily 10–5. BBQ area. Tours invited. Beaches close by. All major credit cards.
Winemakers: Don and Nick Girolamo.

Family owned; founded 1979. Wines include cabernet sauvignon, shiraz, cabernet/shiraz, Rhine riesling, chardonnay, sauvignon blanc and fortified wines. Distribution through cellar door.

Dyson Maslin Beach Wines *Sherriff Road, Maslin Beach SA 5171. (08) 386 1092.*

Cellar door: Daily 10–5. Bankcard, Mastercard, Visa.
Winemaker/owner: Allan Dyson.

Small winery; founded 1977. Key wines include chardonnay, sauvignon blanc, pinot noir, cabernet sauvignon, extra dry vintage champagne and fortified sauvignon blanc. Distribution through Victoria, New South Wales and at cellar door.

Glenloth Winery *Reynell Road, Reynella SA 5161. (08) 381 2566.*

Not open to the public. Grapes are processed from McLaren Vale for Penfolds and wine for the Seaview range is also made here. An outpost of the large Penfolds family, this was formerly known as Allied Vintners.
Winemaker: Mike Farmilo.

Hardy's Reynella Winery *Reynell Road, Reynella SA 5161. (08) 381 2266.*

Cellar door: Daily 10–4.30, tastings finish 4.15. Picnic areas. Self-guided tours. Guided tours by arrangement.
Winemakers: Geoff Weaver (Chief Winemaker), Tom Newton and Bill Hardy (fortifieds).

Owned by Thomas Hardy & Sons Pty Ltd. Founded 1853; premises established by John Reynell 1838 (Chateau Reynella). This is a large and scenic winery complex, surrounded by Chateau Reynella's vineyards, and has been the head office and white-winemaking centre for Hardy's since they bought the historic property from Rothmans of Pall Mall in late 1982. The cellar door, just inside the entrance gate, is large but cosy, and offers undoubtedly the widest range of products available to taste in the area, if not in the country. Notable among Hardy products are Hardy Collection varietal range, Siegersdorf Rhine Riesling, Chardonnay and Cabernet, Show Port and Gold Label tawny ports, vintage ports and reds such as Nottage Hill, plus champagne and late-picked and sweet wines. The company is owned by the Hardy family and the products are distributed nationally and internationally by Hardy's and their associated companies (they also own Ricasoli, a large winery in Tuscany, Italy, and La Baume, in the Midi region of southern France).

Hardy's Tintara *Main Road, McLaren Vale SA 5161. (08) 323 8676.*

Cellar door: Daily 10–4.30. Tastings finish 4.15. Lawns, tables and picnic areas, BYO restaurant opposite, hotel next door. Entertainment areas for hire. Tours by arrangement.
Winemaker: David O'Leary.

Owned by the Hardy Wine Company; founded 1853. The Tintara winery itself dates from 1876 under Hardy's control, and earlier than that under others. It is the largest winery in the area, sited in the middle of the town of McLaren Vale, with a brandy bond store at the front (Hardy's Black Bottle Brandy) and extensive production areas and wood storage at rear. There is also a crafts cottage on the premises, and the Almond Train, featuring local almonds on the old Willunga rail bed at the front of the winery. This winery provides Hardy's premium red and fortified wines, including cabernet sauvignon, pinot noir, shiraz and shiraz blends. These and other group products are available in an extensive tasting area. Distributed nationally by Hardy's.

Hugo *Elliott Road, McLaren Flat SA 5171. (08) 383 0098.*

Cellar door: Daily 10.30–5. Picnic area. Bankcard, Mastercard, Visa.
Winemaker: John Hugo.

Owned by Hugo with others, including Melbourne advertising guru Jamie Aitken; founded 1980. Wines include Rhine riesling, chardonnay, cabernet sauvignon, shiraz, tawny port and liqueur muscat. Good wines.

Ingoldby Wines *Ingolby Road, McLaren Flat SA 5171. (08) 383 0005.*

Cellar door: Monday–Friday 9–5, weekends and holidays 11–5. Tours by appointment. BBQ in park adjacent to winery. Underground cellar with paintings by local artists. All major credit cards.
Winemaker: Walter Clappis.

Owned by Walter and Kerry Clappis; founded 1973. Renowned for cabernet sauvignon, having won an award for 'the most outstanding wine' in 1987, 1988 and 1989. Wines include cabernet sauvignon, cabernet/shiraz/merlot, Rhine riesling, chardonnay and sauvignon blanc. Distributed in Melbourne, Sydney and Adelaide and through cellar door and mailing list.

James Haselgrove Wines *Foggo Road, McLaren Vale SA 5171. (08) 323 8706.*

Cellar door: Daily 9–5. No tours as no winery on these premises. Light two- or three-course Wine Tasters' lunches served daily at reasonable prices; licensed to serve wine at cellar door prices. Occasional art displays. All major credit cards.
Winemaker: James Haselgrove.

Family owned; founded 1981. The Haselgrove family has been closely tied to the Mildara Company, but James Haselgrove is no longer involved there, and James and Julie now run their own business just off Kangarilla Road, near McLaren Flat. Wines marketed include McLaren Vale and Coonawarra (q.v.) products, dry white, dry reds and sweet whites, ports and champagne, plus Coonawarra/McLaren Vale blend of shiraz. Distribution through cellar door and mail order.

Kay Brothers' Amery Vineyards *Kays Road, McLaren Vale SA 5171. (08) 323 8201.*

Cellar door: Monday–Friday 9–5, Saturday, Sunday and public holidays 12–5. BBQs available, picnic area (with scenic views), pottery, home-made pickles and jams for sale. All major credit cards.
Winemaker: Colin Kay.

Family owned; founded 1890. The original stone cellar and homestead still stand, commanding excellent views to the south across the Vale and towards the Gulf of St Vincent. The Kays—father Cud Kay and his winemaker son, Colin—are pillars of the McLaren Vale winemaking establishment, and a powerful force in the area, growing a substantial proportion of their own grapes and still planting more. Like their near neighbour d'Arry Osborn, they are also traditionalists, still making the wines which put the area on the Australian (and English) wine map. And like a few of the older family wineries in the area, they can also offer older vintages of wines, especially reds, at reasonable cellar door prices. Wines include pinot noir, cabernet shiraz, block six shiraz (vines planted 1892), Rhine riesling, late harvest riesling, late harvest frontignac, sauvignon blanc (dry), ruby, tawny and vintage ports, and liqueur muscat. Bulk reds and ports available. Limited distribution in South Australia, cellar door and mail order.

Luong Rice Winery *Off Main Street (opposite Almond Train), McLaren Vale SA 5171. (08) 323 8156.*

Cellar door: Irregular hours.
Winemaker: Peter Bengsen.

This is one of the more unusual operations in the area. Peter Bengsen makes a range of Chinese rice wines which are sold at this outlet (which used to be a Chinese restaurant) alongside some conventional grape wines. The Mei Chiew rice wine has an alcohol content of 22.5 per cent. Other wines include Rhine riesling, spumante, muscatel, frontignan, shiraz, red grenache and some ports and brandies.

Maglieri Wines *13 Douglas Gully Road, McLaren Flat SA 5171. (08) 383 0177.*

Cellar door: Monday–Saturday, 9.30–4; Sunday and public holidays 11–4.30. Large lawn, shaded by trees, for picnics; groups catered for by arrangement. BBQs can also be arranged. Local art on display. All major credit cards.
Winemaker: John Loxton.

Owned by the Maglieri family; founded 1972. Substantial middle-sized winery with an Italian flavour, producing good wines, including full range of red and white wines, plus fortifieds. Good Rhine riesling, but also specialise in wines with an Italian touch, notably lambrusco, a light-style red which is very popular in the US. Distributed in most major States, by mailing list and at cellar door.

Manning Park *Corner Chalk Hill and Olivers Road, McLaren Vale SA 5171. (08) 323 8209.*

Cellar door: Monday–Sunday 9–5. Patio area with BBQ for visitors. Three bedroom, fully self-contained cottage which will sleep eight (enquiries to above telephone number). All major credit cards.
Winemaker: Allan McLean.

Founded 1982. Small outlet about 1.5 kilometres north of McLaren Vale amid almond trees and vineyards. Dry whites, dry reds, sweet whites and tawny port produced under the Manning Park Traditional Wines label. Distribution through cellar door. This small winery also boasts a cooperage with a cooper on view five days a week making beer barrels.

Marienberg *Black Road, Coromandel Valley SA 5051. (08) 270 2384.*

Cellar door: Monday–Friday 9.30–4.30, closed weekends except during Easter, Bushing Festival and Grand Prix. BBQ area for visitors. All major credit cards.
Winemaker: Ursula Pridham.

Owned by Ursula and Geoffrey Pridham; founded 1968. Ursula Pridham, born in Austria, showed (at about the same time as Wolf Blass started marketing his own wines elsewhere in South Australia) that the power of personality *can* successfully market wines. Her wines have a traditional Austrian genesis, with an emphasis on wood treatment. Wines include chablis, sauvignon blanc, gewürztraminer, Rosengarten, sweet whites, shiraz/cabernet, pinot noir and cabernet sauvignon. Distribution in all eastern States and at cellar door.

Maxwell Wines *24 Kangarilla Road, McLaren Vale SA 5171. (08) 323 8200.*

Cellar door: Open seven days including public holidays 10–5. No tours or picnics. All major credit cards.
Winemaker: Mark Maxwell.

Family owned; founded 1979. Products include chardonnay, Rhine riesling, red blend, including cabernet and merlot, and other varieties. Light dry red style. Meads made from fermented honey. Distribution through winery.

Merrivale *Olivers Road, McLaren Vale SA 5171. (08) 323 9196.*

Cellar door: Saturday and Sunday 10–4. No BBQs or picnics. All major credit cards.
Winemaker/owner: Dean Liebich

Founded 1971. Small winery with cellar door and interstate distribution. Wines include Rhine riesling, chardonnay, dry semillon, cabernet sauvignon, shiraz and ports.

Middlebrook *Sand Road, McLaren Vale SA 5171. (08) 383 0004.*

Cellar door: Daily 11–5. Winery and restaurant complex offering sit-down à la carte lunches (12–3) in the the Terrace Restaurant and light grills and salads in the Grillery. Function and reception areas. Pottery and paintings on display, plus various eatables for sale.
Winemaker: Steve Clarkson.

Owned by AMC Investments. The original property, bought by Thomas Hardy in 1880, has seen many changes of owners, including members of the Hardy family. Wines include Rhine riesling, sauvignon blanc, gewürztraminer, chablis, shiraz, cabernet/shiraz/merlot, champagne and—notably—Durus, a honey/cumquat-flavoured liqueur, which tastes much better than it sounds! Vintage and tawny ports. True to its name, Middlebrook is a middle-sized winery, with distribution in most States, plus through cellar door.

Mount Hurtle *Corner Pimpala and Byards Road, Reynella SA 5171. (08) 381 6877.*

Cellar door: Monday–Friday 9–5, Saturday, Sunday and public holidays 8–4. Extensive restorations have taken place

at the winery which include an eighty-seat general facility restaurant (use by prior appointment) and a large outdoor eating facility, again by appointment. Jazz and other concerts are held frequently at the winery. Mastercard, Bankcard, Visa.
Winemakers: Geoff Merrill and Joe De Fabiox.

Historic winery dating from 1897, south-east of Chateau Reynella. Owned by Geoff Merrill, an extremely talented winemaker. Wines under the Geoff Merrill label include chardonnay (made from fruit from McLaren Vale and the Barossa Valley) and cabernet sauvignon (from Coonawarra and McLaren Vale). Under the Mount Hurtle label there is a cabernet sauvignon, sauvignon blanc/semillon and grenache made from grapes from McLaren Vale. Distributed in all States and through cellar door.

Noon's *Rifle Range Road, McLaren Vale SA 5171. (08) 323 8290.*

Cellar door: Open seven days 10–5. Picnic areas available and a BBQ is provided. Bankcard, Mastercard, Visa.
Winemakers: David Noon and Clive Simmonds.

Family owned; founded 1976. A small winery between McLaren Vale and Willunga, with one of the attributes that distinguishes the small winemakers of both McLaren Vale and many other areas of Australia—some really unusual products Key wines include dry whites, *maceration carbonique* reds, big full-bodied reds, unfiltered reds, mulled red spiced wine, and vintage ports. Distributed through cellar door and mail order.

Old Clarendon Winery *Main Road, Clarendon SA 5157. (08) 383 6056.*

Cellar door: Open Friday, Saturday, Sunday and public holidays 11–4 (or by arrangement). Large restaurant (closed to the public on Monday), craft shop (personalised, hand-crafted pottery), home-style bakery and coffee shop open Tuesday–Sunday 10–5 (serving beer and wine). Motel attached. Convention centre.

Old Clarendon 'Winery' is in fact based on an old winery but these days they buy in the wines, and the income is derived from a multiplex of tourist activities sprawling down the side of a hill in the valley that makes up Clarendon. Among the maze are shops, pottery and craft shops and the open-plan Wintergarden Restaurant. Included also are a silversmith, a hairdresser and even a garden plant shop. Above it all is a spartan but comfortable motel. Wines sold under the Old Clarendon Winery label include Rhine riesling, frontignac, shiraz, port and liqueur mead.

Oliverhill *Seaview Road, McLaren Vale SA 5171. (08) 323 8922.*

Cellar door: Daily 10–5. BBQ and picnic areas. Tours invited. All major credit cards. Lunches served daily (Italian and Chinese food).
Winemaker: Vincenzo Berlingieri (owner).

Founded 1973. Table wines available, and the irrepressible Vincenzo (who at another local winery gave the world Plasma Port, complete with an intravenous drip-feed!) specialises in 'all the forgotten' fortified wines. Distribution through cellar door.

Pirramimma *Johnston Road, McLaren Vale SA 5171. (08) 323 8205.*

Cellar door: Monday–Friday 9–5, Saturday 10–5, Sunday and holidays 12–4. Picnickers welcome, small children's play area, tours by appointment. All major credit cards.
Winemaker: Geoffrey Johnston.

Family owned (A. C. Johnston); founded 1892. Pirramimma, headed by amiable general manager Alex Johnston, is one of the lower profile, but nonetheless most significant, of the McLaren Vale larger makers. The wine quality is generally high and, like other older family concerns, older wines and some notable ports can be tasted and purchased from their cellars, to the south-west of McLaren Vale township, at fair prices. Wide ranges of wines, including chardonnay, Rhine riesling, chablis, cabernet sauvignon, shiraz and old ports. Distributed in South Australia, Victoria and New South Wales, by mail order and through cellar door.

Richard Hamilton Willunga Vineyards *Main South Road, Willunga SA 5172. (085) 56 2288.*

Cellar door: Monday–Saturday 9–5, Sunday, holidays 11–5. Tours, picnics welcome. All major credit cards.
Winemakers: Hugh and Richard Hamilton.

Family owned; founded 1971. The Hamiltons, of Hamilton's Ewell Vineyards fame, now operate two small wineries, this one plus Leconfield in Coonawarra. Wines include chardonnay, sauvignon blanc, semillon, Rhine riesling, cabernet sauvignon and port. Distributed in South Australia, Victoria, the Australian Capital Territory, Queensland and Western Australia by National Wine Merchants and in New South Wales by Regional Wines Pty Ltd. Also through cellar door.

Ross McLaren Estate *Victor Harbor Road, McLaren Vale SA 5171. (08) 323 8614.*

Not open to the public as we went to press. Closed for renovations.

Ryecroft *14 Ingoldby Road, McLaren Flat SA 5171. (08) 383 0001.*

Cellar door: Monday–Friday 10–5, Saturday, Sunday and public holidays 12–5. All major credit cards.
Winemaker: Nick Holmes.

A well known Southern Vales name for many years, hidden at the back of McLaren Flat, near Ingoldby. Ryecroft Vineyards Pty Ltd is now owned by Grant Burge, Nick Holmes and Paul Buttery and was purchased in 1987. Wines include chardonnay, semillon, Rhine riesling, frontignac, cabernet shiraz, traditional red and tawny port. Distribution interstate and through cellar door. Nick Holmes also owns Shottesbrooke Vineyards at Myponga and wine under the Shottesbrooke label (sauvignon blanc and cabernet/merlot—generally excellent wines) can be purchased from the cellar door at Ryecroft.

St Francis *Bridge Street, Reynella SA 5161. (08) 381 1925.*

Cellar door: Monday–Friday 8.30–4.30, Saturday, Sunday and holidays 10–5. All major credit cards. Restaurant open daily for lunch and dinner (08) 381 5833. Motel with thirty-seven rooms (two for handicapped). Conference facilities. Spas in all rooms, indoor pool, sauna
Winemaker: Rob Dundon and Jim Irvine.

Family owned; founded 1852. Small but historic winery—just off the Main South Road near the village of Old Reynella. Wines include dry reds, dry whites, ports and sherries. The motel is a recent addition.

Scarpantoni Estate *Kangarilla Road, McLaren Flat SA 5171. (08) 383 0186.*

Cellar door: Daily 10–5. Tours invited. BBQ area available. Paintings on display (not for sale). All major credit cards.
Winemakers: Domenico Scarpantoni, Michael Scarpantoni and Filippo Scarpantoni.

Owned by the Scarpantoni family; founded 1979. Quality small maker with reasonable cellar door prices. Wines include chardonnay, Rhine riesling, sauvignon blanc, late-picked riesling, botrytised riesling, cabernet sauvignon, shiraz, tarrango, fortified very late-picked liqueur Rhine riesling and vintage port. Distributed in Sydney and Perth and through cellar door.

Seaview *Chaffey's Road, McLaren Vale SA 5171. Distribution through Penfolds (08) 323 8250.*

Cellar door: Monday–Friday 9–4.30, Saturday and holidays 10–5, Sunday 11–4. Visitors can inspect the winery, though no organised tours. Lawns, etc., for picnics. Amex, Bankcard, Visa, Mastercard.
Winemaker: Michael Farmilo.

Owned by Penfolds; founded 1850. This famous winery, home of Seaview Rhine Riesling and Seaview Cabernet

Sauvignon, was part of the Adsteam group's takeover in 1985, and its significance as a production centre appears to have diminished inside the reach of the giant Barossa-based wine group. Nevertheless, Seaview's historic buildings, with an impressive tasting room lined with old carved wine vats, sit nestled in the folds of rolling vineyards and yes, indeed, on a clear day you can view the sea—or at least a bit of the Gulf of St Vincent, as you taste a wide range of quality wines. Wines include a select range of Wynn products, including of course their best-known brand, Seaview Rhine Riesling, white burgundy, chardonnay, chablis, cabernet sauvignon, cabernet/shiraz, Seaview Champagne and brut champagne, Grande Cuvée, tawny and Blackwood ports. Also for tasting are Edmund Mazure Champagne, Killawarra dry whites, dry reds and champagne. Distributed through Penfolds.

Settlement Wine Company

Burnt out in a spectacular fire in 1987 (the authors watched it!) and temporarily established in Torresan Wine Estates (08) 323 8808. Owned by Dr David Mitchell;
Winemaker: Janis Gesmanis.

Shottesbrooke

See Ryecroft.

The Vales Wine Company *151 Main Road, McLaren Vale SA 5171. (08) 323 8656.*

Cellar door: Monday–Friday 10–4, Saturday 10–4, Sunday and holidays 12–4. Shops, bakery, delicatessen close by.
Winemaker: Rod Bourchier and Michael Fargos.
Chairman: Michael von Berg MC.

Owned by a group of shareholders since 1987. The cellar door, right in the middle of the main street of McLaren Vale, is one of the most visible in the district. Under the Vales label, wines include cabernet/shiraz, chenin blanc, 1988 Rhine riesling, chardonnay and cabernet/merlot. Under the Wattles label, wines include dry red, semillon/frontignac and Rhine riesling (1989). Founded 1902 and, as we went to press, coming to life again. National distribution.

Thomas Fern Hill Estate *Ingoldby Road, McLaren Flat SA 5171. (08) 383 0167.*

Cellar door: Monday–Friday 9–5, weekends and holidays 12–5. No buses. All major credit cards.
Winemaker: Wayne Thomas.

Owned by Wayne and Pat Thomas; founded 1975. Wines include dry red and dry white table wines, fifteen-year-old tawny port. Distributed in all States and through cellar door.

Tinlin's *Kangarilla Road, McLaren Flat SA 5171. (08) 323 8649.*

Cellar door: Daily 8–4.30. No tours, no BBQ. No credit cards, but cheques accepted.
Winemaker: Don Tinlin.

Family owned; founded 1949. Tinlin's is a medium-sized wine producer specialising in cellar door sales of bottled and bulk wine. They will fill bulk containers from 2 litres up—bring your own or buy a 27 litre plastic containers for $8 plus the cost of the wine; 6 litre casks of dry red and white are available for $10 filled. Wines include full range of dry red and white wines, plus fortifieds. Distributed through cellar door only.

Tonkin's Currency Creek Wines *Winery Road, Currency Creek SA 5214. (085) 55 4069*

Cellar door: Daily 10–5. Restaurant open Tuesday–Sunday for lunch and Friday and Saturday night for dinner; bookings required. All major credit cards.
Winemaker: Brian Barry with Phillip Tonkin.

Owned by Tonkin family; founded 1968 (formerly known as Santa Rosa Wines). Wines produced under the Currency Creek label include sauvignon blanc, chardonnay, fumé blanc, Rhine riesling, late-picked riesling, pinot noir, shiraz, cabernet sauvignon fortified wines and *méthode champenoise.* Distributed in all States and through cellar door.

Torresan's Estate *Martin's Road, McLaren Vale SA 5171.*

Vineyard and winery, but not open to the public. See Torresan's Happy Valley below.

Torresan's Happy Valley *Manning Road, Flagstaff Hill SA 5159. (08) 270 2500.*

Cellar door: Monday–Saturday 8–5.30, closed Sunday and holidays. No tours, no BBQ. Amex, Bankcard, Diner's Club.
Winemaker: Michael Torreson.

Owned by Michael and John Torresan. Founded 1962. Wines include premium Torresan Estate range, cabernet, cabernet/shiraz, riesling, chardonnay, semillon and a lower priced range, plus the Godfather tawny and vintage ports.

Wirra Wirra Vineyards *McMurtrie Road, McLaren Vale SA 5171. (08) 323 8414.*

Cellar door: Monday–Saturday 10–5, Sunday and public holidays 11–5. Bus groups by appointment only. Picnic areas. Major credit cards.
Winemakers: Greg Trott (Principal Winemaker) and Ben Riggs.

Owned by R. G. and R. T. Trott Pty Ltd; founded 1894; re-established 1969. Wirra Wirra is among the most interesting and appealing cellar door operations in McLaren Vale, managed by the gregarious Greg Trott. The restored cellars (about halfway between the Salopian Inn and Middlebrook) are a delight to visit—particularly in winter when a log fire is burning. Regular functions held by the Trott cousins are worth attending, and most importantly of all, wine quality is excellent. Wines include Rhine riesling (dry, hand picked), late-picked chardonnay, sauvignon blanc, sauvignon blanc/semillon, cabernet sauvignon, Church Block Dry Red, vintage and tawny ports, and *méthode champenoise* ('The Cousins'). Distributed in all States and through cellar door.

Woodstock Winery & Coterie *Douglas Gully Road, McLaren Flat SA 5171. (08) 383 0156.*

Cellar door: Monday–Friday 9–5, weekends and holidays 12–5. Picnic area and BBQ available. The Coterie restaurant open Sundays for à la carte lunches 12–5. Group bookings, parties, conventions, wedding and other receptions by appointment only. All major credit cards.
Winemaker: Scott Collett.

Family owned; founded 1974. The Collett family—father Doug and son Scott—are well known around the wine industry as skilled winemakers, and the products from this small winery show this. Reds stand out. Wines include Rhine riesling, sauvignon blanc, chardonnay, shiraz, cabernet sauvignon, botrytis sweet whites, and vintage and tawny ports. Distributed in all States and through cellar door.

Tasmania

It comes as a considerable surprise to most mainland Australians to find that wine is made in Tasmania. Indeed, there is a commercial winery in the suburbs of Hobart.

Climate, so important in viticultural matters, indicates that the production of premium grapes should be entirely possible; after all, Hobart in the south of Tasmania is 43° south of the equator (while, for example, the Champagne region of France is 50° north).

The early settlers realised Tasmania's potential and grapes were grown on the island from the earliest days, though they disappeared until the 1960s. Since the resurgence of Tasmanian viticulture at least a

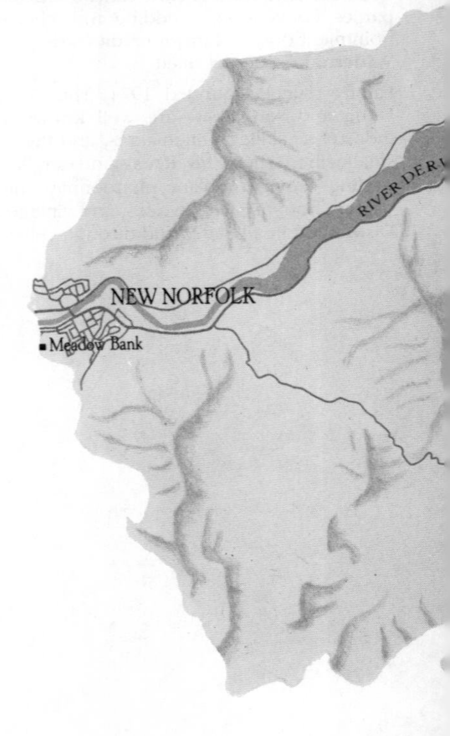

dozen wineries and a number of additional vineyards are now in operation. And it must be said that while quantity is miniscule, quality is generally very good, reflecting the cool climate in which the grapes are grown.

The wine areas are generally centred comparatively close to Hobart in the south, and to the north-east of Launceston in the north. Prices for most of the Tasmanian wines are high, reflecting the small scale of production and the high costs. But to anyone interested in wine Tasmania offers new and exciting prospects.

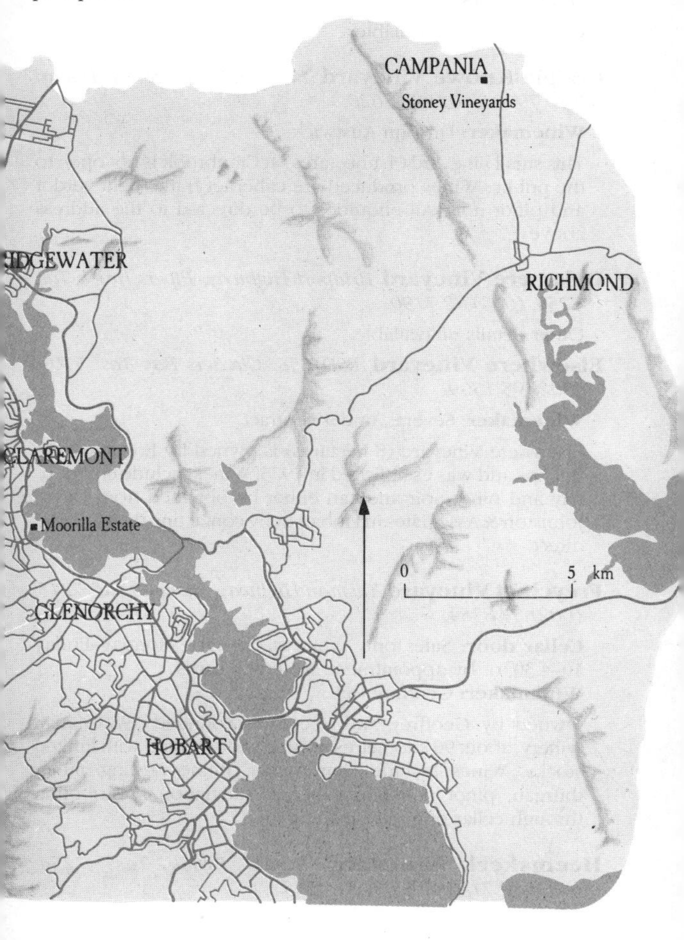

Buchanan Wines *Glendale Road, Sidmouth Tas. 7270. (003) 94 7488.*

Cellar door: By appointment only, while stocks last. No credit cards.
Winemaker: Don Buchanan

Buchanan Wines bought Glengarry Vineyard three years ago. They also own Loira Vineyard. Wines are made under the Buchanan label and include cabernet, pinot noir, chardonnay, sauvignon blanc and Rhine riesling. Agents in Tasmania, Adelaide and Victoria and a few outlets in Sydney.

Cliffhouse Wines *RSD 457, Kayena Tas. 7270. (003) 94 7454.*

Other details unavailable.

Craigie Knowe Vineyard *173 Macquarie Street, Hobart Tas. 7000. (002) 23 5620.*

Winemaker: Dr John Austwick.

This small vineyard (4.1 hectares) at Cranbrook is not open to the public. Wines produced are cabernet franc, petit verdot and pinot noir. All enquiries to be directed to the address above.

Delamere Vineyard *Bridport Highway, Pipers Brook Tas. 7254. (003) 82 7190.*

Other details unavailable.

Elsewhere Vineyard *RSD 558, Glaziers Bay Tas. 7109. (002) 95 1509.*

Winemaker: Several, under contract.

Elsewhere Vineyard (8 hectares) is owned by Eric and Jette Phillips and was established in 1975. Wines include chardonnay and pinot noir and can either be obtained from David Johnston & Associates in Hobart or by contacting the vineyard direct.

Freycinet Vineyard *Tasman Highway, Bicheno Tas. 7215. (002) 57 8384.*

Cellar door: Sales only while stocks last. Monday–Friday 10–4.30, or by appointment. No credit cards.
Winemaker: Geoffrey Bull.

Owned by Geoffrey and Sue Bull. Founded 1980. Small winery, about 90 kilometres north-east of Hobart, with limited stocks. Wines include chardonnay, Rhine riesling/müller thurgau, pinot noir and cabernet sauvignon. Distribution through cellar door and mailing list.

Heemskerk Vineyard *Pipers Brook Tas. 7254. (003) 82 7133 or (003) 31 4585.*

Cellar door: No cellar door sales. Visitors by appointment only.
Winemaker: Graham Wiltshire.

Owned by Fesq, Haselgrove, Wiltshire & Co. Pty Ltd, with an involvement by the French champagne-maker Louis Roederer; founded 1975. This Tamar Valley winery, north-east of Launceston, is the largest in Tasmania, and produces some of the best wines. The timbered winery building, in the splendid, isolated valley, is striking too. Wines include pinot noir, cabernet sauvignon, chardonnay and, of course, *méthode champenoise* sparkling wine. Distributed through Fesq & Co. in New South Wales and Victoria.

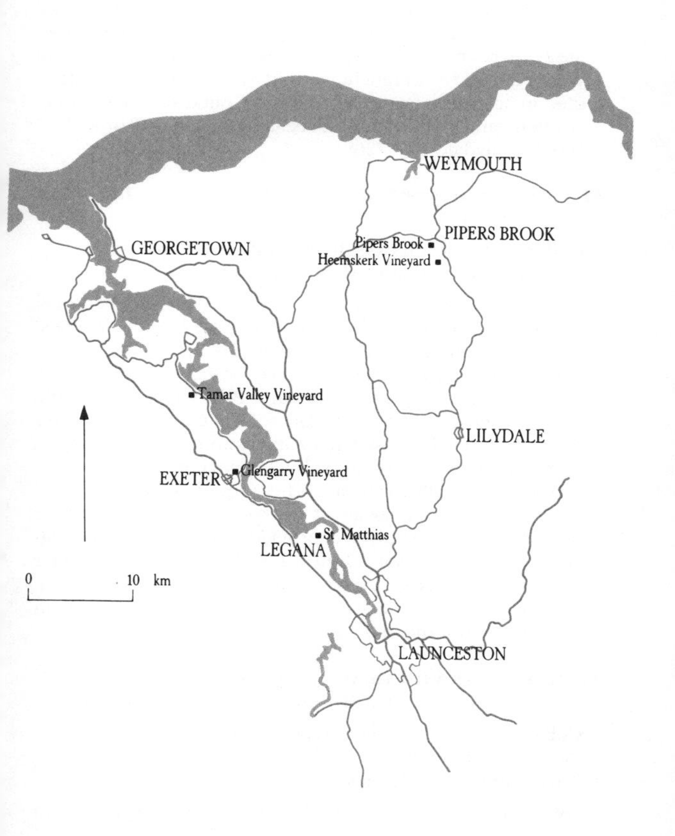

Holm Oak *RSD 258, Rowella Tas. 7270. (003) 94 7577.*

Cellar door: By appointment only.
Winemaker: Consultant Andrew Hood

This winery, established in 1988 and owned by Edward and Nicholas Butler, has 2.5 hectares of pinot noir, 1.7 hectares of cabernet sauvignon and almost 0.5 hectare of merlot and cabernet franc. Wines produced are said to be in the burgundy and bordeaux styles. Various distributions throughout Australia, mail order and through cellar door.

La Provence *Lalla Road, Lalla Tas. 7267. (003) 95 1290.*

Cellar door: Open by appointment only. No credit cards.

Wine is made under contract by Heemskerk. Owner is Stuart Bryce who says La Provence is the oldest established vineyard in Tasmania, the first vines being planted in 1956. There are 4 hectares of vines, and wines include pinot noir and chardonnay, and are in limited supply. The chardonnay vines are perhaps the oldest commercially planted in Australia and were planted by a Frenchman thirty-four years ago. Distributed in selected restaurants and retail outlets in Melbourne, Canberra and Sydney, through cellar door and mail order (PO Box 99, Lilydale Tas. 7268).

Marion's Vineyard *Foreshore Drive, Deviot Tas. 7251. (003) 94 7434.*

Cellar door: Seven days 10–5. Bankcard, Visa.
Winemaker: Mark and Marion Semmens.

Owned by the Semmens family; founded 1980. Another small Tamar Valley winery, which its owners say has 'the loveliest vineyard site in Australia'. A restaurant for special functions by appointment only but serves Sunday brunches to the public. A 40 metre jetty is planned for early 1991 which will enable guests to travel from Launceston or from George Town after they arrive on the Bass Strait catamaran service. A stage is planned for March 1991 to be built in a natural amphitheatre surrounded by the vineyard The Semmens hope to hold concerts and jazz festivals at the site. A couple of smaller buildings set in the bush will provide overnight accommodation at the wine resort. Wines include chardonnay, müller thurgau, pinot gris, cabernet sauvignon, merlot and zinfandel. Distribution through cellar door and selected restaurants in Sydney, Melbourne and Tasmania.

Meadowbank Vineyard *Glenora (in the Derwent Valley, 75 kilometres north-west of Hobart) Tas. 7150. (002) 86 1269.*

Cellar door: Open seven days 9–5 by appointment only. Bankcard, Mastercard.
Winemaker: Ian Holmes

Owned by Gerald Ellis; founded 1974. Grapes were sent to

Victoria and made into wine by the late Stephen Hickinbotham at Anakie. Wine is now made at the winery at Meadowbank and marketed under the Meadowbank Vineyard label. Wines include Rhine riesling, chardonnay, shiraz and cabernet sauvignon. Distributed in Tasmania and Victoria and through cellar door.

Moorilla Estate *655 Main Road, Berriedale Tas. 7011. (002) 49 2949.*

Cellar door: The Moorilla Estate Wine Centre erected recently at the winery is open seven days a week for tastings and tours on a regular basis. Rooms for functions are available by appointment only. All major credit cards.
Winemaker: Julian Alcorso.

Owned by the Alcorso family; founded 1958. One of the most unusual wineries in Australia. The tiny winery is sited on a spit of land projecting into the Derwent River, in the Hobart suburb of Berriedale. The grapes are drawn from their own vineyards there (some of them under bird protection covers, unusual in itself) and from Bream Creek, further to the east. Wines include Rhine riesling, traminer, chardonnay, cabernet sauvignon and pinot noir The long-term aim is to produce predominantly pinot noir. Distribution through Dorado nationally.

Morningside Vineyard *RMB 3002, Middle Tea Tree Road, Tea Tree Tas. 7017 (002) 68 1748.*

Not open to the public.
Winemaker: Peter Bosworth.

This small winery is owned by Peter and Brenda Bosworth and was established in 1981. Small amounts of pinot noir, cabernet and Rhine riesling. Mail order only.

Panorama Vineyard *193 Waterworks Road, Hobart Tas. 7005. (002) 23 1948.*

Cellar door: Monday–Friday 10–5. Weekends by appointment only. No credit cards.
Winemaker: Steve Ferencz.

This small winery is owned by Steve Ferencz. Wines include chardonnay, müller thurgau, pinot noir and cabernet sauvignon. Distributed through cellar door sales and outlets in Hobart, although stocks are limited.

Pipers Brook Vineyard *Pipers Brook Tas. 7254. (003) 82 7197*

Visits by appointment only.
Winemaker: Dr Andrew Pirie (part owner).

Founded 1972. One of the 'big three' in Tasmania (with Heemskerk and Moorilla), this is a high-quality small winery north-east of Launceston. They now own Pellion Vineyard and Ninth Island Vineyard. Wines include Rhine riesling, traminer, chardonnay (extremely good), pinot noir and cabernet sauvignon. Distribution by mailing list and through I. H. Baker in Sydney.

Powercourt *McEwin's Road, Legana Tas. 7251. (003) 30 1225.*

Cellar door: Sales by appointment only. No credit cards.
Winemaker: Ralph Power (owner).

Founded 1970. Very small winery (formerly Chateau Elmslie, renamed for its owner's origins in County Court, Ireland) making good wines, just north of Launceston. Two hectares of vines—wines include chardonnay, pinot noir and cabernet sauvignon. Distribution through cellar door only.

Rochecombe Vineyard *Baxters Road, Pipers River Tas. 7252. (003) 82 7122.*

Cellar door: Open 7 days 9–5. Mastercard, Bankcard, Visa. Small restaurant open for lunches by appointment. One of the attractions at this charming winery is the four or five groups of platypus that swim in the river around the winery. The logo for the winery is, needless to say, a platypus.
Winemaker: Bernard Rochaix.
General manager: Alfred Edgecombe.

This winery, established in 1984, is owned by Bernard and Brigitte Rochaix and Alfred Edgecombe. There are some 20 hectares under vine, and wines include pinot noir, chardonnay, cabernet sauvignon, cabernet franc and chenin blanc. Distributed at cellar door only.

Rotherhythe *Henderson's Lane, Gravelly Beach, Exeter Tas 7251. (003) 34 0188 or (003) 30 1474.*

Owned by Dr Steve Hyde; founded 1972. No cellar door sales; wines from two vineyards are made at Delamere Vineyard by Dr Hyde and produced under the Rotherhythe label. Wines include chardonnay, pinot noir, merlot and cabernet sauvignon. Some wine sold through Delamere.

St Matthias Vineyard *Rosevears Drive, Rosevears, Launceston Tas. 7250. (003) 30 1700 or (003) 31 1840.*

Cellar door: Open seven days 10–5 with the exception of June/July/August when not open at weekends. Bankcard, Visa.
Winemaker: Made under contract by Heemskerk (by Graham Wiltshire).

Owned by Laurie and Adell Wing; founded 1983. Wines include Rhine riesling, chardonnay, cabernet sauvignon and pinot noir. Range of Tasmanian wines from other makers also on sale. Distribution through cellar door and mail order.

Stoney Vineyards *Campania Tas. 7202. (002) 62 4174.*

No tastings; sales by appointment only. Stocks very limited.
Winemaker: Andrew Vasiljuk.

Owned by Peter and Ruth Althaus since June 1989. Founded 1975. Stoney Hill, just north-east of Hobart, produces high-quality wines from just under 1 hectare. Some 15 hectares will be planted over the next two years and a winery is being built. Products include Rhine riesling, sylvaner, traminer, pinot noir and cabernet sauvignon. Distributed through mailing list or Tasman Wine Cellars.

Strathayr Vineyard *Richmond Tas. 7025. (002) 62 2235.*

Owned by Bill Casimaty; founded 1975. Very small winery just north-east of Hobart, with no cellar door sales, making Rhine riesling, pinot noir and cabernet sauvignon. The wine is made by Heemskerk.

Tolosa Vineyard *3 Una Street, Mount Stewart Tas. 7000. (002) 34 33043.*

This winery does not sell wine commercially at this time.

Winterwood Winery *RSD 1057, Gardners Bay Tas. 7112. (002) 951864.*

Cellar door: Seven days a week 10–5 (summer) and Wednesday–Sunday 10–5 (winter). All credit cards except Diner's Club. This winery boasts the only French trellises in Australia.
Winemaker: Bruce and Jane Gillan.

Established in 1985 and owned by Bruce and Jane Gillan. Wines include fruit ports and liqueurs under the Winterwood label and red and white table wines

Queensland

Most all of the Queensland wine industry is centred on the Granite Belt, just south of Stanthorpe on the Darling Downs, near the New South Wales–Queensland border. This area, a new one by Australian standards, shares the problems of all of the other 'new' wine areas of Australia: experimenting with grape varieties, getting to know soils and climate, grappling with technology (or lack of it) and very often the absence of ready capital to buy expertise, new oak and so on.

Still, a number of people have recognised that the areas around Stanthorpe offer attractive conditions for growing wine (and table) grapes: generally cool climate, because of the altitude, 750–900 metres above sea level; good soils; availability of land and reasonable proximity to several large population centres. While wine quality has fluctuated, as one would expect it would with wineries which have emerged in the past decade or so, there is undoubtedly enough performance here—not to mention promise—to believe that in another decade or two this will be a significant area for quality table wine production. After all, how many Australian vineyards can show photographs of snow among the vines, as Robinson's can? If *that's* not cool climate, what is?

An unusual aspect of the Granite Belt (because very few Australian wine areas get together on products) is their development of Ballandean Nouveau, a beaujolais-style light red—an enjoyable summer drink.

Further north, there are several vineyard areas, one particularly of note because of several unique facts. Romavilla, in outback Roma, has been making wines for well over 100 years, and in a fairly significant way. Their Romavilla Liqueur Muscat is quite outstanding, by any standards.

In the Atherton Tablelands, in the far north, the Fosters have been growing the North American grapevine *Vitis labrusca*, and making wines for decades; that puts one Foster's liquor interest at one end of the country, and another at the Top End—though they are rather further apart in dollar turnover, one would suppose!

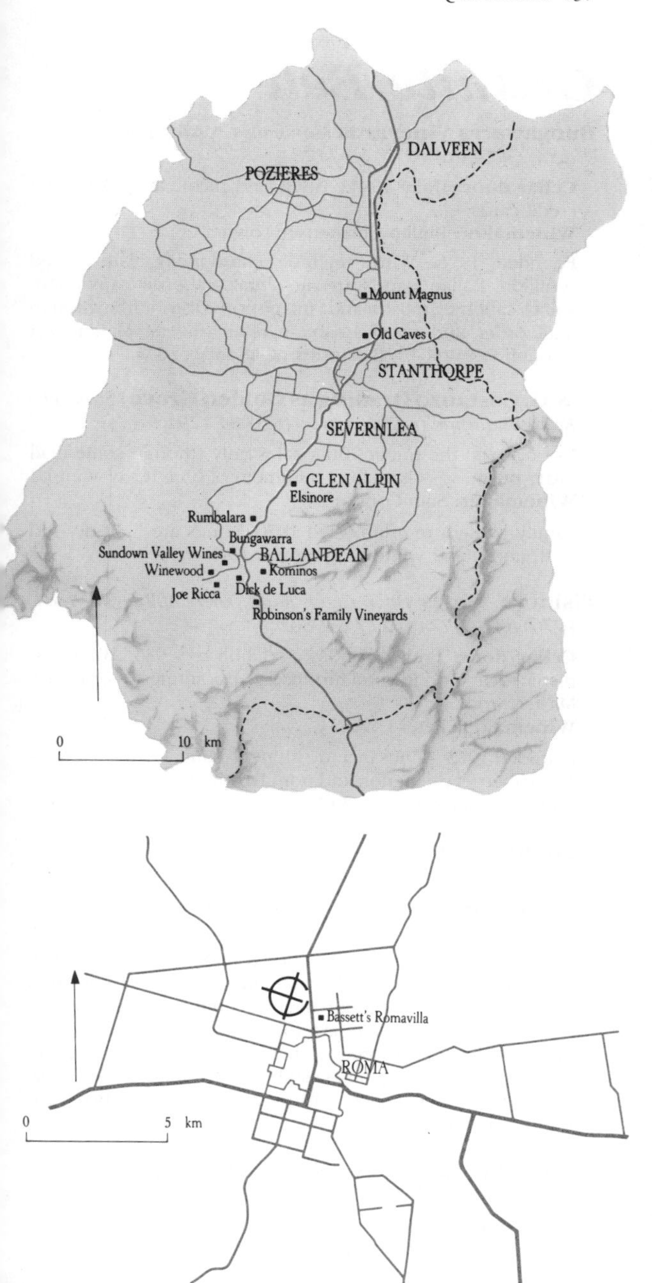
DALVEEN
POZIERES
Mount Magnus
Old Caves
STANTHORPE
SEVERNLEA
GLEN ALPIN
Elsinore
Rumbalara
Bungawarra
Sundown Valley Wines
BALLANDEAN
Winewood
Kominos
Joe Ricca
Dick de Luca
Robinson's Family Vineyards
0
10 km
Bassett's Romavilla
ROMA
0
5 km

Granite Belt

Bungawarra Vineyards *Marshalls Crossing Road, Ballandean Qld 4382. (076) 84 1128.*

Cellar door: Daily 10–4. BBQs and picnic area. All major credit cards.
Winemaker: Phillip Christensen (owner).

Founded 1976. Wines include chardonnay, late–picked semillon, Ballandean Nouveau, shiraz, cabernet sauvignon, shiraz/cabernet, muscat and vintage port. Distribution through mail order and some Brisbane retail outlets. Mailing list through PO Box 10, Ballandean Qld 4382.

S. & G. Costanzo (trading as Golden Grove) *Sundown Road, Ballandean Qld. 4382. (076) 84 1291.*

Not open to the public. Bulk sales only (though some mail order business; will deliver minimum of 63 litres of wine).
Winemaker: Stan Constanzo.

Family-owned; re-established 1976. Wines are light dry red (burgundy) and white burgundy style.

Elsinore Wines *Back Creek Road, Glen Aplin Qld 4381. (076) 83 4234 or (07) 34 39861.*

Cellar door: Friday–Sunday and holidays 9–5. BBQ and picnic area. Catering and groups by appointment. Bankcard, Mastercard.
Winemaker: Peter Love.

Founded 1973. Wines include Rhine riesling, chablis, hermitage, cabernet sauvignon and port. Distribution through cellar door and mail order to PO Box 106, Coorparoo Qld 4151.

Kominos Wines *New England Highway, Severnlea Qld 4352. (076) 83 5275.*

Cellar door: Open seven days 9–4.30. Bankcard, Visa.
Winemaker: Tony Comino.

Family owned; founded 1976; first commercial vintage 1985. Tony Comino's Greek background influenced his decision to make wine here and though the first commercial vintage was only in 1985, the results are looking good. Wines include Rhine riesling, chardonnay, chenin blanc, semillon, shiraz and cabernet sauvignon. Distributed through cellar door, selected Brisbane outlets and by mail order (PO Box 225, Stanthorpe Qld 4380).

Mount Magnus Wines *Donnellys Castle Road, Pozières Qld 4352. (076) 85 3213.*

Cellar door: Daily 9–5. BBQs and picnic facilities. Function room, bus tours by appointment. Bankcard, Visa, Mastercard.

Winemaker: Various, under contract.

Owned by John Matthews; founded 1933. Mount Magnus stands apart from the other Granite Belt wineries off some 15 kilometres to the north-west of Stanthorpe, and surrounded by place names so evocative of World War I: Pozières, Bullecourt and Paschendale. It is also high, approaching 1000 metres about sea level, and wine quality is also high. Wines include chardonnay, sauvignon blanc, semillon, chianti, hermitage, cabernet sauvignon, claret, two tawny ports, marsala, botrytis sauterne and highland cream. Distribution through cellar door and mailing list.

Old Caves Winery *New England Highway, Stanthorpe Qld 4380. (076) 81 1494.*

Cellar door: Monday–Saturday 9–5, Sunday 10–4. Groups by appointment. Souvenirs and pottery. Wood BBQs. All major credit cards.
Winemaker: David Zanatta.

Owned by David and Shirley Zanatta; founded 1980. Wines include chardonnay/semillon, dry white, moselle, rosé, lambrusco, shiraz, tawny, vintage and rummy port, and honey mead. Distributed through cellar door and mail order.

J. & N. Ricca *Sundown Road, Ballandean Qld 4382. (076) 84 1235.*
No formal tastings, but visitors welcome.
Winemaker: Joe Ricca.

Owned by J. and N. Ricca; founded 1930s. Wines include dry red and dry white. Sold to public (minimum 25 litres).

Robinson's Family Vineyards *Curtins Road, Lyra, via Ballandean Qld 4382. (076) 84 1216.*

Cellar door: Daily 9–5. BBQ and picnic facilities. Tours by request. Mastercard, Bankcard, Visa.
Winemaker: John Robinson.

Owned by the Robinson family; founded 1969. John Robinson is a Toowoomba solicitor and his family's winery is one of the best in the State, with a fully equipped winery and large vineyards (14 hectares). Quality wines including chardonnay, traminer, cabernet sauvignon, shiraz/cabernet, ports and liqueurs. Bay Cooler and *méthode champenoise* sparkling wine. Distributed in all States except Tasmania and through cellar door.

Rumbalara Vineyards *Fletcher Road, Fletcher Qld 4381. (076) 84 1206.*

Cellar door: Daily 9–5. BBQ and picnic areas. Groups catered for by arrangement. Bankcard, Mastercard, Visa.
Winemaker: Chris Gray.

Owned by Bob and Una Gray; founded 1974. Well-established winery and vineyards, winning praise from national wine judges. Wines can be purchased at the winery and taken to the Vineyard Cafe nearby in Ballandean. Wines include range of red and white varietals, plus fortifieds, semillons, chardonnay, rosé and muscat. 'English-style' ciders. Distributed through cellar door and mailing list and in Queensland.

Sundown Valley Vineyards *Sundown Road, Ballandean Qld 4382. (076) 84 1226.*

Cellar door: Daily 9–5. Tours. Bankcard, Mastercard, Visa. Lunches by appointment, picnic area.
Winemaker: Angelo Puglisi and Adam Chapman.

Owned by Angelo and Mary Puglisi; founded 1970. One of the most professional winery operations in the district, producing good wines, including Rhine riesling, semillon/sauvignon blanc, chardonnay, auslese sylvaner, hermitage, cabernet sauvignon, moselle and port. Distribution through cellar door and mail order. Their premium range sold under the Ballandean Estate label include cabernet sauvignon, semillon/sauvignon blanc, sauvignon blanc and a light red. This range available in Queensland and New South Wales.

Winewood *Sundown Valley Road, Ballandean Qld 4382. (076) 84 1187.*

Cellar door: Weekends 9–5. Weekdays by appointment. Bankcard, Mastercard, Visa.
Winemaker: Ian Davis (owner).

Founded early 1970s. Ian Davis is a local teacher and he and his wife run the winery, which is close to the township. Wines include light dry reds, full-bodied shiraz and cabernet, semillon and chardonnay. Distribution through cellar door and mailing list (PO Box 84, Ballandean Qld 4382).

Roma

Romavilla Winery *Northern Road, Roma Qld 4455. (076) 22 1822.*

Cellar door: Monday–Friday 9–5; Saturday 9–12 and 2–4, closed Sunday. Bus groups by appointment. Bankcard, Mastercard, Visa.
Winemaker: David Wall.

Owned by David and Joy Wall. Founded 1863; present winery built 1878. One of Australia's most unusual wineries, virtually in the Outback; fortified wines of considerable distinction. Wines include dry whites and dry reds, sherries, ports, muscats, moselle and sauternes. Distribution through cellar door and mail order.

Atherton Tablelands

Foster & Co. *Kalunga, via Herberton Qld 4872. (070) 96 2359.*

Cellar door: Daily 8–5. BBQ for visitors. Two hotels and two cafés 10 kilometres away in Herberton. Bankcard, Visa.
Winemaker: Christopher Foster.

Owned by C. J. Foster and Co.; founded 1978. Wines include riesling, moselle, mataro, claret, shiraz, port and two muscats. Distribution only through cellar door.

Western Australia

Surprisingly, while many Australians do not realise that wine is made in Western Australia, the industry there is one of the oldest in the country. Vines were planted from the very first days of white settlement, and several wineries go back almost as far. Olive Farm winery, for example, was established by the Yurisich family in 1829 and Houghton can date its Swan Valley vineyards to 1836.

The West is crushing some 8000 tonnes of wine grapes each year, depending on vintage conditions. To put this in some sort of perspective, it is just over 1.5 per cent of Australia's typical wine production.

With the exception of the products of a handful of producers, not very much is seen outside its home State. The big makers, dominated by Houghton and Sandalford, are fairly easy to find in the other States and you can usually track down a bottle of Leeuwin Estate or perhaps Evans & Tate, or maybe Plantagenet. But few others.

The home of the wine industry in Western Australia is the Swan Valley, wandering up just to the north-east of Perth Airport, just twenty minutes out of Perth itself. It's a worthwhile trip, even if just to visit the two big boys, Houghton and Sandalford, though a number of the others offer wines of interest. There is a very strong Yugoslav influence, dating back to early settlement (in a similar way to the arrival of Silesian settlers in the Barossa Valley of South Australia). Many of these small family winemakers continue to make distinctive wines, often selling them in bulk or in flagon to the local trade and community.

To the south, on the coast and along the Margaret River area, plus the Great Southern Area near Albany, some very exciting wines have been made over the past two decades. These areas, together with the Swan Valley, offer the wine-interested traveller a delightful way to spend a few days touring through some of the most attractive countryside in the State (last time I visited the Margaret River area I saw a whale blowing in the Indian Ocean, just off the river's mouth). The karri forests alone are worth crossing the continent to see, and further south, toward the vineyard areas, and Albany, one gets a feeling for the splendid isolation of this area, not far from the corner

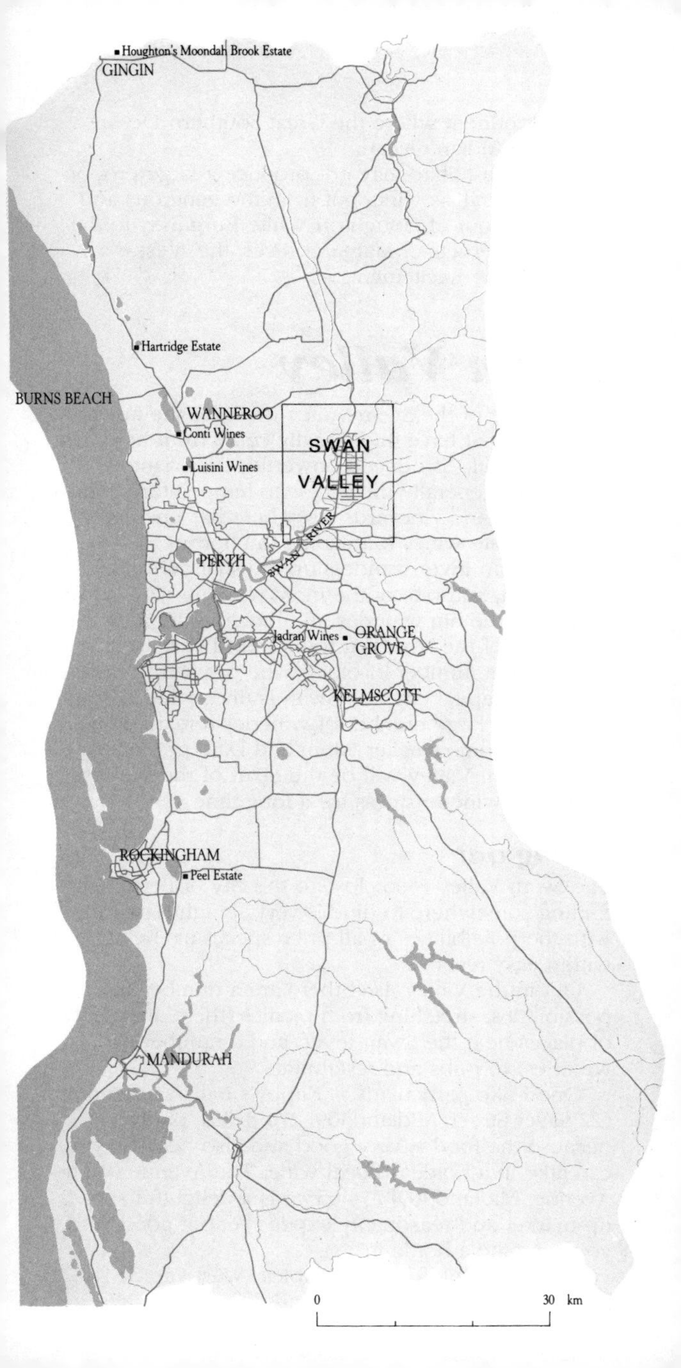

Houghton's Moondah Brook Estate
GINGIN
Hartridge Estate
BURNS BEACH
WANNEROO
Conti Wines
Luisini Wines
SWAN
VALLEY
SWAN RIVER
PERTH
Jadran Wines
ORANGE
GROVE
KELMSCOTT
ROCKINGHAM
Peel Estate
MANDURAH
0
30 km

of the continent where the Great Southern Ocean meets the Indian Ocean.

The largest State may not produce a large proportion of Australia's wine, but from the generous and distinct flavour of Houghton White Burgundy to the elegant cabernets of Margaret River, the West *is* a State of Wine Excitement.

Swan Valley

The climate of the Swan Valley provides the key to the wines that have traditionally come from here. Hot summer weeks produced powerful, even 'jammy', wines, but generally the access to temperature control technology and vineyards elsewhere has enabled more delicate wines to become the norm.

The Swan River wanders up the shallow valley from Perth, and one of the more relaxing ways to see several of the big wineries and lunch in the area is to catch one of the riverboat tours from Perth itself.

As with a number of other wine-producing areas close to a capital city, the Swan is under threat from suburbia. A large number of wineries remain, however, plus some smaller 'Mum and Dad' producers.

The Swan Valley will be the heart of the Western Australian wine business for a long time yet.

Eating out

The Swan Valley is so close to the city of Perth that finding somewhere to dine is very straightforward, with the possibilities of all price spectrums being within easy reach.

Out in the Valley itself there are a number of possibilities, stretching from picnics (there are plenty of places near the Swan River, and a number of wineries) to pubs and restaurants.

One I like particularly is Kappy's Italian restaurant (22 Sayer Street, Midland [09] 274 3430), partly because the food is very good and also because you can take in a bottle of local wine. The Avenue (9 The Avenue, Midland [09] 274 6555) is a delightful spot, up-market and reasonably expensive, but good, and you can take a bottle in.

In South Guildford, the Stables (West Parade [09] 279 3379) is a former Gold Plate winner, and is

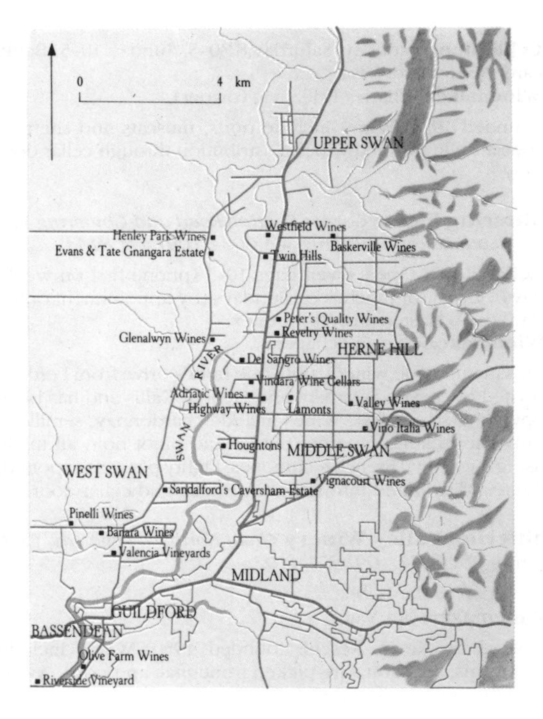

licensed. Dear Friends Restaurant (15 Banara Road, Caversham [09] 279 2815) is relaxed, and licensed, and central to many of the wineries. Finally, the Mulberry Farm (Hamersley Road, Caversham [09] 279 7344) offers bistro-style food, catering heavily for the riverboat trade.

On a sunny day, however, it would be hard to beat a picnic in the extensive grounds of the Houghton winery!

Adriatic Wines *Great Northern Highway, Herne Hill WA 6056. (09) 296 4518.*

Cellar door: Monday–Saturday 8–5, closed Sunday.
Winemaker: P. Jurjevich.

Family owned; founded 1954. Wines include bulk red and white table wines for home bottling, plus a range of fortified and cocktail wines. Distribution through cellar door only.

Banara Wines *Banara Road, Caversham WA 6055. (09) 279 2169.*

Cellar door: Monday–Saturday 8.30–5, Sunday 10–5. Bankcard, Mastercard, Visa.
Winemaker: Charles Knezovic (owner).

Founded 1937. Wines include ports, muscats and sherries; specialise in fortified wines. Distribution through cellar door only.

Chittering Estate *Corner Keating Road and Chittering Valley Road, Lower Chittering WA 6084. (09) 571 8144.*

Cellar door: Open seven days 10–5 (phone first on weekdays). Open for lunches on Sundays (by appointment only). Bankcard, Mastercard, Visa, Amex.
Winemaker: Steven Schapera.

This picturesque winery, only one hour's drive from Perth, is owned by Steven Schapera and George Kailis and has been operating since 1981. Wines include chardonnay, semillon/sauvignon blanc, cabernet/merlot and pinot noir, all made using traditional French techniques. Eighty per cent exported, the rest distributed throughout Australia and cellar door.

Chittering Valley Winery *Great Northern Highway, Chittering WA 6084. (09) 571 4102.*

Not open to the public.
Winemaker: Jim Yates.

Owned by Kevin Neschi; founded 1950. Wines include beaujolais, semillon, late-picked frontignac and ports. Available through retail outlets in Perth.

Cobanov *Lot 1, Stock Road, Herne Hill WA 6056. (09) 296 4210.*

Cellar door: By appointment only. Wine sold mostly in bulk. Cash only.
Winemaker: Steve Cobanov.

Wines include dry reds and whites, ports and sherry, sold locally and in the metropolitan area in 750 millilitre bottles, 2 litre and 20 litre containers.

Coorinja Vineyard *Toodyay Road, Toodyay WA 6566. (09) 574 2280.*

Cellar door: Monday–Saturday 8–5, closed Sunday. Tours possible. Cash only.
Winemaker: Hector Wood.

Family owned; founded 1870. Wines include a range of reds and fortifieds. Distribution through cellar door and selected retail outlets in Perth.

Ellendale Estate *Lot 108, Corona Way, Belhus WA 6055. (09) 296 4581.*

Cellar door: By appointment only. All major credit cards.
Winemaker: John Barrett-Lennard.

Wines include shiraz, cabernet sauvignon, sauternes, vintage and cabernet ports, plus white liqueur muscat. Available through cellar door and some restaurants.

Evans & Tate *Swan Street, Henley Brook WA 6055. (09) 296 4329 or (09) 296 4666.*

Cellar door: Monday–Friday 10–5, weekends 12–4. Amex, Bankcard, Visa.
Winemaker: Bill Crappsley (Senior Winemaker and Manager) and Krister Jonsson.

Owned by John and Toni Tate; founded 1971. The 'Evans' part of the partnership (John Evans) has gone but the quality of this Swan-based maker remains high, perhaps higher than ever. Wines include a range of varietal table wines from the Gnangara (Swan) vineyards and Redbrook (Margaret River) vineyards, including shiraz, cabernet sauvignon, semillon, Margaret River Classic (blend of sauvignon blanc, chenin blanc and semillon) and chardonnay. Distributed in all States.

Faranda Wines *768 Wannneroo Road, Wannneroo WA 6065. (09) 306 1174.*

Cellar door: Daily 8–6. Cash or cheques.
Winemaker: Basil Faranda (owner).

Very small winery producing light, claret-style wine, sold in flagons.

Henley Park Wines *Swan Street, (near Henley Brook), West Swan WA 6055. (09) 296 4328.*

Cellar door: Monday–Saturday 9–6; Sunday 10–6. Bankcard, Mastercard, Visa, Amex. Small à la carte restaurant planned for late March 1991.
Winemaker: Vincent Desplat.

Owned by Claus Buchart Petersen since March 1986; founded 1935. Wines include chenin blanc, chardonnay, Blanc Reserve (semillon, chenin blanc and muscadelle), frontignan, Beaujol Pif (cabernet sauvignon), cabernet sauvignon, Margaret River Cabernet Sauvignon, vintage ports and liqueur tokay. Available through cellar door; some outlets in Western Australia.

Highway Wines *Great Northern Highway, Herne Hill WA 6056. (09) 296 4354.*

Cellar door: Monday–Saturday 8.30–6, closed Sunday. Tastings only by arrangement. No buses. Cash or cheque.
Winemaker/owner: Tony Bakranich.

Founded 1953. Wines include full range of fortifieds in bottles and flagons, with some table wines. Distribution through cellar door only.

Houghton Wines *Dale Road, Middle Swan WA 6056. (09) 274 5100.*

Cellar door: Monday–Saturday 10–5, Sunday 11–4. Tours. BBQ and picnic areas available. Major credit cards.
Winemaker: Peter Dawson.

Owned by the Hardy Family; founded 1836. The splendid Houghton winery (pronounced Haw-ton, unlike the Adelaide suburb of the same name), not far from the Swan River, and about twenty minutes' drive out of Perth, is a must for visitors in the area. The old cellars, the colonial homestead and rolling grounds are simply delightful. The wines demonstrate all the virtues of the varieties for which Western Australia is known—chenin blanc, tokay and verdelho—and show the skills of a large company in putting them together from a number of far-flung vineyard sources.

Wine styles include generic brands such as Houghton White Burgundy and Chablis, plus a wide range of varietals such as chenin blanc (including wood-aged), verdelho (dry and sweet), Rhine riesling from Frankland River, chardonnay, cabernet rosé, cabernet sauvignon, shiraz, fortified tokay and frontignac, and tawny and vintage ports. Separately marketed Moondah Brook Estate range also includes some very good dry white wines. Distribution through Houghton in Western Australia and through the Hardy Wine Company elsewhere.

Ioppolo's Wines *108 Pinjar Road, Wannneroo WA 6065. (09) 405 1064.*

Cellar door: Daily 8–7.
Winemaker: Carmelo Ioppolo.

Family owned. Small winery making sweet white and dry red wines, sold in flagons.

Jadran Wines *445 Reservoir Road, Orange Grove WA 6109. (09) 459 1110.*

Cellar door: Monday–Saturday 9.30–8.30, Sunday 11–5.30. Bankcard..
Winemaker: Steven Radojkovich.

Founded 1927. Wines comprise a full range of red and white table wines, fortified wines and sparkling wines, representing value for money. Distribution: cellar door and mail order.

Jane Brook Estate *Toodyay Road, Middle Swan WA 6056. (09) 274 1432.*

Cellar door: Monday–Saturday 10–5, Sunday 12–5. No tours. Vine-covered courtyard for picnickers. Bankcard, Diner's Club, Mastercard, Visa.
Winemaker: Candy Jonssen.

Owned by Beverley and David Atkinson; founded 1972 (formerly operated as Vignacourt Wine Cellars). Wines include full range of Swan Valley dry whites and dry reds, liqueurs and port, plus Mount Barker reds and whites. Distribution through cellar door, some retail in Perth and mail order to other States.

Lakeville Vineyards *1921 Albany Highway, Maddington WA 6109. (09) 459 1637.*

Cellar door: Daily 9–8 p.m. Cash only.
Winemaker: Mate Maras.

Owned by the Maras family; founded 1954. Wines comprise white and red table wines and fortified wines. Distribution through cellar door. Most wine sold in flagons and larger containers for home bottling.

Lamont *Bisdee Road, Millendon WA 6056. (09) 296 4485.*

Cellar door: Wednesday–Sunday 10–5. Other times by arrangement. À la carte restaurant licensed to sell Lamont wine only. Open Wednesday–Sunday for lunch and Friday and Saturday for lunch and dinner. All major credit cards.
Winemaker: Corin Lamont.

Founded 1979. Small winery owned by Neil and Corin Lamont, members of the family of the late Jack Mann, legendary Swan Valley winemaker and 'father' of Houghton White Burgundy. The highly regarded restaurant is run by Kath and Fiona Lamont, the owners' daughters. Wines include white burgundy, cabernet rosé, shiraz, cabernet sauvignon, sweet white, vintage and tawny ports, and liqueur muscat. Distribution through cellar door.

Little River Wines *West Swan Road, West Swan WA 6055. (09) 296 4462.*

Cellar door: Seven days 10–6 Bankcard, Mastercard, Visa, Amex.
Winemaker: John Smith (owner).

Founded 1934 (formerly Glenalwyn wines); owned by the Murfit family since 1987. Wines include verdelho (dry and late-picked), chenin blanc, cabernet sauvignon, sauternes, late harvest frontignac, liqueur frontignac, tawny port, vintage port and white port. Distribution through cellar door.

Long Valley Wines *Lot 34, Haddrill Road, Baskerville WA 6056.*

Open by appointment only.
Winemakers: Tony and Rita Vallalonga (owners).

Wines include shiraz and malbec, chardonnay and chenin blanc.

Mann's Vineyard *Memorial Avenue, Baskerville WA 6056 (09) 296 4348.*

Cellar door: By appointment only.
Winemaker: Dorham Mann.

Small family cellar producing *méthode champenoise* wines exclusively from the red grape cabernet sauvignon.

Moondah Brook Estate *Gingin WA 6503. (09) 274 5100.*

No cellar door sales at the vineyards, some 80 kilometres north of Perth, but wines can be purchased at the Houghton winery.
Winemaker: Paul Lapsley.

Owned by Houghton Wines; founded 1969. The superb Moondah Brook Estate (complete with a real brook) was established to help provide grapes for Houghton White Burgundy, and the wines under the MBE label are made by Houghton; they are very pleasant drinking, notably the dry white verdelho. Wines also include chenin blanc, chardonnay and cabernet sauvignon. Distribution nationally by the Hardy Wine Company.

Neroni Wines *Lot 1, Great Northern Highway, Muchea WA 6501. (09) 571 4080.*

Cellar door: Daily 8–6. No tours. Bankcard, Mastercard, Visa.
Winemaker: Vince Nesci.

Family owned; founded 1964. Wines include red and white table wines, sparkling and fortified wines. Distribution through cellar door.

Olive Farm Wines *77 Great Eastern Highway, South Guildford WA 6055. (09) 277 2989.*

Cellar door: Monday–Friday 10–5.30; weekends and holidays 9–3. Tours possible. Bankcard, Mastercard, Visa.
Winemaker: Ian Yurisich.

Owned by Judi and Ian Yurisich; founded 1829. Probably the oldest working winery in Australia, standing now, almost incongruously, beside Perth International Airport. Good comprehensive range of wines, especially fortifieds and whites (including verdelho); also reds and *méthode champenoise* sparkling wine. Distribution through cellar door and mailing list and outlets in Perth.

Paul Conti Wines *529 Wanneroo Road, Wannneroo WA 6065. (09) 409 9160.*

Cellar door: Monday–Saturday 9.30–5.30, closed Sunday. Restaurant on premises (Conti's [09] 409 1516) open Wednesday–Saturday for dinner, Sunday for roast lunch. Picnic areas and toilets. Bankcard, Mastercard, Visa.
Winemaker: Paul Conti.

Owned by Paul and Anne Conti; founded 1948 (formerly Contiville). Paul Conti is a well-established Western Australian wine identity (and a charming man) making good wines at reasonable prices, using coastal fruit from near his winery, plus Swan Valley fruit. Wines include a range of premium white and red table wines, notably chenin blanc, chardonnay, late-picked frontignacs, hermitage, cabernet sauvignon and vintage port. Premium wines are labelled Paul Conti Wines; flagons Conti Estate Wines. Flagons at cellar door only. Sold through cellar door and available at a number of Perth retail outlets, and in Victoria and Sydney.

Penwill Wines *Swan Street, West Swan WA 6055. (09) 447 3614.*

Not open to public. Makes ports.

Pinelli Wines *18 Bennett Street, Caversham WA 6055. (09) 279 6818, after hours (09) 279 3805.*

Cellar door: Monday–Saturday 9–5, Sunday 10–6. Cash or cheque.
Winemaker: Robert Pinelli.

Family owned; founded 1976. Wines include range of reds and whites, fortified and sparkling wines. Colombard won a bronze medal in the Royal Perth Show in 1988 and the chenin blanc another bronze in the 1989 Royal Perth Show. Although they bottle under the Pinelli label, they sell mainly in flagons.

Sandalford *West Swan Road, Caversham WA 6055. (09) 274 5922.*

Cellar door: Monday–Saturday 10–5, Sunday 11–4. All major credit cards.
Winemaker: Christian Morlaes (General Manager).

Owned by the Roe family and others; founded 1840. Second-largest, and one of the oldest, of the West's wineries, making a range of good wines, particularly those from Margaret River Estate. Products include wide range of dry and sweet white wines, dry red wines and fortified wines, marketed under Sandalford and Caversham Estate labels, with fruits from the Swan Valley (Caversham) vineyards and extensive vineyards at Margaret River. Chenin blanc, verdelho, moselle, semillon, chardonnay, rosé, cabernet sauvignon and zinfandel (unusual Californian red variety), plus outstanding liqueur wines, Liqueur Sandalera. Wines available through cellar door, mailing list and national distribution, mainly through Taylor Ferguson.

Swan Cooperage *Lot 4, 52 Great Northern Highway, Herne Hill WA 6056. (09) 296 4477.*

The interest in this establishment lies in the skills of its owner, A. G. Lypka, who is a cooper—that is, he makes barrels for the wine industry—the only one in the Swan Valley. It is a truly admirable craft and, if you have not seen oak casks being put together or refurbished, it is well worth a look. You can purchase the barrels ($180 each at the time of writing, for the cheapest one) and can even buy them full of Swan Valley Port.

Talijancich Wines Pty Ltd *121 Hyem Road, Herne Hill WA 6056. (09) 296 4289.*

Cellar door: Sunday–Friday 8.30–5.00, closed Saturday. All major credit cards.
Winemakers: Peter and James Talijancich.

Family owned; founded 1932. Wines include verdelho, semillon, grenache rosé, shiraz, liqueur hermitage, liqueur tokay, 1961 liqueur muscat and magnum ruby port. Distribution through some Perth outlets, cellar door and mailing list.

Twin Hills Wines *Great Northern Highway, Millendon WA 6056. (09) 296 4272.*

Cellar door: Monday–Saturday 8.30–5.30, Sunday 10–4. Cash or cheque.
Winemaker: Mark Kraljevich.

Family owned; founded 1937. Wines include rosé, white burgundy, chenin blanc, verdelho, reds, port and sherry. Bottles and flagons. Distribution through cellar door only.

Valley Wines *Lot 41, Lennard Street, Herne Hill WA 6056. (09) 296 4416.*

Cellar door: Most days.

Dry whites and reds, port, sherry, marsala and vermouth, in bulk.

Vindara Wine Cellars *Great Northern Highway, Herne Hill WA 6056. (09) 296 4556.*

Cellar door: Monday–Friday 8.30–5, Saturday 8–6, Sunday 9–12. Cash or cheque.
Winemaker: Ivan Viskovich.

Family owned; founded 1978. Wines include Rhine riesling, chenin blanc, moselle, rosé, claret, port and sherry. Distributed at cellar door.

Westfield Wines *Corner Memorial Avenue and Great Northern Highway, Millendon WA 6056. (09) 296 4356.*

Cellar door: Monday–Saturday 8.30–5.30, closed Sunday. Bankcard, Mastercard, Visa.
Winemaker: John Kosovich.

Family owned; founded 1922. Well-established smaller maker with quality products, including Rhine riesling, chardonnay, chenin blanc, semillon, verdelho, merlot, cabernet sauvignon, shiraz, liqueur muscat, vintage port and champagne. Distributed through cellar door and some retail outlets in Perth.

Perth Hills

The Perth Hills (some 30 kilometres east of Perth) is home to a number of Western Australia's newest wine producers. This elevated region, long famous for apple and cherry production, possesses an ideal combination of soils and climate for fine wine production. Some are produced in small quantities and are only available direct from the producer. A number of vineyards specialise in the production of only one wine. This hilly, picturesque wine region boasts numerous excellent restaurants and places of interest for the touring wine lover.

Eating Out

The Mundaring Weir Hotel (09) 295 1106 serves lunch daily and dinner on Friday and Saturday. A relaxed atmosphere with authentic turn-of-the-century surroundings and motel-style accommodation, situated at the Mundaring Weir. The Châlet Rigi, Mundaring Weir Road, Piesse Brook (09) 293 1261, serves lunch, afternoon tea and dinner daily. Continental and Swiss cuisine; fully licensed with elegance and style, surrounded by a native forest. Loose Box Restaurant, 45 Great Eastern Highway, Mundaring (09) 295 1787, serves lunch on Friday and Sunday, and dinner Wednesday–Sunday; French cuisine, BYO.

Ashley Park *284 Aldersyde Road, Bickley WA 6076. (09) 293 1415.*

Winemaker: Peter Fimmel.

Owned by John and Noval Ashley who grow and produce only pinot noir. The vineyard was established in 1988 and the first wine will be available by mail order in 1992.

Avalon Wines *Lot 156, Bailey Road, Glen Forrest WA 6071. (095) 298 8049.*

Winemaker: Jim Elson.

Owned by Catherine and David Brown; founded 1986. Wines include chardonnay, semillon, cabernet sauvignon and merlot. Distribution through above address and selected Perth outlets.

Carosa Vineyard *Lot 3, Houston Street, Mount Helena WA 6555. (09) 572 1603.*

Cellar door: Weekends 10–5 and public holidays.

Winemaker: Jim Elson.

Owned by Carole and Jim Elson. Established in 1985 with vines planted to chardonnay, cabernet sauvignon, merlot, pinot noir and Rhine riesling. Distribution through cellar door, mail order and selected liquor stores.

Chidlow Brook Vineyard *Lakeview Road, Chidlow WA 6556. (095) 72 4021.*

Cellar door: By appointment only. Nearest restaurant is the Loose Box in Chidlow, 8 kilometres away.
Winemaker: Les Johnston.

Owned by Les and Susan Johnston; founded 1970. Wines include chardonnay, cabernet sauvignon and cabernet/shiraz. Distribution through cellar door.

Cosham Vineyard *Lot 44, Union Road, Carmel WA 6076. (09) 291 6514.*

Winemaker: Anthony Sclanders.

Owned by Rod, Maxine and Anthony Sclanders. This vineyard was founded in 1989 with plantings of cabernet sauvignon, merlot, cabernet franc, pinot noir and chardonnay. A limited first vintage of a cabernet blend was produced in 1990.

Darlington Estate *Lot 39, Nelson Road, Darlington WA 6070. (09) 299 6268.*

Cellar door: Wednesday–Sunday 12–5. Visa, Bankcard, Mastercard. Light lunchtime snacks available.
Winemaker: Balt van der Meer. Consultant: John Smith.

Owned by Balt van der Meer; founded 1983. Wines include chardonnay, Symphony (blend of chenin blanc/colombard), Prelude (blend of semillon and sauvignon blanc), Vin Primeur (light red), cabernet sauvignon, shiraz and port. Distribution through retail outlets in Perth and cellar door.

Hainault Vineyard *255 Walnut Road, Bickley WA 6076. (09) 293 8339.*

Cellar door: Saturday, Sunday, holidays 10–5 or by appointment. Bankcard, Mastercard, Visa.
Winemaker: Peter Fimmel.

Owned by Peter and Helen Fimmel; founded 1979. Wines include chardonnay, semillon, gewürztraminer, cabernet/merlot pinot noir. Distribution through cellar door, Perth, Sydney and Melbourne.

Piesse Brooke Wines *226 Aldersyde Road, Bickley WA 6076. (09) 293 3309 or (09) 293 3449.*

Cellar door: Sunday 10–5. Otherwise by appointment. No credit cards.
Winemaker Brian Murphy (manager).

Founded 1974; owned by Dianne Bray and Ray and Lee Boyanich. Wines include cabernet sauvignon and shiraz blend. Distribution through cellar door and mailing list.

Scarp Valley Wines *6 Robertson Road, Gooseberry Hill WA 6076. (09) 454 5748.*

Not open to public. Shiraz wine made by Peter Fimmel. Owned by Doris and Robert Duncan; founded 1974. Limited amounts of light red made and sold by private sale.

Woodthorpe Estate *Lot 62, Richardson Road, Parkerville WA 6553. (09) 299 6268.*

Under Darlington Estate management. Not open to the public.

South-West Coastal Plain

This is a curious area, in geographical terms. The description is quite straightforward: the coastal plain just inland from the Indian Ocean coast. What is a little misleading is that it encompasses, geographically and certainly to the winemakers involved, the areas both north *and* south of Perth. We therefore have wineries and vineyard separated by quite considerable distance, though sharing the same tuart sands in which most of their grapes grow.

The district stretches from Yanchep, some 50 kilometres north of Perth, to Busselton, not far from Margaret River, 250 kilometres south of the capital.

As this is essentially a guide to the wineries themselves, rather than to the wines, the northern establishments have been included in the Swan Valley, even though their proprietors will probably be outraged at my liberty. Clearly, however, for the tourist in the Swan Valley, the coastal area around Wanneroo is just a hop and half a skip away, whereas Bunbury is a good day's drive. Among the wineries I have 'moved' into the Swan are Paul Conti, Hartridge and Luisini.

Eating out

The Blackwood Inn (South-Western Highway, Mullalyup—between Kirup and Balingup—[097] 64 1138) is pleasant and gives you a chance to take a bottle of wine to your meal. In Bunbury, the Chartroom offers à la carte food and seafood at the Admiral Motor Inn (56 Spencer Street [097] 21 7322). The Lord Forrest (Symmond Street, Bunbury [097] 21 9966) is recommended. A little further out of town, the Forest Lodge in Pemberton (2 kilometres north of the town)

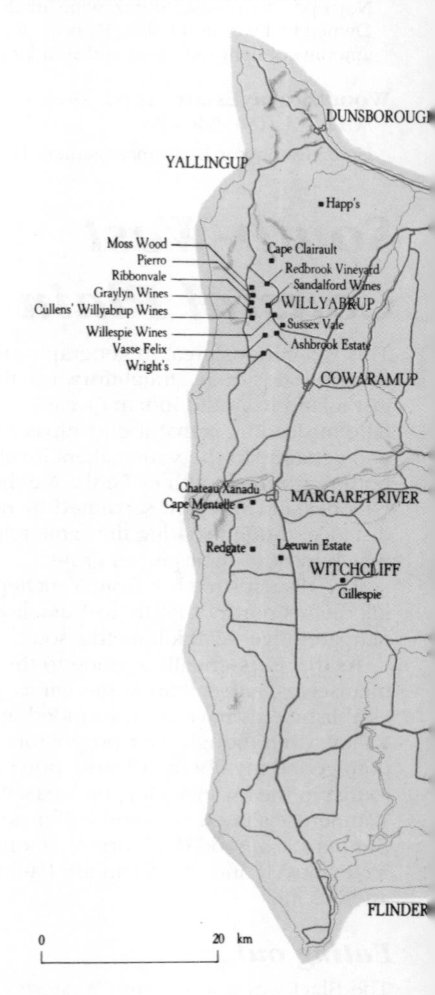

BUNBURY
Thomas Wines
Leschenault
BOYANUP
Capel Vale Wines
CAPEL
USSELTON
DONNYBROOK
Albert Vinci
KIRUP
BRIDGETOWN

(097) 76 1113 shares home cooking with timber views. In the township of Donnybrook, not far south-east of Bunbury, the Preston Gourmet Restaurant (097) 31 1553 is à la carte and BYO.

Baldivis Vines *River Road, Baldivis WA 6171. (095) 25 2066.*

Cellar door: By appointment only. Mastercard.
Winemaker: Andrew Spencer-Wright.

This small vineyard is owned by Peter Kailis and was established in 1982. Wines include chardonnay, sauvignon blanc, semillon and cabernet/merlot. Available through cellar door and some outlets in Western Australia, Victoria, Sydney, Brisbane and Darwin. Few restaurants in Sydney and Melbourne.

Capel Vale Wines *Lot 5, Capel North West Road, Stirling Estate, Capel WA 6271. (097) 27 2439.*

Cellar door: Monday–Friday 10–4.30, weekends 9–4 (closed during vintage). BBQ site available beside river, by arrangement. Mastercard, Visa, Bankcard.
Winemaker: Andrew Phillips.

Owned by Dr Peter Pratten; founded 1975. Small winery 27 kilometres from Bunbury, established by a local doctor, which had its first vintage in 1980 from five-year-old vines. Wines include Rhine riesling, sauvignon blanc/semillon, chardonnay, riesling/traminer, shiraz, cabernet sauvignon and Baudin (merlot/cabernet/shiraz). Available through cellar door and mailing list (PO Box 692, Bunbury WA 6230) and some outlets in Perth, Melbourne, Sydney and Brisbane.

Leschenault Wines *Minnimup Road, off Lakes Road, Gelorup WA 6230. (097) 95 7222.*

Cellar door: Monday–Friday 10–5, Saturday and Sunday 10–6. BBQ and picnic area available by appointment. Tours by appointment. Bankcard, Mastercard, Visa.
Winemaker: Dr Barry Killerby (owner).

Founded 1973. Wines include chardonnay, semillon, traminer, April Red (light sweet red), pinot noir, shiraz, cabernet sauvignon and vintage port. Distribution through cellar door and mailing list (PO Box 1058, Bunbury WA 6230) and through limited retail outlets in Perth, Melbourne and Sydney.

Peel Estate *Fletcher Road, Baldivis (near Mandurah) WA 6210. (095) 24 1221.*

Cellar door: Daily 10–5. BBQs on request. Visa, Mastercard, Bankcard.
Winemaker: Will Nairn (owner).

Founded 1980; owned by Will Nairn. Wines include chenin blanc, chardonnay, sauvignon blanc, verdelho, shiraz, cabernet sauvignon, zinfandel and vintage port. Distribution: cellar door and some outlets in Perth, Melbourne, Sydney and Brisbane (mail order through PO Box 37, Mandurah WA 6210).

Thomas Wines *Briar Holme Vineyard, 23–24 Crowd Road, Gelorup WA 6230. (097) 95 7085.*

Tastings and sales by appointment only.
Winemaker: Gill Thomas (owner).

Founded 1976. Claimed to be the smallest vineyard in Western Australia. Wines are pinot noir and cabernet sauvignon. Distribution through winery and some outlets in Perth.

Margaret River

This is undoubtedly one of the most exciting 'new' wine areas of Australia, with some marvellous red and white wines emerging from its scattered vineyards. It's a fair drive from Perth, but if you have the time, make the effort. It is Australian motoring at its best, if the weather is good, and there are plenty of sights other than vineyards and wineries. There is also some excellent surfing on the Indian Ocean coast. Hotels are so-so, for the most part, but some good motels, notably the Captain Freycinet, have sprung up over the past few years.

Eating out

The Casuarina Restaurant in the Captain Freycinet Motel (097) 57 2033 presents better-than-average motel food, and has a local wine list. Also in Margaret River is the Settler's Tavern (097) 57 2398, with fresh salads and counter meals, plus Margaret River wines. The 1885 Restaurant (Farrelly Street, Margaret River [097] 57 2302) has excellent atmosphere and good à la carte food; licensed.

Out of town, just 5 kilometres, is the restaurant and functions centre at the astonishing Leeuwin Estate winery (097) 57 6253—a must to visit.

Amberley Estate *Thornton Road, Yallingup WA 6282. (097) 55 2248.*

Cellar door: Open seven days 10–4.30. All major credit cards. Light lunches daily with special summertime lunch hampers. Musical evenings and special art displays.
Winemaker: Eddie Price.

A partnership of family and friends own Amberley Estate with 40 hectares of vines established in 1986, the first vintage being in 1990. Wines include chenin blanc, sauvignon blanc, semillon, semillon/sauvignon blanc, a big wooded semillon/sauvignon blanc 'graves' blend, chardonnay, varietal cabernet, and cabernet/merlot nouveau. Traditional red blends will be forthcoming in a year or two. Available through cellar door and all major retail outlets in Western Australia. As from 1991 available in all capital cities.

Ashbrook Estate *Harmans Road South, Willyabrup WA 6284. (097) 55 6262.*

Cellar door: Weekends and holidays 10–5. Tours by appointment. Bankcard, Mastercard, Visa.
Winemakers: Brian and Tony Devitt (owners).

Founded 1975. Tony Devitt is in charge of horticultural research at the Department of Agriculture and, as such, experienced in the difficulties, and the opportunities, of small vignerons; his brother is a retired schoolteacher who has, for the last four years, been full-time Winemaker and Vineyard Manager. Between them they hold the promise of some good wines from this small winery. Products include sauvignon blanc, semillon, verdelho, chardonnay, Rhine riesling (two) and cabernet blend. Distribution through cellar door, plus selected retail outlets in Perth, Sydney and Melbourne.

The Berry Farm *Bessell Road, Rosa Glen WA 6285. (097) 57 5054.*

Cellar door: Open seven days 9.30–4.30. Bankcard, Visa, Mastercard. Lunches served in cottage daily—blackboard menu changed frequently.
Winemaker: Eion Lindsay (with consultants).

Eion and Andrea Lindsay have owned this farm for fifteen years and it has been open to the public for five years. Their unusual wines made from berries and kiwi fruit have been a popular tourist attraction. Wines made from raspberries, strawberries, boysenberries, pears and plums are available at cellar door. There is also a very popular plum port and two lots of kiwi wine (sauternes and a dry wine). Vinegar made from the fruit is also available and jams. Distribution through cellar door and retail outlets in Perth.

Brookland Valley Vineyard *Caves Road, Willyabrup WA 6284. (097) 55 6256.*

Cellar door: 11.30–4.30 every day except Monday (winter), 10.30–5.30 seven days (summer). Restaurant open for morning tea, lunch and afternoon tea every day and dinner on Saturday throughout the year. Wine-arts related gallery. All major credit cards.
Winemaker: Wine made at Cape Mentelle.

Owned by Deirdre and Malcolm Jones since its establishment in 1984. Wines include chardonnay and cabernet sauvignon/cabernet franc blend. Vines also planted are sauvignon blanc and merlot. Available at cellar door and liquor outlets in Perth and Melbourne.

Cape Clairault Wines *Henry Road (off Pusey Road), Willyabrup WA 6284. (097) 55 6225.*

Cellar door: Open seven days 10–5. BBQ (large enough for forty people) available, in natural bushland setting near winery. All major credit cards.
Winemaker: Ian Lewis and Mike and Jan Davies.

Owned by Ian and Ani Lewis; founded 1977; first vintage 1981. Wines include straight sauvignon blanc, semillon/sauvignon blanc, Rhine riesling and cabernet sauvignon. From cellar door only sweet table wines and fortifieds are available. Others available through cellar door, mailing list (CMB Carbunup River WA 6280) and selected outlets in Sydney, Melbourne and Perth.

Cape Mentelle Vineyards *Wallcliffe Road, Margaret River WA 6285. (097) 57 2070.*

Cellar door: Daily 10–4.30. Tours by appointment only. Picnic areas in landscaped outdoor area (liquor can be consumed on the premises). All major credit cards.
Winemaker: David Hohnen.

Owned by French champagne house Veuve Clicquot since April 1990; founded 1977. Cape Mentelle, run by experienced winemaker David Hohnen, has been 'on the map' since he won the Jimmy Watson Trophy for Best One-Year-Old Red Wine at the Melbourne Wine Show two years running, 1983 and 1984. While he is clearly a red specialist, the whites are also full of flavour and are good drinking. Products include Rhine riesling, semillon, sauvignon blanc, shiraz, zinfandel and cabernet sauvignon. The winery also has interests in Cloudy Bay, New Zealand, which gives it a fascinating product range. 'Quaffing' red and white wines also available in 1.5 litre magnums at reasonable prices. Distribution nationally or by mailing list and there is a good newsletter (PO Box 110, Margaret River WA 6285).

Chateau Xanadu *Off Wallcliffe Road, Margaret River WA 6285. (097) 57 2581.*

Cellar door: Monday–Saturday 10–4.30, Sunday 11–4.30. Tours by appointment. BBQ and picnic area. Bankcard, Mastercard, Visa.
Winemaker: Conor Lagan.

Owned by the Lagan family; founded 1977. Wines have been improving rapidly in recent years, and include semillon, chardonnay, cabernet sauvignon, sauvignon blanc and cabernet franc. Distribution through cellar door and mailing list (PO Box 144, Margaret River WA 6285) and selected outlets in Sydney and Perth.

Cullen Wines *Caves Road, Cowaramup WA 6284. (097) 55 5277.*

Cellar door: Monday–Saturday 10–4, closed Sunday except long weekends. Light snacks available all day. Seats outside. Cash or cheque. Tours by appointment.
Winemaker: Vanya Cullen.

Family owned; founded 1971; first vintage 1974. The Cullens were among the pioneers of the district and the wine quality is generally high; also an interesting winery. Products include chardonnay, sauvignon blanc, classic dry white, Rhine riesling, sauternes-style, cabernet/merlot, fumé cabernet (light red) and pinot noir. Distribution: cellar door and outlets in Adelaide, Melbourne, Sydney, Brisbane, Perth and Canberra.

Fermoy Estate *Metricup Road, Willyabrup WA 6284. (097) 55 6285.*

Cellar door: Open by appointment only.
Winemaker: Michael Kelly.

Owned by a unit trust of businessmen. Established in 1982 with first vintage in 1988. Wines include cabernet sauvignon, sauvignon blanc and chardonnay. Available through cellar door and mailing list (PO Box 123, Cowaramup WA 6284).

Foxhaven Estate *Canal Road, Yallingup WA 6282 (097) 5 5223 or (09) 291 6052.*

Cellar door: By appointment only.
Winemaker: David Hunt.

Owned by David and Libby Hunt; established in 1978, with first vintage in 1985. Wines available include Rhine riesling and cabernet sauvignon. Semillon and sauvignon blanc planted. Distributed through cellar door and mailing list (43 Falls Road, Lesmurdie WA 6076).

Freycinet Wines *Lot 1, Gnarawary Road, Margaret River WA 6285. (097) 57 6358.*

Cellar door: Seven days 10–4.30. Bankcard, Mastercard, Visa.
Winemaker: Peter Gherardi.

Owned by Peter and Jennifer Gheradi; first vintage 1984. Wines include chenin blanc, sauvignon blanc, semillon, chardonnay and cabernet sauvignon. Distribution: cellar door and retail outlets in Perth, Sydney, Queensland and Canberra.

Gralyn Wines *Caves Road, Willyabrup WA 6284. (097) 55 6245.*

Cellar door: Daily 10.30–4.30. Tours invited. Blackboard lunches served 12–2 daily, bookings advisable. Bankcard, Mastercard, Visa.
Winemakers: Graham and Merilyn Hutton (owners).

Founded 1975; first vintage 1978. Wines include white and red table wines (dry and sweet) from Rhine riesling, hermitage and cabernet sauvignon, but specialise in ports—six available, plus white port and liqueur shiraz port. Distribution through cellar door.

Green Valley Vineyard *Sebbes Road, Forest Grove, via Margaret River WA 6285. Enquiries (09) 384 3131.*

Cellar door: Weekends only 11–4. Mastercard, Visa.
Winemaker: Wine made at Vasse Felix.

This vineyard is owned by E. D. and E. Green; the land bought in 1979, with their first vintage in 1987. Wines include müller thurgau, Rhine riesling and chardonnay. Their first red was made in 1990. Available through cellar door.

Happ's Vineyard *Commonage Road, near Dunsborough WA 6282. (097) 55 3300.*

Cellar door: Daily 10–5. Tours for large groups by appointment. Bankcard, Mastercard, Visa.
Winemaker: Erland Happ.

Family owned; founded 1978. Wines include cabernet/merlot, shiraz, Fuchsia (slightly sweet, pink, spritzig wine), chardonnay and verdelho. Distribution through selected outlets in Perth and Sydney and through cellar door.

Leeuwin Estate *Lot 688, Gnarawary Road, Margaret River WA 6285. (097) 57 6253.*

Cellar door: Daily 10–4.30. Tours and tastings for a small fee. À la carte restaurant for lunch 12–2.30. Saturday for dinner in summer. All major credit cards.
Winemaker: Bob Cartwright.

Owned by Denis Horgan; founded 1978. A stunning winery in a magnificent bushland setting, clearly the show place of the area, and one of the highlights of the Australian wine industry. Money was apparently no concern in siting, building and equipping this winery. While quality is generally high., the costs are also reflected in the prices for the wines. Wines include Rhine riesling, chardonnay, sauvignon blanc, gewürztraminer, pinot noir and cabernet sauvignon. Distributed as Leeuwin Estate wines, with an art series as premium range, nationally and internationally.

Lenton Brae *500 metres north of intersection of Caves and Metricup Roads, Willyabrup WA 6284. (097) 55 6255.*

Cellar door: Weekends and public holidays only 10–5.30. Visa, Mastercard, Bankcard.
Winemaker: Consultants.

Owned by the Tomlinson family since 1983 with first vintage in 1987. Wines include chardonnay and cabernet sauvignon. Semillon and sauvignon blanc planted. Distribution through cellar door and liquor outlets in Perth.

Morrison Estate Vineyard *Harmans Mill Road, Willyabrup WA 6284. (097) 55 6234.*

Not open to the public at this stage. This run-down vineyard was previously Sussex Vale Vineyard, and was bought by Dr B. T. Morrison in June 1989. No wine produced yet, but hopes to be open in a year or two.

Moss Wood Wines *Metricup Road, Willyabrup WA 6284. (097) 55 6266.*

Cellar door: By appointment only. Cash or cheque.
Winemaker: Keith Mugford.

Owned by Clare and Keith Mugford; founded 1969. An unpretentious winery, established by local medico Dr Bill Pannell, and his wife, which has produced—and does produce—some of the best wines of Western Australia. Wines are wood-matured semillon and a non-wood-matured semillon, chardonnay, pinot noir and fine cabernet sauvignons. Distribution: cellar door, mailing list (PO Box 52, Busselton WA 6280) and specialist outlets in capital cities.

Pierro Margaret River Vineyards *Caves Road, Willyabrup WA 6284. (097) 55 6220 or (097) 52 1125.*

Cellar door: Open seven days 10–5. Picnics possible. Bankcard, Mastercard, Visa.
Winemaker: Michael Peterkin (owner).

Founded 1980. Blanc de blanc, blanc de noir, spätlese riesling, chardonnay, pinot noir. Distribution through cellar door and mailing list (PO Box 552, Busselton WA 6280) and selected capital city outlets. Wines of quality from an unusual winery run by another doctor; distinctive and attractive packaging.

Redbrook Vineyard *Corner Caves and Metricup Road, Willyabrup WA 6284. (097) 55 6244.*

Cellar door: Open seven days 10.30–4.30. Mastercard, Visa, Bankcard, Amex.

This vineyard is owned by Evans & Tate (see Swan Valley—Evans & Tate) All their wines can be tasted at Redbrook Vineyard in this Federation-style building.

Redgate Wines *Boodjidup Road, Margaret River WA 6285. (097) 57 6208.*

Cellar door: Daily 10–5. BBQ facilities. Bankcard, Mastercard, Visa.
Winemakers: Bill and Paul Ullinger.

Owned by Bill Ullinger; founded 1981. Wines include dry and sweet whites and dry reds. Distribution through cellar door, all eastern States, London, Singapore and New Zealand.

Ribbon Vale Estate *Lot 5, Caves Road, Willyabrup WA 6284. (097) 55 6272.*

Cellar door: Weekends and major holidays 10–5. Mastercard, Bankcard, Visa.
Winemaker: Jan Davies.

Owned by John James; this winery was established in 1977 and had its first vintage in 1982. Wines include unwooded and wooded semillon, sauvignon blanc, semillon/sauvignon blanc, cabernet sauvignon and cabernet/merlot. Available through cellar door and in Victoria, New South Wales and Western Australia.

Rivendell Vineyard *Wildwood Road, Yallingup WA 6282. (097) 55 2090.*

Cellar door: Open seven days 10–5. Bankcard, Mastercard, Visa. Tea rooms open 10–5. Gallery of local art. Home-made jams, pickles. Pick-your-own strawberries and other seasonal flowers and fruit. Plenty of room for children and picnics. Potted herbs for sale.
Winemaker: Michael Davies.

Owned by Mark and Lu Standish and established in 1987 with first vintage in 1990. Wine from the first vintage is semillon/sauvignon blanc but nine varieties planted, including cabernet, shiraz and verdelho. Available through cellar door.

Rosa Brook Estate *Location 990, Rosa Brook Road, Margaret River WA 6285. (097) 57 2286.*

Cellar door: Friday, Saturday and Sunday 10–4.30. All major credit cards. Tastings are held in the 65-year-old building, built by early settlers as an abattoir, which has been renovated, but to its earlier style.
Winemaker: Rick Hoyle-Mills.

Owned by a partnership of four, John and Richard Cooper, Hugh Crock and Rick Hoyle-Mills. Established 1979 with first vintage in 1990. Wines include Rhine riesling, semillon, limited quantities of chardonnay, pinot noir/malbec, cabernet sauvignon/merlot and merlot. Available through cellar door.

Sandalford Margaret River Estate *Metricup Road, Cowaramup WA 6284. (097) 55 6213.*

Cellar door: Daily 11–4. Bankcard, Mastercard, Visa, Amex.
Winemaker: Christian Morlaes.

Vineyard established 1972. For other details see Swan Valley—Sandalford.

Vasse Felix *Harman's Road South, Cowaramup WA 6284. (097) 55 5242.*

Cellar door: Open seven days 10–4.30 Bankcard, Mastercard, Visa.
Winemaker: David Gregg.

Founded 1967. This was a pioneer vineyard in the area, established by Dr Tom Cullity with David Gregg as winemaker, which showed the way in wine quality for the area. Owned since 1987 by Heytesbury Holdings (a Holmes à Court company). Interesting winery; good products. Wines include Rhine riesling, semillon/sauvignon blanc, classic dry red, hermitage and cabernet sauvignon. Distribution through cellar door and mailing list, plus selected retailers in major cities.

Willespie *Harman's Mill Road, Cowaramup WA 6284. (097) 55 6248.*

Cellar door: Open seven days 10–4.30. Light meals served at weekend. Bankcard, Mastercard, Visa.
Winemaker: John Smith (consultant).

Owned by the Squance family; founded 1976. Wines include Rhine riesling, semillon, verdelho, sauvignon blanc, cabernet sauvignon, merlot and vintage port. Distribution through cellar door, mailing list and in Perth, Melbourne, Cairns and Sydney.

Woodlands Wines *Lot 1, Corner Woodlands and Caves Roads, Willyabrup WA 6284. (09) 294 1869.*
Winemaker: David Watson.

Founded 1973; first vintage 1979. Small maker, resident in Perth, specialising in good red wines. One wine only made: cabernet sauvignon (includes 15 per cent malbec, with some merlot and cabernet franc). Pinot noir also planted and some chardonnay. Sales by phone and mail to 29 Spring Park Road, Midland WA 6056, or ask for Heather on (09) 274 6155, or fax (09) 274 6421.

Woodynook Wines *Metricup Road, Metricup WA 6282. (097) 55 7547.*

Cellar door: Weekends and public holidays 10–4. Bankcard, Mastercard, Visa. Lunch-time restaurant open 10–4 with indoor and courtyard dining.
Winemaker: Neil Gallagher.

Owned by H. J. Gallagher; winery established in 1982 with first vintage in 1987. Wines include cabernet sauvignon/merlot, merlot, semillon, late harvest semillon and sauvignon blanc. Available through cellar door and retail outlets in Perth.

Wrights Wines *Harman's Road South, Cowaramup WA 6284. (097) 55 5314.*

Cellar door: Daily 10–4.30. Bankcard, Mastercard, Visa.
Winemaker: Henry Wright.

Family owned; founded 1973. Wines include chardonnay, Rhine riesling, semillon, hermitage and cabernet sauvignon. Distribution through cellar door, mailing list (PO 25, Cowaramup WA 6284) and selected retail outlets in New South Wales and Victoria.

Mount Barker/ Frankland River

You can experience a sense of beautiful isolation in visiting the wine areas around the south-western corner of the Australian continent. It is a 'new' area in the sense of wine and, indeed, commercial settlement on any meaningful scale. Vineyards were established in the area, which is large, only a few decades ago.

Because of the time scale involved in experimenting first with vines, then with wines, it is sometimes tempting to say of new areas: 'Only time will tell.' However I think that in the case of Mount Barker/ Frankland River, which is the preferred name of most local wine people (as opposed to the other name sometimes used: Great Southern area), the runs are on the board, even if it is simply the 'First Test'. Wines of outstanding quality have come from area producers, such as Plantagenet, and excellent commercial wines (that is to say in quantities that consumers can readily buy) from makers such as Houghton, with their Frankland River products.

It is also an area of spectacular and rugged beauty. Though some 400 kilometres from Perth, the driving is pleasant enough to make the trip worthwhile, particularly if you have enough time to make a leisurely circuit of Margaret River/Albany and back to Perth. Allow four days if you wish to relax, taste and sightsee a bit.

Eating out

This vast tract of Australia offers excellent outdoor picnic environments. The major town is the former whaling port of Albany, which has spectacular views of the harbour and good licensed/BYO restaurants. Penny Post Restaurant and Grill Room in the old Post Office building (33 Stirling Terrace [098] 41 1045), is one and Kookas Restaurant (204 Stirling Terrace [098] 41 5889) offers fine locally prepared food in an excellent environment and is open Tuesday–Friday for lunch and Friday and Saturday for dinner. The Alouette (63 Grey Street East [098] 41 5388) offers contemporary international food and is open for dinner only Tuesday–Saturday.

To the north in the town of Mount Barker, Sophie's Restaurant (34 Albany Highway, Mount Barker [098] 51 1728) has an old-world atmosphere with home-

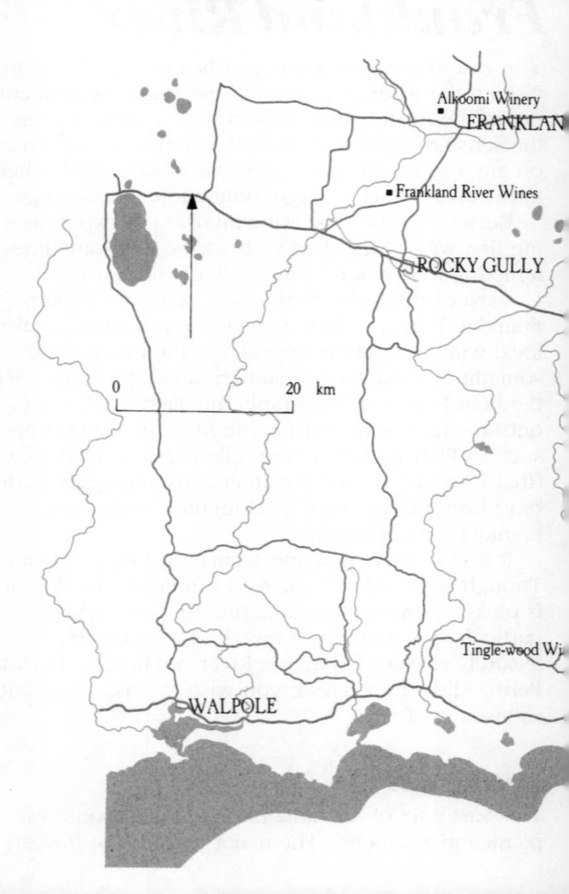

cooked food and is open for lunches Wednesday–Friday and Sunday; Friday and Saturday for dinner.

Alkoomi Wines *Wingeballup Road, Frankland WA 6396. (098) 55 2229.*

Cellar door: By appointment only at the winery. BBQ and picnic area at the winery. Albany Cellar, at 225 Lower Stirling Terrace, Albany WA 6330, handle tastings and sales: Monday–Saturday 10–5; Sundays 1–5. Bankcard, Mastercard, Visa.

Winemaker: Kim Hart.

Owned by Mervyn and Judith Lange; founded 1976. Wines include Rhine riesling, chardonnay, semillon, sauvignon

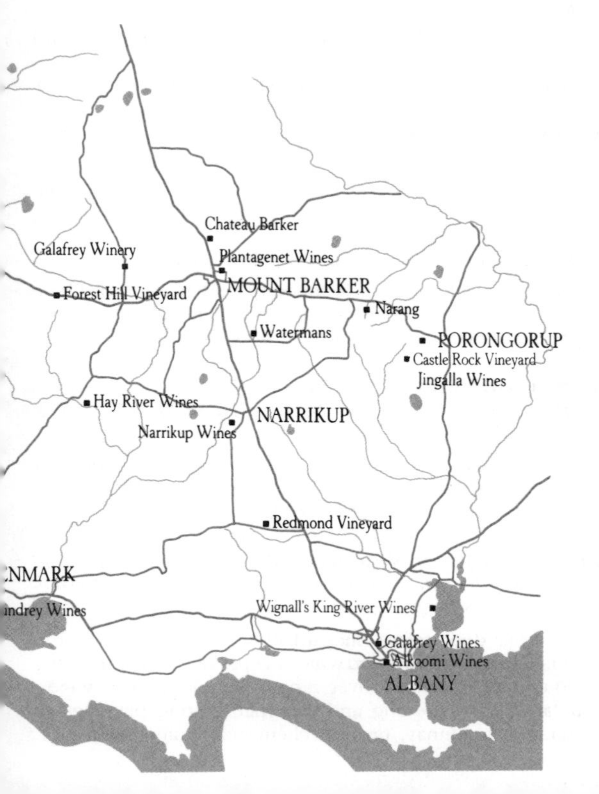

blanc, cabernet sauvignon, malbec and shiraz. Distributed through cellar door, mailing list (enquiries to RMB 234, Frankland WA 6396) and limited retail outlets in Sydney, Melbourne, Canberra, Adelaide and Perth.

Blackwood Crest Wines *Chamber's Road, Boyup Brook WA 6244. (097) 67 3029.*

Cellar door: Daily 10–5. Tours by appointment. BBQ and catering for light lunches by appointment also. Cash or cheque.
Winemaker: Maxwell Fairbrass (owner).

Founded 1976. Wines include Rhine riesling, semillon/sauvignon blanc, hermitage, cabernet sauvignon, sauterne and port. Distribution through cellar door and some Perth outlets.

Bolgonup Heritage *RMB 1129, Porongorup WA 6324 (098) 53 1030.*

Not open to the public. Three holiday units available on the property.
Winemaker: David McNamara.

Owned by Russell and Dianne Faulkner. This small vineyard produces limited amounts of cabernet sauvignon. Enquiries to the managers, Carl and Maureen James on (098) 53 1030.

Chatsfield Wines *O'Neil Road, Mount Barker WA 6324. (098) 51 1704.*

Cellar door: 10–30–4.30 Tuesday–Sunday and public holidays. Morning and afternoon teas, soup and rolls. Bankcard, Mastercard, Visa.
Winemaker: Wine made at Goundrey Wines.

Owned by Dr Ken Lynch; founded 1976. Wines include Rhine riesling, traminer, chardonnay, shiraz and cabernet sauvignon. Distribution through cellar door and local outlets.

Forest Hill Vineyard *142 kilometre peg, Muir Highway (18 kilometres west of Mount Barker), Forest Hill WA 6324. (098) 51 1971.*

No longer open to the public. This vineyard was taken over by Robert Holmes à Court who also owned Vasse Felix. All wine sales are at Vasse Felix. See Margaret River—Vasse Felix.

Frankland River Vineyard *Off Rocky Gully–Frankland Road (north of Muir Highway), Rocky Gully WA 6397. Vineyard (098) 55 1563.*

No cellar door sales, vineyard only, leased by Houghton Wines. Extensive vineyard which has provided the fruit for the Houghton Frankland River range of good varietal wines, notable Rhine riesling and cabernet, among plantings of shiraz, chardonnay, malbec, chenin blanc and pinot noir.

Distribution through Hardy's throughout Australia. Owned by John Roche, a former Lord Mayor of Adelaide.

Galafrey Wines *145 Lower Stirling Terrace, Albany WA 6330. (098) 41 6533.*

Cellar door: In old (1910) wool store Monday–Saturday 10–5. Open Sunday, school holidays and long weekends. Bankcard, Mastercard, Visa, Amex.
Winemaker: Ian Tyrer.

Owned by Ian and Linda Tyrer; founded 1977. Wines include Rhine riesling, Müller thurgau, frontignan, chardonnay, pinot noir, shiraz, cabernet sauvignon and port. Distribution through cellar door and retail liquor outlets in Western Australia.

Goundrey Wines *11 North Street, Denmark WA 6333. (098) 48 1525.*

Cellar door: Monday–Saturday 10–4, Sunday 12–4. Mary Rose tea shop next door, open daily 9–5. Bankcard, Mastercard, Visa.
Winemaker: Claudio Radenti.

Owned by Goundrey Wines Limited; founded 1975 and operating from an old butter factory. Wines include Rhine riesling, sauvignon blanc, shiraz and cabernet sauvignon. Distribution through cellar door and liquor outlets in Perth and New South Wales.

Hay River Wines *The Springs, Denmark Road, Mount Barker WA 6324. (09) 328 3120 (Perth).*

Not open to the public; vineyard only.
Winemaker: Goundrey Wines.

Owned by a syndicate; founded 1974. Cabernet sauvignon only produced. Limited retail distribution in Perth only.

Jingalla Wines *RMB 1114, Bolganup Dam Road, Porongurup WA 6324. (098) 53 1023 or (098) 53 1014.*

Cellar door: Open daily 10–5.30. Picnic area and BBQ; national park and other BBQs adjacent.
Winemaker: Carl Radenti (at Goundrey).

Owned by Geoff and Nita Clarke and Barry and Shelley Coad. First vintage 1983. Wines include Rhine riesling (dry and sweet), dry verdelho, cabernet sauvignon (light and heavy bodied) 'rouge' (sweet red) and port. Sold locally through cellar door under Jingalla Wines, Porongurup label.

Karrivale Wines *Woodlands Road, Porongurup WA 6324. (098 53 1009.*

Cellar door: Saturday, Sunday and holidays 10–5 (or by appointment). Porongurup National Park next door. Sales by cash and cheque.

Winemaker: John Wade at Plantagenet Wines.

Owned by Campbell McGready. Founded 1980 and originally Narang Wines. Rhine riesling only produced. Available through cellar door or several local bottle shops.

Patterson's *St Werburghs Road, Mount Barker WA 6324. (098) 51 1629.*

Cellar door by appointment only. Small vineyard owned by teachers A. F. and S. M. Patterson, and planted to chardonnay, pinot noir and shiraz. Distribution through cellar door and mail order.

Plantagenet Wines *46 Albany Highway, Mount Barker WA 6324. (098) 51 1150.*

Cellar door: Monday–Friday 9–5, Saturday and Sunday 10–4. BBQ available. All major credit cards.
Winemaker: John Wade.

Owned by Tony Smith; founded 1974. Plantagenet is the most respected winery in the area, making the best range of wines, and also making wines for a number of others. Named after a local government area, it produces generally top-flight wines though, sadly, it has stopped producing a superb rosé it once made. Wines include Rhine riesling, frontignan, chardonnay, cabernet sauvignon, cabernet/hermitage, Fleur de Cabernet and port. Distribution nationally though mailing list (PO Box 155, Mount Barker WA 6324), and through cellar door and a reasonable range of retail outlets in major capital cities.

Porongorup Wines *Porongurup Road, Porongurup WA 6324. (098) 53 1105.*

Winemaker: John Wade, Plantagenet Wines.

This small vineyard, owned by Peter and Lesley Thorn, producing Rhine riesling, is not at this stage open to the public. Limited amounts of wine were to be released towards the end of 1990 and all enquiries should be made by telephone.

Tingle-Wood Wines *Glenrowan Road, 8 km north-west of Denmark, WA 6333. (098) 40 9218.*

Cellar door: Daily 9–5. Large farm, picnickers welcomed, craft shop. Bankcard, Mastercard, Visa.
Winemaker: John Wade at Plantagenet.

Owned by Bob and Judy Wood; founded 1981. Wines include Rhine riesling and cabernet/shiraz. Distribution through cellar door and mailing list (PO Box 160, Denmark WA 6333).

Wignall's King River Wines *Chester Pass Road, Highway 1, Albany WA 6330. (098) 41 2848.*

Cellar door: Open seven days 10–4, except during the month of August 12–4. Picnic area and children's playground. Bankcard, Mastercard, Visa.
Winemaker: John Wade at Plantagenet Wines.

Owned by Bill, Pat and Robert Wignall; founded 1985. Wines include chardonnay, sauvignon blanc, frontignan, pinot noir and cabernet sauvignon. Distribution through cellar door, mail order (PO Box 248, Albany, WA 6330) and liquor retail outlets in Perth, Brisbane, Sydney and Melbourne.

William's Rest *Albany Highway (7 kilometres north of town), Mount Barker WA 6324. (098) 51 1452.*

Cellar door: Every day except Wednesday and Thursday from 10–4. Mastercard, Bankcard, Visa.
Winemaker: Claudio Radenti.

Owned by Goundrey Wines Limited since 1987 (used to be Chateau Barker). Wines available under the William's Rest label are Rhine riesling, late harvest riesling, dry white, dry red, pinot noir and port. Wines under the Goundrey label are also available (see Goundrey Wines, this section). Distribution through cellar door and Perth.

Victoria

Victoria's important place in Australia's wine history is largely unknown to most of today's wine drinkers. But towards the middle of the nineteenth century it was realised that Victoria had much in common with some of the European growing districts and vines started marching out of Melbourne. The gold rush speeded up this viticultural spread and by all accounts some very good wines were made in the State in the latter half of the century.

The arrival of the vine louse *Phylloxera vastatrix* put a rapid end to the hopes and aspirations of Victoria's winemakers. The louse—actually a type of aphid that attacks the roots of the vines—could not be controlled, even though it was realised from similar experiences in Europe that grafting onto American rootstock would solve the problem. Thousands of hectares of vines were in desperation ripped out of the ground and for more than half a century wines were made in quantity in only two major regions (excluding Chateau Tahbilk in the Goulburn Valley, where some pre-phylloxera vines still exist, alongside phylloxera-infected vines).

The north-eastern area around Rutherglen (and I take the licence to include Brown Brothers at Milawa in this general area) continued making the splendid ports, muscats and other fortifieds which made the area famous. And in the north-west of the State the waters of the Murray helped establish a great irrigation system which made possible the planting of vast vineyards; it is these Murray Valley vineyards which help provide the economical cask wines which make up some three-quarters of the wines we enjoy today.

This is the paradox of Victoria's vineyards and wineries: at one end of the State are some enormous wineries, such as the Lindeman/Penfolds' Karadoc plant near Mildura, producing oceans of good, clean *vin ordinaire* wines; while scattered around the rest of the State, in a dozen different areas and more sub-areas, are over 150 wineries, most of them small to very small. The climate and the soils combine to offer winemakers with sufficient skill and determination (not to mention money!) the opportunity to produce some very fine wines indeed. The classic cabernets, other reds and some whites which come from the better producers of Victoria are world class wines, many of the reds with a deliciously 'minty' character which is quite different to the wines of other States.

Central and Southern Areas (Bendigo)

It is fitting that Balgownie is the first entry in this region's listings as it was the first winery established here when vines were replanted from 1969. The reds that emanate from the district have great power and intensity, usually with a 'minty' flavour thrown in, too. Within easy driving distance of Melbourne, the wineries loosely scattered about the civilised city of Bendigo (population 67 000), are well worth a visit, if in the area or passing nearby.

Eating out

Bendigo has plenty of pubs which serve fair to very good food, in the civilised manner of Victorian pubs. Among other eateries in Bendigo are the Metropolitan Restaurant and Brasserie (corner Bull and Hargreaves Street [054] 43 4916) specialising in French and European food; the Copper Pot (Howard Place [054] 43 1362); and the Jolly Puddler (101 Williamson Street [054] 43 9859) with à la carte food. There is further information on accommodation and eating available from the Bendigo and District Tourism Association (054) 41 5244.

Balgownie Estate *Hermitage Road, Maiden Gully Vic. 3551. (054) 49 6222.*

Cellar door: Monday–Saturday 10–5, closed Sunday. Tours by appointment. BBQ and picnic areas. Bankcard, Mastercard, Visa.
Winemaker: Lindsay Ross.

Now owned by Mildara Wines but founded in 1969 by Stuart Anderson, a small maker who used to be a pharmacist—the results of his prescriptions remain excellent, especially the reds! Cabernet sauvignon, hermitage, pinot noir, chardonnay and Rhine riesling. National distribution through Mildara.

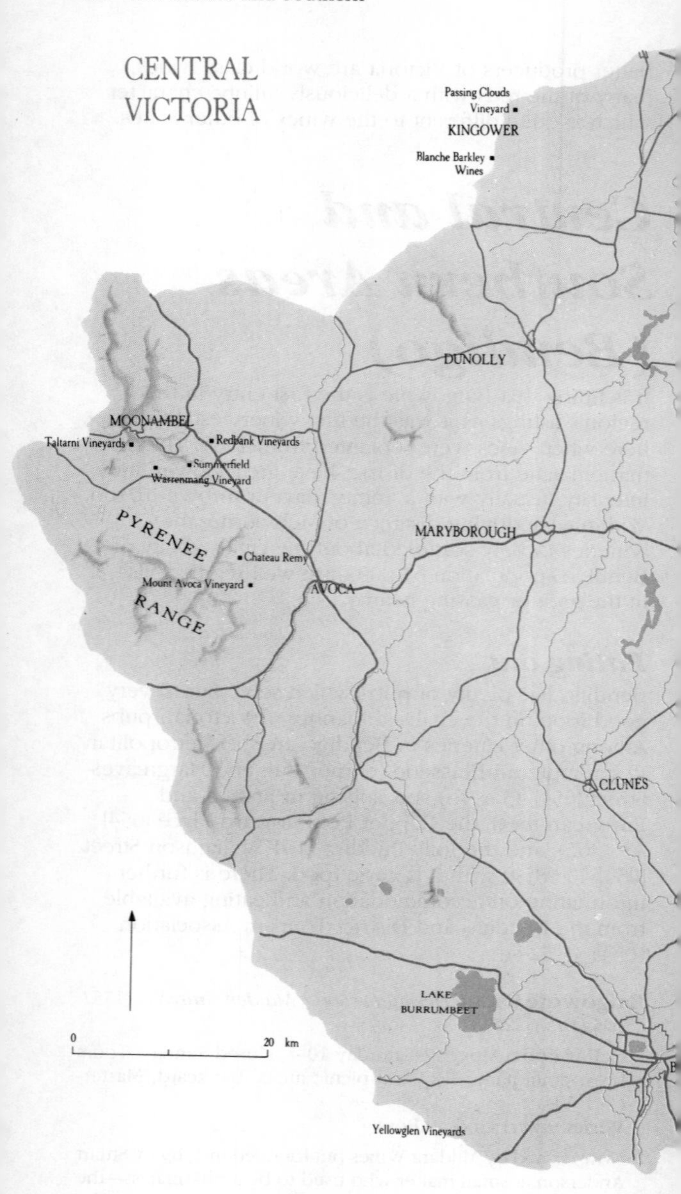
CENTRAL VICTORIA
Passing Clouds Vineyard
KINGOWER
Blanche Barkley Wines
DUNOLLY
MOONAMBEL
Taltarni Vineyards
Redbank Vineyards
Summerfield
Warrenmang Vineyard
PYRENEE RANGE
Chateau Remy
Mount Avoca Vineyard
AVOCA
MARYBOROUGH
CLUNES
LAKE BURRUMBEET
0
20 km
Yellowglen Vineyards

Balgownie Vineyard
BENDIGO
Chateau Dore
Chateau Le Amon
Huntleigh Vineyards
Jasper Hill
LAKE EPPALOCK
Mt Ida Vineyards
HEATHCOTE
The Heathcote Winery
Zuber Estate
Romany Rye Vineyards
Harcourt Valley Vineyard
CASTLEMAINE
BAYNTON
Knight's Granite Hills
Vineyard
The Mill Winery
Flynn and Williams
Virgin Hills Vineyard
KYNETON
DAYLESFORD
WOODEND
MACEDON
GREAT
DIVIDING
RANGE
Mt Aitken Winery
GISBORNE
Craiglee
SUNBURY
St Annes Vineyard

Blanche Barkly Wines *Rheola Road, Kingower Vic. 3517. (054) 38 8223 or (054) 43 3664.*

Cellar door: Saturday 9–5 or by appointment. Bankcard, Mastercard, Visa.
Winemaker: David Reimers.

Owned by David and Alvin Reimers; founded 1972. Wines include cabernet and shiraz. Distribution through some retail outlets in Melbourne, cellar door and mailing list (RMB 348, Kingower Vic. 3517).

Chateau Doré *Mandurang Road (8 kilometres south of Bendigo), Mandurang, Vic. 3551. (054) 39 5278.*

Cellar door: Tuesday–Saturday 10.30–4.30. Sunday by appointment. Tours of winery. Bankcard, Visa.
Winemaker: Ivan Grose.

Owned by Ivan and Jan Grose; founded 1851; re-established 1979 by the fourth generation of the same family. Wines include Rhine riesling, moselle, chardonnay, shiraz and cabernet sauvignon. Distributed through cellar door only.

Chateau Le Amon *140 kilometre post, Calder Highway, Bendigo Vic. 3550. (054) 47 7995.*

Cellar door: Monday, Wednesday–Friday 10–5, Saturday and holidays 9–6. Sunday 12–6. Bankcard, Mastercard, Visa.
Winemaker: Ian Leamon.

Owned by the Leamon family; founded 1973; first vintage 1977. Maker of good wines, especially reds. Wine include Rhine riesling, semillon, chardonnay, shiraz and cabernet sauvignon. Distribution through selected outlets in Melbourne, Sydney, Brisbane and Adelaide, cellar door and mailing list (PO Box 487, Bendigo Vic. 3550).

Crawford River Wines *Crawford, via Condah Vic. 3303. (055) 78 2267.*

Cellar door: Sales by appointment only.
Winemaker: John Thompson (owner).

Founded 1975. Wines include Rhine riesling (dry and sweet), beerenauslese (riesling style—limited amounts), semillon/sauvignon blanc and cabernet sauvignon. Distribution through cellar door, limited Victorian retail and mail order (PO Box 3, Condah Vic. 3303).

Delatite Vineyards *Pollards Road, Mansfield Vic. 3722. (057) 75 2922.*

Cellar door: Daily 9–6. Electric BBQs. Picnic area with swings. Mastercard, Bankcard, Visa.
Winemaker: Rosalind Ritchie.

Owned by Robert and Vivienne Ritchie; founded 1969. Wines from this quality maker include Rhine riesling, chardonnay, sauvignon blanc, gewürztraminer, shiraz, pinot noir, red blend, malbec and merlot. Distribution through retail outlets in Sydney, Melbourne, Adelaide and Brisbane, plus cellar door.

Eppalock Ridge *Metcalf Pool Road, Redesdale Vic. 3444. (054) 25 3135.*

Cellar door: Open weekends, public and school holidays 10–6. Usually open weekdays, but phone first.
Winemaker: Rod Hourigan.

Founded 1978. Wines include semillon, chardonnay, shiraz and cabernet. Distributed through cellar door and the Rutherglen Wine Company in Victoria.

Flowerdale *RMB 6513, Yea Road, Flowerdale Vic. 3717. (057) 80 1432 or (057) 80 1225.*

Cellar door: Saturday 10–5, Sunday 12–5, only in summer. Bankcard.
Winemaker: Rosalind Ritchie

Owned by Peter Geary; founded 1976. Wines include chenin blanc, chardonnay, traminer and pinot noir. Distribution mainly through cellar door.

Harcourt Valley Vineyards *118 kilometre post, Calder Highway, Harcourt Vic. 3453. (054) 74 2223.*

Cellar door: Monday, Thursday, Friday and Saturday 10–6; Sunday 12–6. Bankcard, Mastercard, Visa.
Winemaker: Ray Broughton.

Owned by John Livingston; founded 1976. Wines include Rhine riesling, chardonnay, shiraz, cabernet sauvignon and pinot noir. Distribution through cellar door and selected outlets in Canberra, Adelaide, Sydney, Melbourne and elsewhere in Victoria.

Heathcote *183 High Street, Heathcote Vic. 3523. (054) 33 2595.*

Cellar door: Daily 10–6. Bankcard, Mastercard, Visa.
Winemaker: Stephen Reed.

Owned by Ken and Doris Tudhope; founded 1982. Wines include chardonnay, wood-matured chenin blanc, gewürztraminer, viognier (a rare dry white variety from France), pinot noir, shiraz, cabernet sauvignon and cabernet/shiraz. Distribution through cellar door and outlets in Sydney, Melbourne and Adelaide.

Huntleigh Vineyard *Tunnecliffs Lane, Heathcote Vic. 3523. (054) 33 2795 or (03) 857 7647.*

Cellar door: Weekends and holidays 10–5. Bankcard, Mastercard, Visa.

Winemaker: Leigh Hunt (owner).

Founded 1975; first vintage 1979. Wines include traminer, shiraz and cabernet sauvignon. Distribution through cellar door and mail order.

Jasper Hill Vineyard *Drummonds Lane, Heathcote Vic. 3523. (054) 33 2528.*

Cellar door: Weekends 10–6, mid-week by appointment, while stocks are available. Picnic area. All major credit cards.
Winemaker: Ron Laughton (owner).

Founded 1976; first vintage 1982. Wines include shiraz (George's Paddock), shiraz/cabernet franc (Emily's Paddock) and riesling (George's Paddock). Distributed through cellar door and nationally.

McIvor Creek Wines *Costerfield Road, Heathcote Vic. 3523. (054) 33 3000.*

Cellar door: Open seven days 10–5.30. BBQ facilities and picnic area with beautiful views. Amex, Bankcard, Visa, Mastercard.
Winemakers: Peter and Robyn Turley (owners).

Established in 1973. Range of red and white table wines and fortifieds. Available through cellar door and retail liquor outlets in Victoria and New South Wales

Mount Aitken Estates *Calder Highway, Gisborne Vic. 3437. (03) 744 6122.*

Cellar door: Daily 9–5. Licensed restaurant for 150. Functions room, art gallery and port room. All major credit cards.
Winemaker: Roger McLean.

Owned by Roger and Ann McLean; founded 1974. Wines include large range of Victorian and South Australian wines and ports. Resident cooper (barrel maker). Distribution through cellar door and nationally.

Mount Ida Vineyards *147 High Street, Heathcote Vic. 3523. (054) 82 1911.*

No cellar door sales; vineyard only.
Winemaker: Tisdall Wines.

Owned by Tisdall Wines; founded 1976; first vintage 1980. Products include shiraz, shiraz/cabernet and cabernet sauvignon. All wines available through Tisdall Wines (see Goulburn Valley—Tisdall Wines).

Murrindindi Vineyards *RMB 6070, Murrindindi Vic. 3717. (057) 97 8217.*

Not open to public.
Winemaker: Hugh Cuthbertson.

Family owned; founded 1984. Wines include chardonnay,

sauvignon blanc and cabernet/merlot/cabernet franc. Distribution by mailing list (address above).

Passing Clouds *Kurting Road, Kingower Vic. 3517. (054) 38 8257.*

Cellar door: Daily 10–6, by appointment 'to genuine red wine drinkers only'. Bankcard.
Winemaker: Graeme Leith.

Owned by Graeme Leith and Sue Mackinnon; founded 1974; first vintage 1980. Small maker of excellent reds, including shiraz/cabernet, cabernet sauvignon and pinot noir. Limited retail distribution in Victoria, New South Wales, Adelaide, Queensland, Western Australia and Hobart and by mail order.

Seppelt's Drumborg Vineyard *Henty Highway, Portland Vic. 3305. (055) 27 9257.*

Vineyard only, growing Rhine riesling, chardonnay, cabernet sauvignon, pinot meunier and rose-cross (a hybrid developed by Karl Seppelt). Source of some excellent wines, and a bold experiment in cool climate grape-growing by the Seppelt company (see Barossa Valley—Seppelt's Wines).

Water Wheel Vineyards *Lyndhurst Street, Bridgewater-on-Loddon. Vic. 3516. (054) 37 3060*

Cellar door: Monday–Friday 9–5, Saturday and holidays 10–5, Sunday 12–5. Bankcard, Mastercard, Visa.
Winemaker: Peter Cumming.

Owned by Peter Cumming; founded 1972; first vintage 1974. Wines include Rhine riesling, chardonnay, chablis, fumé blanc, sauvignon blanc, pinot noir, hermitage, cabernet sauvignon, vintage port and liqueur port. Distribution through cellar door and some retail outlets in Victoria and Sydney.

Yellowglen Vineyards *White's Road, Smythesdale Vic. 3551. (053) 42 8617.*

Cellar door: Monday–Saturday and holidays 9–5, Sunday 12–5. Lawn area for picnics. Tours by appointment. Amex, Bankcard, Diner's Club, Mastercard, Visa.
Winemaker: Jeffrey Wilkinson.

Owned by Mildara Wines; founded 1971. A fascinating operation, set up by imaginative local businessman Ian Home, a board member of adoptive parent Mildara Wines. Excellent Australian sparkling wines, both white and pink. Wines are exclusively *méthode champenoise* sparkling wines, distributed nationally by Haselgroves.

Zuber Estate *Northern Highway, Heathcote Vic. 3523. (054) 33 2142.*

Cellar door: Daily 10–6. Cash or cheque only.
Winemaker: Lew Knight.

Founded 1981. Wines are reds—a claret and a burgundy—sold only through cellar door.

East Gippsland

This new viticultural area is centred around the large towns of Sale and Bairnsdale, to the east of Melbourne along Highway 1. While the Bass Strait oil rigs are busy tapping the oil resources offshore, several small winemakers are busy showing the potential inland.

The area is very new but clearly has the potential to produce wines with attractive varietal characters of light to medium body.

Eating out

In Sale there is Pipek's Bistro (308 York Street [051] 44 1933), with Mediterranean food; Celebrations (94 Raymond Street [051] 44 4855) with French and Italian food; and the Gippsland Palace (58 Macarthur Street [051] 44 7399), which is a BYO restaurant specialising in a variety of Asian dishes. In Maffra, there's Powerscourt Historic Homestead (Stratford Road [051] 47 1897) with 'classical' cuisine with an emphasis on local produce.

Bairnsdale has the Commercial Hotel (corner Bailey and Main Streets [051] 52 3031) which serves counter lunches and dinners; the Mitchell Motor Inn Restaurant (Princes Highway [051] 52 5012) serves dinners only, specialising in fresh seafood from the Lakes; while Waters Wine and Food (131 Main Street [051] 524 3360) is open Fridays for lunch, Wednesday–Saturday for dinner and focuses on French cuisine.

In Lakes Entrance, a floating restaurant, the Sloop John D. (Western Boat Harbour, Princes Highway [051] 55 1400) has a seafood theme, is BYO, and is open for dinner; Sally's (Bulmer Street [051] 552 1000) is also BYO.

Coalville Vineyard *Moe South Road, Moe South Vic. 3825. (051) 27 2555.*

Cellar door: By appointment only.
Winemaker: Stewart Mair.

Small winery, established in 1974. One wine only, Coalville

Red (100 per cent cabernet sauvignon). Available through cellar door.

Golvinda *RMB 4635, Lindenow South, via Bairnsdale Vic. 3875. (051) 57 1480.*

Cellar door: Open seven days 9–6. Picnic area and BBQ. Ploughman's lunch to order. Bankcard, Mastercard, Visa.
Winemaker: Robert Guy.

Owned by Robert and Ann Guy; founded 1972. Wines include Rhine riesling, semillon, chenin blanc and cabernet/merlot. Distribution through cellar door and mail order.

McAlister Vineyards *Golden Beach Road, Longford Vic. 3815. (051) 49 7229.*

Cellar door: By appointment only. Bankcard.
Winemaker: Peter Edwards (owner).

Founded 1975. One wine only, a red blend of cabernet, cabernet franc, petite verdot and merlot named 'the McAlister'. Distribution through cellar door.

Nicholson River *Liddells Road, Nicholson Vic. 3882. (051) 56 8241.*

Cellar door: By appointment preferably. No credit cards.
Winemaker: Ken Eckersley.

Owned by Ken and Juliet Eckersley; founded 1978. Wines include Rhine riesling, semillon, chardonnay, pinot noir, cabernet franc, merlot, and cabernet sauvignon. Distribution through cellar door and mail order.

Parish Wines (Briagolong Estate) *Valencia–Briagolong Road, Briagolong Vic. 3860. (051) 47 1011.*

Not open to public.
Winemaker: Dr G. E. McIntosh (owner).

Wines include red and white burgundy (chardonnay and pinot noir). Available through mail order (118 Boisdale Street, Maffra Vic. 3860).

Wyanga Park Vineyards *Baades Road, Lakes Entrance Vic. 3909. (051) 55 1508.*

Cellar door: Monday–Saturday 9–5, Sunday 10–5. Tours available. BBQ and picnic facilities. Water access. Bankcard, Mastercard, Visa.
Winemaker: Andrew Smith.

Family owned; founded 1970. Formerly Lulgra Winery, this was the first winery re-established in the area as wine interest was reborn in the 1970s. Wines include Rhine riesling, chardonnay, crouchen, traminer, sauvignon blanc, pinot noir and cabernet sauvignon. Distribution through cellar door.

Geelong

Here is another area where nineteenth-century viticultural blood, sweat, toil and tears were repaid with the disaster of phylloxera. The area was a prosperous winegrowing district 125 years ago, with a strong European influence. It is also an area with a European-like coolness of climate, producing wines (at their best) of great flavour and finesse. Several characters in the area stand out: notably the Seftons of Idyll Vineyards, who replanted vines in the mid-1960s and whose vigorous promotion of the area has done much for it; and the multi-talented Hickinbotham family at Anakie. The Hickinbothams have contributed much to Australian wine, from Alan Hickinbotham's work establishing the winemaking course at Roseworthy in South Australia through to his son Ian's great red wines at Wynn's and his work on pioneering fruity sparkling wines at Kaiser Stuhl. To Ian's late son Stephen Hickinbotham, who produced a 'new' style of red which he called Cab Mac, which has been quite successful.

It will probably take a large company to move into this area—which most are loath to do because of the low yields of grapes—to really show its potential to the wine world at large. There are certainly some extremely good wines emerging from Geelong and surrounding areas.

Eating out

Geelong offers rather more sophisticated food than many other areas, probably because of its proximity to Melbourne. A gratifying number of the restaurants are BYO and there are good counter lunches and dinners available at many of the hotels. The Source (Moorabool Street [052] 21 1375) won an award as top country restaurant in Australia and offers 'new style European/French cooking with an Indonesian influence'; the Bush Inn (58 Corio Street [052] 9 5194) offers similar food to the Source, but somewhat simpler; Fisherman's Pier (Yarra Street, Eastern Beach [052] 22 4100) has seafood; the Man-Bo Tower (395 Moorabool Street [052] 21 7888) has top-flight Chinese cuisine; while two French cuisine restaurants (both BYO) are Usther's (93 Yarra Street [052] 9 7529) and le Parisien (16 The Esplanade, South Geelong [052] 9 3110).

Asher Vineyard *360 Goldsworthy Road, Lovely Banks Vic. 3221. (052) 76 1365.*

Cellar door: Open first and third weekends in the month and by appointment.
Winemaker: Brian Moten.

Founded 1975. Wines are cabernet/malbec and sauvignon blanc. Distributed through the cellar door.

Bannockburn Vineyards *Midland Highway, Bannockburn Vic. 3331. (052) 81 1363.*

Not open to the public.
Winemaker: Gary Farr.

Owned by Stuart Hooper; founded 1973. Wines include Rhine riesling, sauvignon blanc, chardonnay, shiraz, pinot noir and cabernet sauvignon. Distributed nationally.

Clyde Park *Midland Highway, Bannockburn Vic. 3331. (052) 81 7274.*

Not open to the public.
Winemaker: Garry Farr (owner).

Founded 1978. Private venture by Bannockburn's winemaker, making his own chardonnay and cabernet, which are distributed through Seabrooks, the Melbourne merchants.

Idyll Vineyard *265 Ballan Road, Moorabool Vic. 3221. (052) 76 1280.*

Cellar door: Tuesday–Sunday and public holiday Mondays 10–5. All major credit cards.
Winemaker: Dr Daryl Sefton.

Owned by Dr Daryl and Nini Sefton; founded 1966. Dr Sefton, a veterinary surgeon, and wife Nini have pursued their winemaking dream for twenty-five years in this area with great talent, gusto and dedication. Wines include chardonnay, gewürztraminer, Idyll Blush (rosé) and cabernet/shiraz. Distribution through cellar door and retail liquor outlets in Melbourne and Canberra.

Innisfail Vineyard *Cross Street, Batesford Vic. 3221. (052) 76 1258.*

Cellar door: By appointment only. Visa, Diner's Club, Mastercard.
Winemaker: Gary Farr

Owned by Ron and Sharon Griffiths; established 1980. Planted to cabernet sauvignon, pinot noir, chardonnay and Rhine riesling. Available through cellar door, local restaurants and retail outlets and some outlets in Melbourne.

Mt Anakie *Staughton Vale Road, Anakie Vic. 3221. (052) 84 1256.*

Cellar door: Monday–Saturday 11–5, Sunday 12–5. All major credit cards. The vineyard is opposite Brisbane Ranges National Park and between the You Yangs and Steiglitz Historic Park. BBQ facilities.
Winemaker: Otto Zambelli.

Owned by Otto and Bronwyn Zambelli (and sometimes described as Zambetti Estate); founded 1968. This winery was leased by Hickinbotham winemakers until late 1986 and is now run by the owner. Some good wines include Rhine riesling, chardonnay, semillon, Dolcetto (light red), Biancone (light summertime red), cabernet sauvignon, shiraz and tawny port. Distribution through cellar door, local restaurants and some retail outlets in Melbourne. Some exports to Germany.

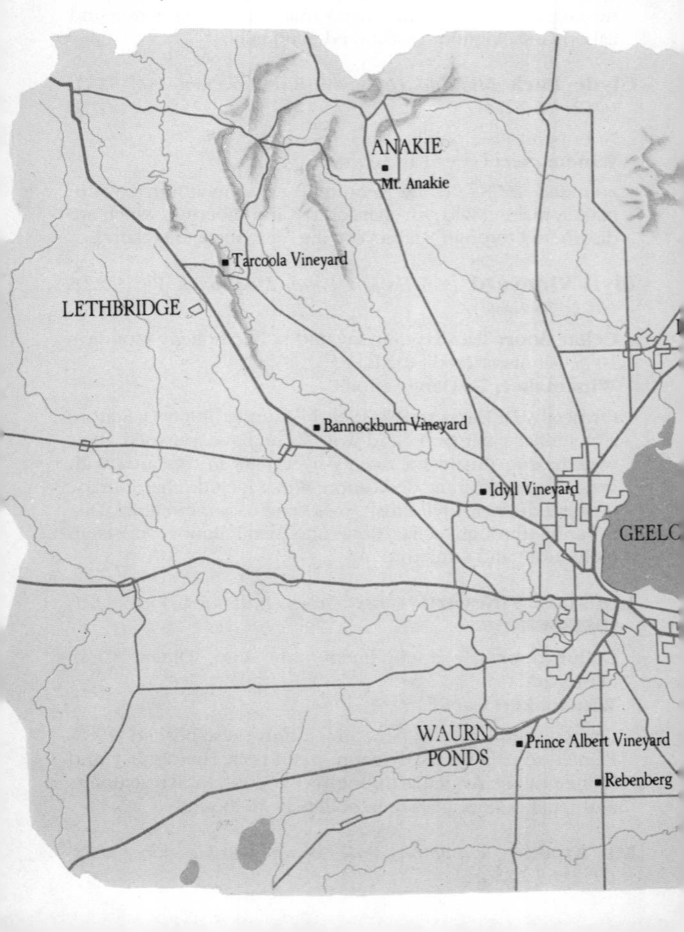

Prince Albert Vineyard *Lemins Road, Waurn Ponds Vic. 3221. (052) 43 5091.*

Cellar door: By appointment only. No credit cards.
Winemaker: Bruce Hyett.

Owned by Bruce and Susan Hyett; founded 1975. The only wine is pinot noir. Distributed through selected outlets in Sydney and Melbourne, cellar door and mail order.

Rebenberg Vineyard *Feehans Road, Mount Duneed Vic. 3221. (052) 64 1281.*

Cellar door: Saturday and school holidays 10–5, Sunday 12–5 or by appointment. Bankcard, Visa.
Winemaker/owner: Ken Campbell.

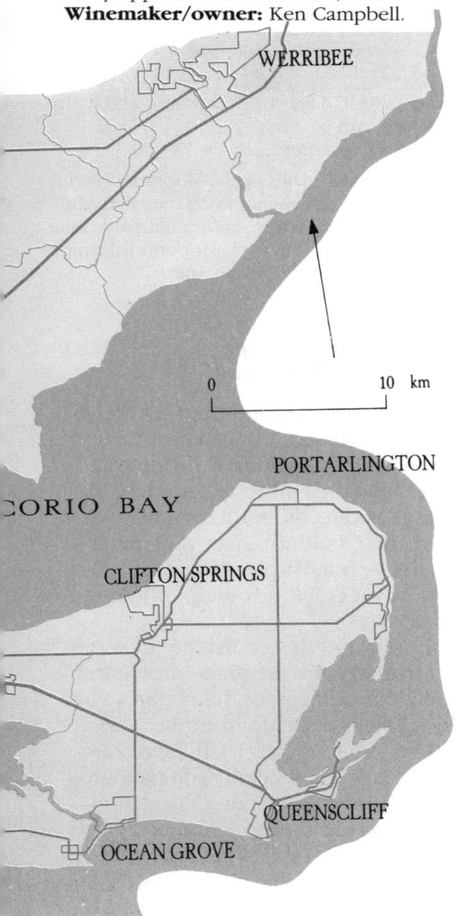

Operated by Ken Campbell and Peter Caldwell for Rebenberg Pty Ltd. Vineyard planted 1971; winery built 1980. Planted to semillon, sauvignon blanc, muscadelle, cabernet sauvignon, malbec, merlot and shiraz. Available through cellar door.

Scotchmans Hill Vineyard *Scotchmans Road, Drysdale Vic. 3222. (052) 51 3176.*

Not open to the public.
Winemaker: Peter Cummings.

Owned by D. W. and V. J. Browne and managed by Rob Burgess. Planted to cabernet sauvignon, cabernet franc, chardonnay, pinot noir, merlot and Rhine riesling. Available through local restaurants and some in Melbourne.

Tarcoola Estate *Maude Road, Lethbridge Vic. 3332. (052) 81 9245.*

Cellar door: Open seven days 10–5, but preferably by appointment. Bankcard, Amex, Visa.
Winemaker: Keith Wood (owner)

Founded 1971. Smallish vineyard beside the Moorabool River, 30 kilometres from Geelong, producing several unusual white varieties. Wines include Rhine riesling, müller thurgau, chasselas, cabernet sauvignon and shiraz. Distribution through cellar door, mailing list and several restaurants.

Goulburn Valley

The Goulburn Valley stretches to the north of Melbourne—an hour or so's drive from Tullamarine Airport. Just to the north of Seymour, the Hume Highway (Route 31) branches off to the north-east and the wine track goes directly north towards the town of Nagambie. The Goulburn River runs into nearby Nagambie Lake—a most pleasant place to relax—and then runs, via Goulburn Weir, to join the Murray near Echuca.

The climate, the soils and the availability of water make the Valley a natural for wine-grape-growing. It has much in common with many of the nation's wine 'valleys'. The wines which emanate from this Valley, however, do not lose much flavour by the introduction of river waters. They are generally full-flavoured, even full-bodied, wines of considerable distinction.

Chateau Tahbilk (curiously, not far from the differently spelt township of Tabilk—a historical accident) is the wine doyen of the valley; it is challenged by the equally dramatic winery of Mitchelton, though the former is ninety years older than the latter.

It is a delightfully green and graceful part of Victoria; a place to wander by car, picnic, drink the young white wines and keep the big, gutsy red wines for as long as you can.

Don't hesitate to make a very brief detour if driving between Sydney and Melbourne.

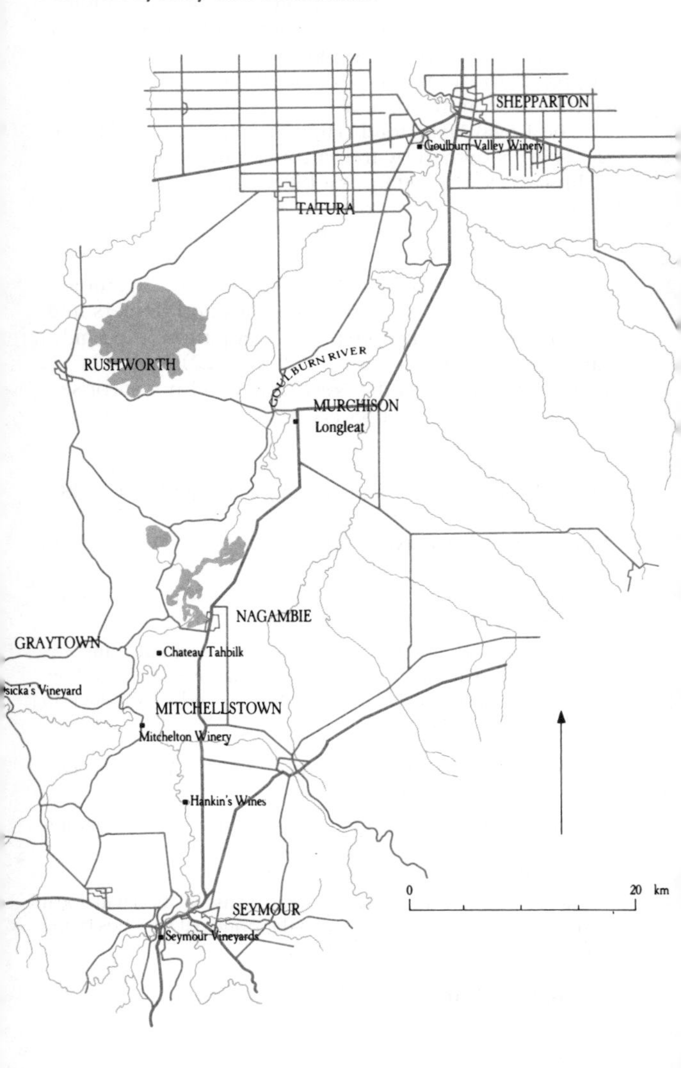

Eating out

Anyone scanning this small tome will by now have picked my preference for buying a bottle of local wine and having a picnic at winery, roadside or somewhere else quiet and pleasurable. One of the most enjoyable such occasions was a delightful afternoon spent beside the shores of Lake Nagambie on a sunny day; but there are plenty of other spots in this area which will please just as much. If that approach to eating out does not attract you, try some of these recommendations:

The Royal Mail Hotel (High Street, Nagambie [057] 94 2488) is owned by the Purbrick family of Chateau Tahbilk. It looks rough, *is* a bit rough around the edges, but has a heart of gold, good counter lunches and old-fashioned, reasonably priced pub accommodation.

Niggy's Bistro/Steakhouse (High Street, Nagambie [057] 94 2492) has very good lunches and dinners in a pleasingly cosy atmosphere. In Shepparton, the Emily Jane (481 Wyndham Street [052] 21 5822) is an à la carte restaurant; and the New China will not surprise you with its cuisine at 55 Fryers Street (058) 21 1166. In Mitchelton there is only one real choice for the wine-interested traveller: the various eating areas at Mitchelton winery (Mitchelton Vintners [057] 94 2388).

Belvedere Vineyard *399 High Street, Nagambie Vic. 3608. (057) 94 2514.*

Cellar door: Open daily 10–5. Bankcard, Mastercard, Visa.
Winemaker: David Traeger.

Winery established in 1968; owned by a pastoral company. Vines planted to cabernet, shiraz and small amount of riesling. Available through cellar door, mailing list and a few outlets in Melbourne.

Broken River Wines *RMB 4881, Cosgrove Road, Shepparton Vic. 3631. (058) 29 9486.*

Cellar door: Thursday–Sunday 10–5. Other times by appointment. Bankcard, Mastercard, Visa.
Winemaker: Frank Dawson.

Owned by Frank and Helen Dawson, in association with local shareholders. Estate wines, with the principal varieties being chenin blanc and cabernet franc.

Chateau Tahbilk *Tabilk, via Nagambie Vic. 3607. (057) 94 2555.*

Cellar door: Monday–Saturday 9–5; Sunday and holidays 11–5. Picnic areas. Bankcard, Mastercard, Visa.
Winemaker: Alister Purbrick.

Owned by the Purbrick family; founded 1860. Chateau Tahbilk is something of a Victorian institution—a beautiful, historic winery set amid stunning gardens and still run by the charming Purbricks. No wonder Sir Robert and Dame Pattie Menzies listed it as their number one watering hole, and the royal family enjoyed Chateau Tahbilk's wines at the coronation of Elizabeth II in 1953! Powerful and emphatic reds, whites full of character—both types of wines which will repay cellaring. Wines include chardonnay, marsanne (including wood-aged), semillon, shiraz and cabernet sauvignon. National distribution through the Hardy Wine Company.

Glenmour Estate *Johnson's Lane, Northwood, Vic. 3660. (057) 92 1229.*

Cellar door: Saturday and holidays 9–5; Sunday 12–5.
Winemaker : Alister Purbrick.

Small winery some 10 kilometres north of Seymour making a different range of wines, such as malbec, mataro, trebbiano/crouchen dry white and a sweet white. Distribution through cellar door sales and mailing list (PO Box 355 Seymour Vic. 3660).

Goulburn Valley Winery *52 Vaughan Street, Shepparton Vic. 3630. (058) 21 2051.*

Cellar door: Monday–Friday 9–6, Saturday 9–5, closed Sunday and holidays. Cash or cheque.
Winemaker: Don Phillips.

Owned by Don Phillips; founded 1908. Small winery in the centre of Shepparton's shopping centre, which has been through troubled times—it closed in the 1950s and reopened again to make wine quite recently. Wines include shiraz and fortifieds. Distribution through cellar door and several Melbourne outlets.

Hankin's Wines *Johnsons Lane, Northwood, via Seymour Vic. 3660. (03) 465 2866.*

Cellar door: Open weekends 10–5. Cash and cheque only.
Winemaker: Dr Max Hankin (owner).

Founded 1977. Wines include cabernet/shiraz/malbec, semillon, sauvignon blanc and shiraz. Distribution by mail order (351 High Street, Lalor Vic. 3075, phone as above).

Haywards of Whiteheads Creek *Hall Lane, Whiteheads Creek, via Seymour Vic. 3660. (057) 92 3050.*

Cellar door: Monday–Saturday 9–6, Sunday 10–6.
Winemaker: Sid Hayward.

Established 1975. Owned by the Hayward family, with vines planted to shiraz, cabernet sauvignon, riesling, pinot noir and malbec. Available through cellar door and mail order (RMB 4270, Seymour Vic. 3660).

Longleat *Old Weir Road, Murchison Vic. 3610. (058) 26 2294.*

Cellar door: Monday–Saturday and holidays 9–6; Sunday 10–6. Picnic area on Goulburn River. All major credit cards. Nearest restaurant (2 kilometres away in town) in Murchison is the Gallery Tea Rooms, open for morning and afternoon tea and lunch.

Winemaker: Peter Schulz.

Owned by Peter and Mark Schulz; founded 1975. Wines include Rhine riesling, chardonnay, sauvignon blanc, semillon, shiraz, cabernet sauvignon, vintage and tawny port, muscat and non-vintage champagne. Labelled as Wines of Longleat. Distributed through cellar door and retail outlets in Victoria and New South Wales (PO Box 25, Murchison Vic. 3610).

Mitchelton *Mitchellstown (off Goulburn Valley Highway) Vic. 3608. (057) 94 2710.*

Cellar door: Monday–Saturday 9–5, Sunday 10–5. Educational guided tours by appointment. BBQ and lawn picnic areas available; swimming pool, aviary; observation tower. Restaurant open each day for lunch (dinners by appointment). Coffee shop open seven days. Victorian wine museum. Major Mitchell river boat cruises operating at weekends between Mitchelton and Chateau Tahbilk. Functions. All major credit cards.

Winemaker: Don Lewis.

Owned by the Valmorbida family; founded 1969. Mitchelton is certainly the most prominent Goulburn Valley winery, and not just because of the 55 metre high observation tower which dominates the complex. It makes a lot of wine, from some very diverse sources (including Western Australia and South Australia) and some very good wines, especially whites; an excellent Coonawarra sweet white was on Qantas First Class for some time. Wines include wide range of red and white table wines, plus sparkling and fortified wines. Distributed nationally and through cellar door, under both Mitchelton and Thomas Mitchell labels.

Monichino Wines *Berrys Road, Katunga Vic. 3640. (058) 64 6452.*

Cellar door: Open seven days 9–6. BBQs, picnic areas and swings. Bankcard, Mastercard, Visa.

Winemaker: Carlo Monichino (owner).

Founded 1962. Wines include Rhine riesling, frontignac, gewürztraminer, chardonnay, semillon, sauvignon blanc, cabernet sauvignon and malbec. Distribution through cellar door and several Melbourne outlets.

Osicka's (Major's Creek Vineyard) *Off Heathcote–Nagambie Road, Graytown Vic. 3608. (057) 94 9235.*

Cellar door: Monday–Saturday 10–5, Sunday by appointment. Buses by appointment only. BBQ available. Cash or cheque.
Winemaker: Paul Osicka.

Owned by the Osicka family; founded 1955. A family from Czechoslovakia producing good wines from a hand-made brick-built winery begun 100 years ago. Skilful vintage port maker (won Rutherglen Show vintage port class three years running). Other wines include good dry reds (shiraz, and cabernet sauvignon) plus some good dry whites (chardonnay and Rhine riesling).

Somerset Crossing Winery *1 Emily Street, Seymour Vic. 3660. (057) 92 2445.*

Cellar door: Open daily 10–6. Bankcard, Mastercard, Visa. Riverview restaurant next door, open every day except Saturday for lunch. Open for dinner Tuesday–Saturday. Bookings (057) 92 3877.
Winemaker: David Traeger.

Owned by Dr Ian Rafter; founded 1970 (formerly River View Wines). Wines include wide range of white and red varietal table wines including a light red, Le Rouge Nouveau. Distribution through cellar door, mailing list and a few Sydney and Melbourne retail outlets.

Thomas Mitchell

See Mitchelton.

Tisdall Wines *Cornelia Creek Road, Echuca Vic. 3564. (054) 82 1911.*

Cellar door: At Radcliffe Street, Echuca. Monday–Saturday and holidays 10–5; Sunday 11–5. All major credit cards. Restaurants nearby in Echuca.
Winemaker: Jeff Clarke.

Owned by Dr Peter Tisdall; founded 1979. A quality maker at the northern end of the Goulburn Valley, drawing fruit from a number of different, scattered vineyards. The chardonnays and some of the cabernets and cabernet/merlot wines have been impressive. Products include chenin blanc, chardonnay/Rhine riesling, sauvignon blanc/semillon, shiraz/cabernet and cabernet/merlot (under Tisdall label); chablis, cabernet sauvignon and Rhine riesling (under Hopwood Estate label, the economy range); chardonnay, cabernet sauvignon, pinot noir and fumé blanc (under Mt Helen label). Distribution through cellar door, and widely available nationally.

Walkershire Wines *Segafrados Lane, Greytown Vic. 3608. (057) 94 9257.*

Cellar door: Open daily 10–6. All major credit cards.
Winemaker: John B. Walker.

Owned by John B. and Megan C. Walker; founded 1976. Mr Walker, who wishes to make it clear he is not related to several other John Walkers in the Australian wine business, came from Yorkshire, bringing an unorthodox yet apparently successful approach to making his red wines. These include one dry red cabernet/shiraz blend plus an occasional late-picked fortified wine. Available through cellar door and mailing list (PO Box 74, Nagambie Vic. 3608).

Yarck Vineyard Estate *Lot 30A, Henke Lane, Yarck Vic. 3719. (057) 97 6277.*

Cellar door: By appointment only. No credit cards.
Winemakers: Tim and Caroline Miller.

Established in 1969. This small winery is undergoing renovations and will eventually be open to the public. Wines include full-bodied reds.

Great Western

Many could be forgiven for believing that Great Western is simply the name of a brand of Australian champagne (it is also the brand name of another firm established in 1860 in Hammondsville, New York, which was apparently described as 'the great champagne of the west', hence 'Great Western'). In fact, Australia's Great Western is a tiny town in central-western Victoria which obtained *its* name from a steamship of the middle part of the last century, the *Great Eastern,* and a man who was a mining warden in the area, by the name of Western!

The Victorian gold rush of the 1850s gave its stimulus to the Great Western area, boom times that in wine terms were only to reappear with the extraordinary champagne boom of the late 1970s and 1980s.

Among the millions of Australians who have regularly or occasionally consumed Great Western Champagne, how many would think that Great Western is not just a grape-growing area, but an area that also produces some very good table wines? Few, probably, would know that the maker of Great Western is a South Australian based company (now owned by the diverse SA Brewing Company), B. Seppelt & Sons.

They have made some of Australia's greatest sparkling wines, and quite a few of the best table wines, over a very long period. Perhaps that was the reason for their appeal as a takeover target.

There are other winegrowers in the district, north of the town of Ararat. And on the whole the name Great Western suggests great wines—even if it is a fair way west of most of the rest of populated Victoria.

Eating Out

There is not much available in this area, but several opportunities do stand out. In Ararat the Pyrenees Country Kitchen (319 Barkly Street [053] 52 3292) offers very good food; as does the Kookaburra Restaurant at Hall's Gap, just to the west (053) 56 4222, with French and Italian influenced food, dinner Tuesday–Saturday. In Great Western itself the Great Western Hotel (053) 56 2270 has counter lunches and dinners.

Best's Wines *Western Highway (1.1 kilometres off Western Highway at the 219 kilometre post), Great Western Vic. 3377. (053) 56 2250.*

Cellar door: Monday–Friday 9–5, Saturday and holidays 9–4, open Sundays 12–4 of long weekends and Victorian school holidays only. Picnic areas, tables and chairs. BBQs can be brought in. Bankcard, Mastercard, Visa. Nearest restaurant 13 kilometres at Stawell.

Winemakers: Viv Thomson, Trevor Mast and Simon Clayfield.

Owned by the Thomson family; founded 1866. Medium-sized winery not far from—and in the popular eye often overshadowed by—Seppelt's Great Western. Maker of some extremely good wines, notably reds, with whites catching up rapidly.

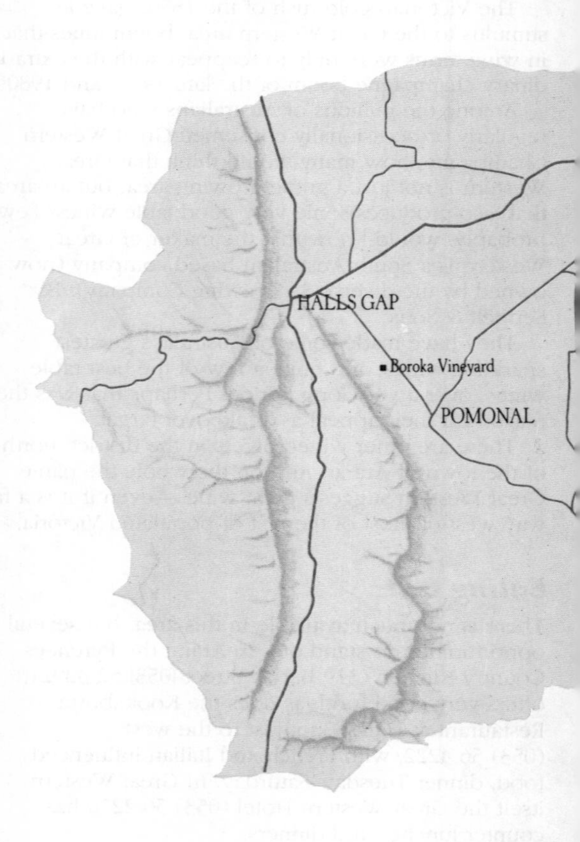

Products include white table wines (Rhine riesling, chardonnay, golden chasselas, ondenc (or Irvine's White, Hans Irvine being a pioneer of the area), pinot meunier, hermitage and cabernet sauvignon. Also sparkling and fortified wines. Mailing list plus wide national distribution.

Boroka Vineyards *Pomonal Road, Halls Gap Vic. 3381. (053) 56 4252.*

Cellar door: Monday–Saturday 9–5, Sundays of school holidays and general holiday periods 11–5 or by appointment. Groups by arrangement. Picnic and BBQ facilities available. Gourmet picnic baskets available—please order previous day. Bankcard, Mastercard, Visa, Amex.
Winemaker: Bernie Breen (owner).

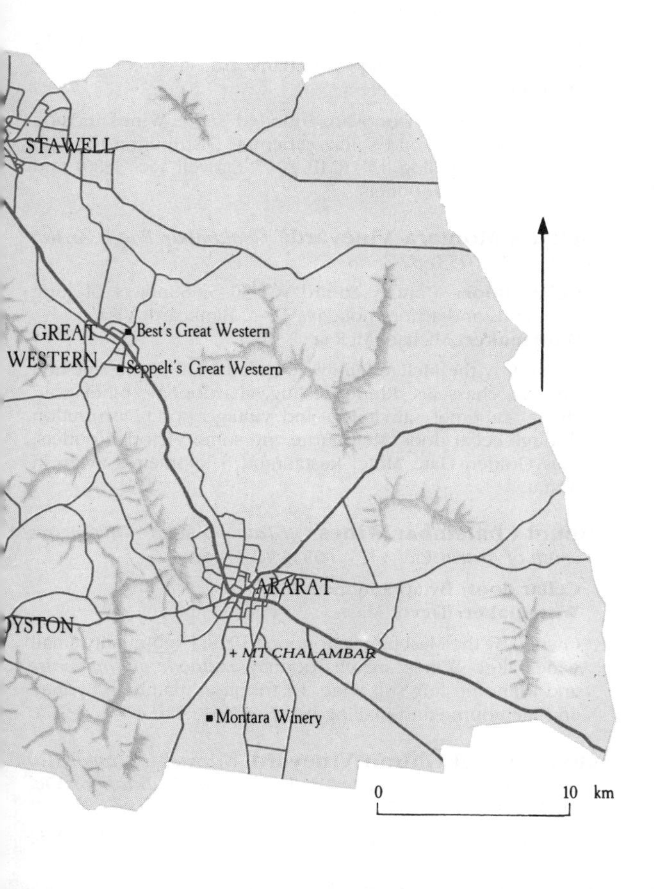

Small winery; founded 1976. Wines include sauvignon blanc, colombard, light red, shiraz, cabernet sauvignon and vintage port. Distribution through cellar door and mailing list (RMB 2072, via Stawell Vic. 3380).

Cathcart Ridge Estate *Byron Road, Cathcart, via Ararat Vic. 3377. (053) 52 231 or (053) 52 4082.*

Cellar door: By appointment.
Winemaker: Dr Graeme Bertuch.

Family owned; founded 1977. Wines include chardonnay, shiraz, cabernet sauvignon, merlot and cabernet franc. Distribution through Fesq & Co. plus mailing list (PO Box 367, Ararat Vic. 3377).

Donovan Wines *Pomonal Road (5 kilometres south-west of Stawell), Stawell Vic. 3380. (053) 58 2727.*

Cellar door: Monday–Saturday 10–4, Sunday of long weekends and school holidays 1–5. Bankcard, Visa.
Winemaker: Chris Peters.

Owned by Peter Donovan; founded 1977. Wines include crouchen, shiraz and shiraz/cabernet. Distribution through cellar door, mailing list (RMB 2017, Stawell Vic. 3380) and some Melbourne outlets.

McRae's Montara Vineyards *Chalambar Road, Ararat Vic. 3377. (053) 52 3868.*

Cellar door: Monday–Saturday 9.30–5, Sundays of long weekends and school holidays 12–4. Bankcard, Visa.
Winemaker: Michael McRae.

Owned by the McRae family; founded 1970. Wines include ondenc, chasselas, Rhine riesling, chardonnay, pinot noir, shiraz, cabernet sauvignon and vintage port. Distribution through cellar door, Melbourne and some Victorian outlets, plus Golden Gate Motel Restaurant, 3 kilometres away in Ararat.

Mount Chalambar Wines *Off Tatyoon Road, 3 kilometres south of Ararat Vic. 3377. (053) 52 3768.*

Cellar door: By appointment only.
Winemaker: Trevor Mast.

Owned by the Mast family; founded 1978. High-quality small winemaker. Wines are chardonnay *méthode champenoise* and Rhine riesling still wine. Distribution mainly in Sydney and Melbourne and mailing list (Box 301, Ararat Vic. 3377).

Mount Langi Ghiran Vineyard *Warrack–Buangor (20 kilometres from Ararat on Melbourne Road), Buangor Vic. 3375. (053) 54 3207.*

Cellar door: Monday–Friday 10–5 and weekends 12–5.

Picnic area and BBQ. Bankcard, Mastercard, Visa, Amex.
Winemaker: Trevor Mast.

Owned by Trevor Mast and Ian Menzies; founded 1970. Wines include Rhine riesling, late-picked Rhine riesling, chardonnay, shiraz and cabernet sauvignon. Distribution through cellar door and in Sydney and Melbourne and local area.

St Anne's Vineyard *Western Freeway, Myrniong Vic. 3341. (053) 68 7209.*

Cellar door: Monday–Saturday 10–5, Sunday 12–5. Home BBQ and picnic area. Bankcard, Mastercard, Visa.
Winemaker: Alan McLean.

Owned by the McLean family; founded 1971. Wines include dry whites, reds and port. Distribution through cellar door and mail order.

Seppelt's Great Western *Western Highway, Great Western Vic. 3377. (053) 56 2202. Head office: 181 Flinders Street, Adelaide SA 5000. (08) 236 3400.*

Cellar door: Monday–Saturday 9–5 (with tours at 9.30, 10.30, 1.30 and 3.00), Sunday 12–4 during Victorian school holidays and Victorian public holidays and long weekends (tours 12.15, 1.30 and 2.45). Electric BBQs available in attractive gardens. Major credit cards.
Winemakers: Michael Kluczko is Senior Champagne Maker; the Chief Winemaker and Technical Manager of the company is Ian McKenzie.

Owned by B. Seppelt & Sons (SA Brewing Co.); winery founded 1918. Wine-show-winning company based in Adelaide with other major wineries in the Barossa Valley. But Great Western is Australia's biggest selling sparkling wine, and the underground champagne cellars here at Great Western are really worth a visit. Extraordinary range of top white and red table wines from various vineyards in Victoria and South Australia—plus, of course, Great Western sparkling wines of various sources, pedigrees and ages, such as the excellent Salinger. Great Western is not just a sparkling wine, but a whole range offering all sorts of variations and, obviously, all price brackets. Many people will also enjoy the remarkable sparkling (red) burgundies of Great Western.

Macedon

The Macedon region is a small one, set in rolling hills spreading out to the north-west of Melbourne, as the land climbs to Mount Macedon (1020 metres). The climate can be cold, and the conditions windy, both bringing problems for the grape-growers of the area—

and opportunities to make good wines. Adversity often seems to be the father of good wines, even if the economics can make those wines expensive.

Most of the seven area wineries listed here are very small (for example, Flynn and Williams make just seventy to eighty dozen bottles of wine a year), and they are spread around the area, with decidedly different micro-climates and altitude variations. The two best known vineyards, with reasonable availability in the main capital cities, are Knight's Granite Hills and Virgin Hills Vineyards—both producers of some very good reds.

Eating out

The Shamrock Hotel (Mollison Street, Kyneton [054] 22 1570) offers good tucker. Three other restaurants present the attraction of BYO wines (or other bottles), which I find hard to resist! The Mill restaurant (054) 22 2267 in Malmsbury, just north of Kyneton, has international cuisine; Piper's Row (Piper Street, Kyneton [054] 22 2108); and at a more economical level, Kyneton Cottage, also in Piper Street (054) 22 2581.

Cleveland Winery *Shannons Road, Lancefield Vic. 3435. (054) 29 1449.*

Open by appointment only.
Winemaker: Keith Brien.

Owned by Lyn and Keith Brien; established 1983. Wines include chardonnay, pinot noir and cabernet. Distribution through cellar door and mail order.

Cope-Williams' Romsey Vineyards *Glenfern Road, Romsey Vic. 3434. (054) 29 5428.*

Cellar door: Open during the week in summer 10–6. Phone first during winter. Visa, Mastercard.
Winemakers: Gordon and Michael Cope-Williams.

Family owned; founded 1982. Relatively new but exciting cool-climate winery operated by English-born architect, in a lovely park setting. Cricket matches are hosted during the summer months on the cricket pitch in a village green setting with a three course lunch served. Wines include Macedon *méthode champenoise,* pinot noir and chardonnay. Wines under the Coat of Arms label from fruit from other vineyards include cabernet sauvignon, cabernet sauvignon/pinot noir, Rhine riesling/chardonnay and Cricketers' Portwine.

Cowbaw Ridge *RSD 391, Perc Boyers Lane, East Pastoria, via Kyneton Vic. 3444. (054) 235 2277.*

Not open to the public.
Winemaker: Alan Cooper.

Owned by Alan and Nelly Cooper; established 1985. Wines include chardonnay, shiraz and cabernet sauvignon. Distribution through cellar door only.

Craiglee *Sunbury Road, Sunbury Vic. 3429. (03) 744 1160 or (03) 744 4489.*

Cellar door: Open every day except Tuesday 10–5; Apex park next door. Bankcard, Mastercard, Visa.
Winemaker: Pat Carmody.

Family owned; established 1864. Re-established with new vines 1976. Wines include chardonnay, shiraz, cabernet sauvignon and pinot noir Distribution through cellar door and some Melbourne outlets.

Fearn Hyll Estate *Hogans Road, Daylesford Vic. 3460. (053) 48 6539.*

Cellar door: Seven days 10–5.
Winemaker: David Farnhill.

New, small maker producing good white burgundy and riesling, with reds (pinot noir, shiraz and cabernet) to come. Limited distribution through cellar door and in Victoria.

Flynn and Williams *Flynn's Lane, Kyneton Vic. 3444. (054) 22 2427.*

Cellar door: By appointment. Cash or cheque.
Winemakers: John Flynn and Laurie Williams (owners).

Founded 1980. Wine is a good cabernet sauvignon. Distribution mainly in selected Melbourne outlets or to 'those who make it to the cellar door'.

Goonawarra Vineyard *Sunbury Road, Sunbury Vic. 3429. (03) 744 1180.*

Cellar door: Monday–Saturday 10–6, Sunday 12–6. Restaurant open for Sunday lunch and Devonshire afternoon tea only. Special pre-booked dining dates. Functions. Plant nursery. Bankcard, Mastercard, Diner's Club, Visa.
Winemaker: Not named at press time.

Owned by Elizabeth and John Barnier; founded 1863. Re-established 1982. Splendid old bluestone winery owned by Melbourne lawyer. The name (not to be confused with Coonawarra) means 'Resting Place of the Black Swan'—presumably having nothing to do with Swan Lager! Wines include chardonnay, semillon (originally from Cowra in New South Wales), cabernet franc (notably), merlot, pinot noir and viognier. Distribution through cellar door and mailing list only.

Hanging Rock Winery *Jim Road, Newham Vic. 3442. (054) 27 0544.*

Cellar door: Open daily 10–5. Bankcard, Mastercard, Visa.
Winemakers: John Ellis and Gary Duke.

An interesting venture in a scenic location (you've seen the movie ... now drink the wine!). First vintage was 1987. Winemaker John Ellis did great things for Rosemount in their early days, then later for Tisdall, before moving on to start this project. His wife and co-owner Anne is the daughter of the Hunter Valley's Murray Tyrrell. Estate-grown wines include semillon and sauvignon blanc. Pinot noir and chardonnay are used for sparkling wine production (to be released towards the end of 1991), plus other premium fruit from vineyards in the Macedon and Victorian area. Distributed nationally and through cellar door.

Knight's Granite Hills Winery and Vineyard *Burke and Wills Track, Baynton, via Kyneton Vic. 3444. (054) 23 7264.*

Cellar door: Monday–Saturday 9–6, Sunday 12–6. Picnics possible. Bankcard, Mastercard, Visa.
Winemaker: Lew Knight.

Family owned; founded 1971. Small but high-quality winemaker, with a range of estate-grown as well as their excellent wines from the local area vineyards. Wines include Rhine riesling, chardonnay, shiraz, cabernet sauvignon and cabernet franc. Distributed through cellar door and in Melbourne, Sydney and Brisbane.

Lancefield Estate *Woodend Road, Lancefield Vic. 3435. (054) 29 1217.*

Cellar door: Open weekends 12–6 or by appointment. Spit roast lunches with live music every Sunday—best to book. Mastercard, Bankcard, Visa, Diner's Club.
Winemakers: Andrew Pattison, with John Ellis as consultant.

Owned by Andrew Pattison; vineyard founded 1982. New winery (founded 1985) just ten minutes from Hanging Rock; you can buy a bottle of their wine and have a picnic nearby. Wines include chardonnay, traminer, colombard, pinot noir, merlot, shiraz, cabernet/merlot, sparkling Macedon *méthode champenoise*. Distribution through cellar door and in Melbourne.

Rochford Vineyard *Romsey Park, Rochford Vic. 3442. (054) 29 1428.*

Cellar door: By appointment only.
Winemaker: Bruce Dowding.

Established 1983; owned by Bruce Dowding. Vines planted to riesling, cabernet sauvignon, bordeaux style (cabernet franc/malbec/merlot) and pinot noir. Available mainly through mail order and some cellar door trade, also retail and restaurant outlets in Melbourne and Sydney.

Virgin Hills Vineyards *Salisbury Road, Lauriston West Vic. 3444. (054) 23 9169.*

Cellar door: By appointment only. Cash or cheque.
Winemaker: Mark Sheppard.

Owned by Marcel Gilbert; founded 1968. Wines are 90 per cent red (blend of 70 per cent cabernet, plus shiraz, malbec and merlot), plus one white wine, representing 10 per cent of Virgin Hills' production, a chardonnay. National distribution through selected retail outlets, mailing list and cellar door.

Wildwood Winery *St Johns Lane, Wildwood, Bulla Vic. 3428. (03) 307 1118.*

Cellar door sales: Weekends, phone first.
Winemaker: Dr Wayne Stott.

Extremely small maker, with promising chardonnay, cabernet sauvignon, cabernet franc, merlot and pinot noir.

Mornington Peninsula

This is a jackboot of land extending to the south-east of Melbourne, between Port Phillip Bay and Western Port. Again, a tiny winegrowing area with proliferating wineries (we listed five in the last edition of this book; this time twenty-eight!). Given that it's early days, wine quality can be outstanding, in spite of urban expansion and climatic problems. There is an authentication stamp indicating 100 per cent local area grape content in wines so stamped.

Eating out

Essentially a seaside area of Victoria, the eating-out scene is varied, and seasonal to some extent. If you like a good view, try the Mountain Peak Restaurant, Arthurs Seat, Dromana (059) 87 2330; the Royal Hotel Restaurant (the Esplanade, Mornington [059] 75 2605) has good counter lunches. Johnny Come Lately (Red Hill Road, Red Hill [059] 89 2326) has English-style foods at weekends and bistro for the rest of the week. La Colomb (Vale Street, Mornington [059] 75 5155) has French food, dinners only. Pendle Farmhouse

(6 Purues Road, Main Ridge [059] 89 6130) is open at weekends and serves 'French international' cuisine. For exceptional cuisine it's hard to beat Herman Schneider's Two Faces in Delgany Country House Hotel, Nepean Highway, Portsea (059) 84 4000, and Tuerong Estate Restaurant (see Tuerong winery listing below).

Allen's Vineyards *Red Hill–Shoreham Road, Red Hill Vic. 3937 (059) 89 2044.*

Bill Allen established this 0.5 hectare vineyard at Red Hill in 1983 with plantings of cabernet sauvignon and chardonnay. The wines are made and marketed by Peninsula Estate of Red Hill and are available by mail order from PO Box 115, Red Hill Vic. 3937.

Balnarring Vineyard *Bittern–Dromana Road, Balnarring Vic. 3926. (059) 89 5258.*

Cellar door: Open daily 10–4.

This 5 hectare vineyard, established by Bruce and Stan Paul in 1982, has plantings of pinot noir, gewürtztraminer, merlot, cabernet sauvignon and chardonnay. Distribution through cellar door, mail order, selected restaurants and retailers.

Coolart Valley Vineyard *Thomas Road, Red Hill South, Vic. 3937. (059) 89 2087.*

Winemaker: 1990 vintage: Peter Cummings.

This 1.8 hectare vineyard was established by Don and Betty Currie at Red Hill in 1981 with plantings of cabernet sauvignon, followed later by chardonnay, semillon, riesling and merlot. The vines are maintained by the Curries and the wine has been made by Hickinbothams since 1987. Available by mail order or at Herman Schneider's Two Faces Restaurant, Portsea.

Cotton Springs Vineyard *9B Musk Creek Road, Flinders Vic. 3929. (059) 89 6193.*

Winemakers: Kathleen Quealy and Kevin McCarthy.

Established by Bill and Gwen Ulbrick in 1973 and managed by Kevin McCarthy and Kathleen Quealy. This 1 hectare vineyard has plantings of sauvignon blanc, chardonnay, malbec and cabernet sauvignon. Wines, which are made at Hickinbothams, are available through mail order.

Craig Avon Vineyard *Craig Avon Lane, Merricks North Vic. 3916. (059) 89 7465.*

Winemaker: Consultancy advice from Nat White of Main Ridge Estate.

This vineyard was established by Ken and Helen Lang in 1986

with further plantings in 1987 and 1988. Varieties grown are chardonnay, pinot noir, cabernet sauvignon, cabernet franc and merlot over an area of 2.2 hectares. First release was expected late 1990. Distribution by mailing list.

Darling Park Vineyards *Browne Lane and Red Hill Road, Red Hill Vic. 3937. (059) 89 2732.*

Owned by John and Delys Sargeant, this 2.5 hectare vineyard is planted to cabernet sauvignon, cabernet franc, merlot, chardonnay and pinot noir. The 1989 vintage was made and marketed by Hickinbotham Winemakers and the 1990 vintage is being marketed by Peninsula Estate.

Dromana Estate *Harrisons Road, Dromana Vic. 3936. (059) 87 3275.*

Cellar door: Open January every day; February at weekends; March weekends of 2–3 and 9–10. Bankcard, Visa.
Winemaker: Garry Crittenden.

Owned by Garry and Margaret Crittenden; founded 1981. Very small family winery producing promising wines including chardonnay, merlot, pinot noir and cabernet sauvignon. Under the Schinus Molle label (horticultural name for peppercorn tree) are wines made from fruit purchased from other vineyards. Distribution through mailing list (PO Box 332, Mornington Vic. 3931), cellar door and nationally.

Elgee Park *Wallaces Road, Merricks North Vic. 3926. (059) 89 7338.*

Not open to the public; wines available through selected restaurants, retailers and mail order.
Winemakers: Daniel Greene with assistance from consultants Gary Baldwin and Ian Macrae.

Owned by S. Baillieu Myer Vineyard; founded 1972; winery built 1984. Wine quality is high and products include wooded chardonnay, riesling and cabernet sauvignon/cabernet franc/merlot blend. Distribution through mailing list and some local outlets and in Melbourne and Sydney.

Erinacea *Devonport Drive, Rye Vic. 3941. (059) 88 6336.*

Owned by Ron and Carol Jones; established in 1985. Planted to cabernet sauvignon, cabernet franc and merlot. Their first release, a bordeaux-type blend of the three varieties, was expected in 1990.

Hickinbotham *Corner Nepean Highway and Wallaces Road, Dromana Vic. 3936. (059) 81 0355 or (03) 379 1872.*

Winemakers: Ian Hickinbotham and family and Peter Cummings.

This vineyard, purchased by Ian Hickinbotham in 1987, is now planted to 2.4 hectares of cabernet sauvignon, merlot, cabernet franc and 'The Antcliff Collection' of chardonnay clones, the first release of which is expected in 1991. The Hickinbotham family is currently making and marketing wines from a wide variety of grapes grown at selected Victorian vineyards. Most wines are very good.

Hoffert Balnarring Estate Vineyard *87 Bittern–Dromana Road, Balnarring, Vic. 3926. (059) 89 5330.*

Winemakers: Bud and Patrick Hoffert (owners).

Bud Hoffert and his son Patrick established this non-irrigated vineyard in 1975. It is planted to sylvaner, traminer, chardonnay and cabernet sauvignon. Wines are currently available through selected retailers and restaurants and through cellar door sales which were expected to open late in 1990.

R. R. Hollick Vignerons *50 Red Hill–Shoreham Road, Red Hill Vic. 3937. (059) 89 8660.*

Originally established in 1981 and formerly known as Red Hill Estate, this 2 hectare vineyard was acquired late in 1988 by Vinecraft Pty Ltd. They planted another 6.5 hectares of equal quantities of semillon, chardonnay, pinot meunier and Rhine riesling in 1990 to add to the existing varieties of cabernet sauvignon, merlot, cabernet franc and chardonnay. The first release, a bordeaux-type blend, is expected in 1991.

Karina Vineyard Dromana *Harrisons Road, Dromana Vic. 3936. (059) 81 0137.*

Cellar door: Open weekends 11–4 or by appointment.
Winemaker: Graeme Pinney.

Owned by Jan and Graeme Pinney, this 3 hectare vineyard is planted to sauvignon blanc, Rhine riesling, cabernet sauvignon, merlot and chardonnay. Available through local retailers and restaurants or directly from cellar door.

Kings Creek Vineyard *237 Myers Road, Bittern Vic. 3918 (059) 83 2102 or (03) 376 3775.*

Winemakers: Kevin McCarthy and Kathleen Quealy.

Established in 1982, this 3 hectare vineyard is owned and operated by the Bell, Glover, Perraton and Scarborough families. It is planted to chardonnay, pinot noir and cabernet sauvignon. Wines, including some older wines, available through cellar door, mail order and at selected restaurants.

Main Ridge Estate *Lot 48, William Road, Red Hill Vic. 3937. (059) 89 2686.*

Cellar door: Saturdays 12–5; other days phone first. Mastercard, Visa.
Winemaker: Nat White.

Founded 1975. Wines include chardonnay, pinot noir, pinot meunier and cabernet sauvignon. Limited availability in major capital cities.

Massoni Main Creek Vineyard *Mornington–Flinders Road, Red Hill Vic. 3937. (059) 89 2060.*

Winemaker: Peter Cummings.

This vineyard, formerly the Warren Estate, was established in 1984. It is owned by Melbourne restaurateur Leon Massoni and his wife Vivienne, and produces complex and finely structured Chablis-style wines such as the Red Hill chardonnay. Available through retail outlets in Melbourne and selected restaurants.

Merricks Estate *Thompsons Lane, Merricks Vic. 3916. (059) 89 8416.*

Cellar door: By appointment only.
Winemaker: George Kefford.

Owned by George and Jackie Kefford; founded 1978. Wines include chardonnay, shiraz, pinot noir and cabernet savignon. Wines available through cellar door and in Sydney.

Moorooduc Estate *Derril Road, Moorooduc Vic. 3933. (059) 78 8585 or (03) 699 3191.*

Winemaker: Dr Richard McIntyre.

Established in 1983 and owned by Rick and Jill McIntyre, this 2.5 hectare vineyard is planted to chardonnay, pinot noir, cabernet sauvignon, merlot and cabernet franc. Nat White is consultant winemaker with Garry Crittenden of Vitinational as consultant viticulturist. Mail order from PO Box 239 Albert Park Vic. 3206.

Mornington Vineyards *Moorooduc Road, Mornington Vic. 3931. (059) 74 2095 or (03) 817 3156.*

Established by Hugh and Isabelle Robinson and family in 1988, this 2.4 hectare vineyard is planted to chardonnay and pinot noir. Winemaker is Tod Dexter with advice from viticulturist Garry Crittendon. First release is expected in late 1990. Available by mail order and at selected outlets.

Paringa Estate *44 Paringa Road, Red Hill South Vic. 3937. (059) 89 2669.*

Cellar door: By appointment only.
Winemaker: Consultant Tod Dexter.

Established in 1985 with plantings of cabernet sauvignon, cabernet franc, shiraz, pinot noir and chardonnay, this 3.2 hectare vineyard is owned by Lindsay and Margaret McCall. Available through cellar door, mail order and selected restaurants.

Peninsula Estate Winery *44 Paringa Road, Red Hill South Vic. 3937. (059) 89 2866.*

Established in 1985 and owned by Tim and Jamie Sutcliffe, the vineyard and impressive new winery were entirely planned, planted and built by the two brothers. They are also making and marketing wine from grapes grown at Allens, Darling Park, St Neot's, Ocean View and Kewley's Vineyards. Wines available through mail order. Cellar door expected to be open late 1990.

Peninsula Hills Vineyard *Buddina, Shoreham Road, Red Hill South Vic. 3937. (059) 89 2532.*

Gordon Brennan established this 1 hectare vineyard in 1978. It is planted to cabernet sauvignon, shiraz, Rhine riesling and merlot. Available through mail order.

Shoreham Vale *Red Hill–Shoreham Road, Red Hill South Vic. 3937. (03) 822 6624.*

David and Jill Heathershaw established their 2 hectare vineyard in 1985. It is planted to chardonnay, cabernet sauvignon, Rhine riesling and shiraz.

Bob Hollick is consultant viticulturist and winemakers are Gordon and Michael Cope-Williams. Available through mail order.

St Neot's Estate *63 Red Hill–Shoreham Road, Red Hill South Vic. 3937. (059) 89 2023 or (03) 867 1515*

This 2 hectare vineyard, owned by Philip and Elvala Ayton, was established in 1980–81. There is no cellar door or winery and the wine is made by Peter Cumming. Wines include traminer, chardonnay, sauvignon blanc, riesling, pinot noir and cabernet. Available through retail outlets on the Mornington Peninsula.

Stonier's Merricks Vineyard *62 Thompsons Lane, Merricks Vic. 3916. (059) 89 8352 or (03) 699 8922.*

Established in 1978 by Noel and Brian Stonier with chardonnay and cabernet sauvignon, this vineyard has been extended to 15 hectares with plantings of pinot noir, merlot and cabernet franc.

Wines from 1982 to 1986 were made by the late Stephen Hickinbotham, and since 1986 by Tod Dexter. A winery was being built for completion in December 1990. Available through mail order, Gatehouse Cellars (03) 690 1277 and selected restaurants.

Tanglewood Downs Estate *Bulldog Creek Road, Mornington Rural Vic. 3931. (059) 74 3325.*

Cellar door: During summer first Saturday of every month and every Sunday and public holiday from first weekend in

September to second weekend in March. Otherwise by appointment.
Winemaker: Kevin McCarthy.

This 2 hectare vineyard, owned by Ken and Wendy Bilham and established in 1985, is planted to chardonnay, gewürztraminer, merlot, cabernet sauvignon and pinot noir. Available by mail order, cellar door and through selected restaurants and licensed outlets.

Tuerong Estate Vineyard and Restaurant *Mornington–Flinders Road, Red Hill Vic. 3937. (059) 89 2129.*

Cellar door: Was planned for late 1990. Restaurant open Friday, Saturday, Sunday and most public holidays.
Winemaker: Peter Cumming.

Established in 1984, this 2.8 hectare vineyard is owned by Gennaro Mazzella and Gwen Riggs, with plantings of chardonnay, cabernet sauvignon, merlot and malbec. Wines available through the restaurant; however, they are expensive.

Vintina Estate *1282 Nepean Highway, Mount Eliza Vic. 3930. (03) 787 8166.*

Cellar door: Weekends and public holidays from 9–4 or by appointment.
Winemaker: Kevin McCarthy.

Established in 1985 and owned by Jim and Tina Filippone. This 1.5 hectare vineyard is planted to chardonnay, cabernet sauvignon, pinot noir and semillon. Available through cellar door.

Murray Valley

This is one of the 'big three' irrigated areas of Australia (the others being the South Australian Riverland, just downstream, and the Murrumbidgee Irrigation Area of New South Wales). Here, around the green and appealing city of Mildura, the water drawn from the mighty Murray will make just about anything grow, from avocado pears to citrus fruit, not to mention grapes. The vast irrigation schemes devised by the Chaffey brothers from California made it happen, literally turning desert into highly productive farmlands. The Chaffeys, incidentally, have another link with the Australian wine industry, with Ben Chaffey's involvement with Seaview. Some of their descendants still live in Adelaide.

Vast quantities of grapes are grown along this stretch of the Murray, which by the time it reaches Mildura, not far short of its confluence with the Darling, has flowed over 1500 kilometres from its source high in the Australian Alps, alongside Mount Kosciusko.

This area has a handful of wineries, running from just above Swan Hill downstream to Wentworth, the junction of the Murray and Darling Rivers. It does incorporate several very large producers, including Lindemans' enormous Karadoc plant, Mildara Wines and Stanley Leasingham's plant at Buronga. It is the home of this handful of giant juice factories, taking advantage of cheap gordo and sultana grapes, the backbone of Australia's cask wine production.

Eating out

The Grand Hotel (Seventh Street, Mildura [050] 23 0511) has always been a favourite, straddling a city block and overlooking the river. It has good counter lunches and a number of restaurants, including a Spanish Grill. The hotel also features a good

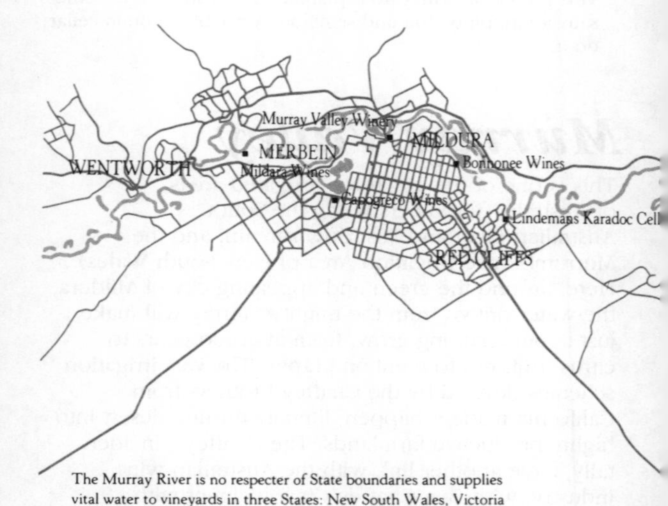

The Murray River is no respecter of State boundaries and supplies vital water to vineyards in three States: New South Wales, Victoria and South Australia.

range of Mildara's excellent older reds. Swan Hill is also a pleasant city, with its attractive riverboat museum beside the eucalypt-lined banks of the Murray.

The River Boat Restaurant (Horseshoe Bend, Swan Hill [050] 32 2463) will put you in the mood, with à la carte and table d'hôte cuisine. The White Swan Hotel (Campbell Street, Swan Hill [050] 32 2761) also has à la carte meals, while Rick's Charcoal Grill (Murray Valley Highway, Beverford [050] 37 6443) has an Italian theme.

Alambie Wines *Nangiloc Road, Nangiloc Vic. 3494 (050) 29 1546.*

Not open to public—bulk maker of quality wines which are sold to other winemakers.
Winemaker: David Martin.

Best's St Andrews *Tresco West Road, Tresco West, via Lake Boga Vic. 3584. (050) 37 2154.*

Cellar door: Monday–Friday 9–5, Saturday 10–4, Sundays of long weekends only 12–4. Picnic facilities. Tours weekdays 10, 11, 2, 3 and 4. Bankcard, Mastercard, Visa.
Winemakers: Bob Deighton and Simon Clayfield.

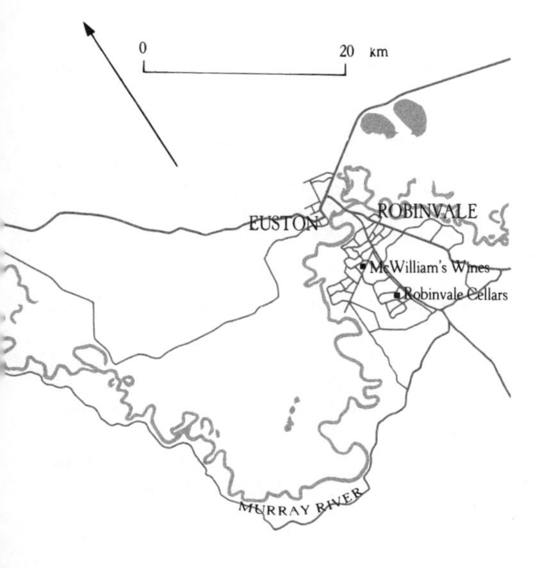

Owned by the Thomson family; founded 1930 This is the Murray River arm of Best's Wines at Great Western, making a range of good local wines but also offering the Great Western range. Products include a wide range of varietal whites, two reds (shiraz and cabernet sauvignon) and fortifieds. National distribution.

Buller's *Murray Valley Highway, Beverford Vic. 3590. (050) 37 6305.*

Cellar door: Monday–Saturday and holidays 9–5, Sunday 10–5. Bankcard, Mastercard, Visa.
Winemaker: Richard Buller junior.

Owned by the Buller family; founded 1952. Buller's are another company using this area as an outpost of their empire, being based in Rutherglen, where they produce typical north-east Victorian fortifieds, using spirit from here to fortify their muscats and so on. Wines include range of table and good fortified wines and spumante. Distribution in Melbourne, Sydney and South Australia, and cellar door, plus mailing list.

Buronga Hill *Buronga Hill NSW 2648. (050) 22 2344.*

Winery not open to the public, sells wine in bulk to others. Quite large operation started by former Hungerford Hill staff, just over the River Murray on the New South Wales side, selling bulk wines and grape juice.

Capogreco Winery Estate *Riverside Avenue, via Seventeenth Street (near Lake Hawthorne), Mildura Vic. 3500. (050) 22 1431.*

Cellar door: Monday–Saturday 10–6, Sundays of long weekends only 10–6. Tours possible. Bankcard, Mastercard, Visa.
Winemaker: Bruno Capogreco.

Family owned; founded 1976. Wines include red and white table wines, fortifieds, vermouth, marsala, Italian-style wines, such as a red made from barbera, and the locally popular Rossa Dolce flavoured wine, plus flagons. Distribution through cellar door and mailing list (PO Box 7, Cabarita, via Merbein Vic. 3505).

Lindemans' Karadoc *Edey Road (28 kilometres south-east of Mildura), Karadoc, via Red Cliffs Vic. 3496. (050) 24 0303.*

Cellar door: Monday–Friday 9–5, Saturday, Sunday and public holidays 10–4.30. Tours Monday–Friday 11, 2 and 3.30. BBQ, tables and chairs. Amex, Bankcard, Mastercard, Visa.
Chief Winemaker: Wayne Falkenberg.

Owned by Penfolds since early 1990, in turn acquired by SA Brewing Holdings in November 1990; founded (winery) 1973. This giant winery, perhaps the largest in Australia, processes some 40 000 to 50 000 tonnes of grapes annually and is now Lindemans' chief production and packaging centre. The company makes an extraordinary range of high-quality wines. While Karadoc might dispel some of your illusions about how good wines are made today, it is worth making the fifteen minute drive out of Mildura to see where it's done. Wines include Ben Ean Moselle, Leo Buring Leibfrauwine, Matthew Lang range, plus cask and flagon wines, and others. National and international distribution.

McWilliam's Robinvale *Moore Street, Robinvale Vic. 3549. (050) 26 4004.*

Cellar door: Monday–Friday 9–12 and 1–4.30. Conducted tours 10 and 3. Closed weekends and public holidays. Bankcard, Mastercard, Visa.
Winemakers: M. D. McWilliam and Matthew McWilliam.

Owned by the McWilliam family; winery founded 1963; company founded 1877. Wines include a wide range of company products (see Murrumbidgee Irrigation Area (Griffith)—McWilliam's vineyards), notably McWilliam's Cream Sherry and Bodega sparkling wines. Distribution nationally.

Mildara Wines *Wentworth Road, Merbein Vic. 3505. (050) 25 2303. Melbourne office (03) 690 9966.*

Cellar door: Monday–Friday 9–5, Saturday 10–4, Sundays and public holidays 11–4 (Easter and other long weekend holidays open 9–5). Pleasant park adjacent with BBQs.
Winemakers: Alan Harris and Andrew Peace.

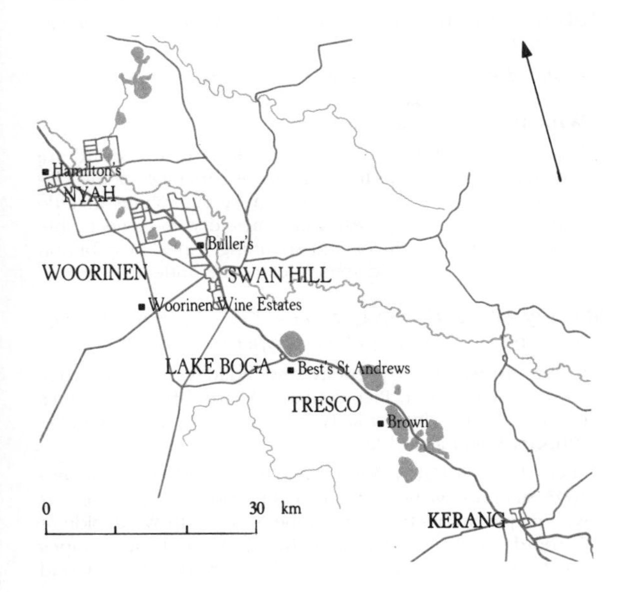

Owned by a listed public company; founded 1888. Mildara, ten minutes' drive to the west of Mildura, overlooks the river and has an excellent tourist and visitors' centre. The winery is one of the wine cornerstones of the Sunraysia area and in recent times has been an aggressive marketer on the national scene. Excellent sherries are still made here, for example, Mildara's splendid extra dry George Fino Sherry. Wines include a wide range of white and red table wines from the Sunraysia district plus the company's Coonawarra vineyards in South Australia, yielding excellent products such as Jamieson's Run (red and chardonnay), fortified wines (sherries, ports and brandy) plus Windsor Brut Méthode Champenoise and other wines. National and international distribution.

Mildura Vineyards *Campbell Avenue, Irymple Vic. 3498. (050) 24 5843.*

Cellar door: Open Monday–Saturday 10–4.30, closed Sundays. Picnic area. Bankcard, Mastercard, Visa.
Winemaker: Neville Hudson.

Owned by Murray Land Fruit Juices Pty Ltd; founded 1974 as Bonnonee Wines and more recently Fitzpatrick Estate. A surprisingly large operation, making a wide range of wines, and worth a visit and a taste. Wines include dry and sweet white wines, plus red wines, sparkling wines and 'fun' wines such as spumante. Also fortified range. Distribution through cellar door and mailing list (PO Box 695, Irymple Vic. 3498).

Robinvale Wines *Block 436, Sea Lake Road, Robinvale Vic. 3549. (050) 26 3955.*

Cellar door: Monday–Saturday 9–6, Sundays and holidays 1–6. Picnic area. Bankcard, Mastercard, Visa.
Winemaker: Bill Caracatsanoudis.

Family owned; founded 1976. Grapes on this vineyard are grown chemical-free as the company is a member of the Biodynamic Growers' Association of Australia. Wines include non-alcoholic grape juices, fruit wines, dry and sweet table wines, dry reds, fortifieds and sparkling wines. Distribution through cellar door and some Melbourne outlets.

Stanley Wine Company *Silver City Highway, Buronga NSW 2648. (050) 23 4341, head office (08) 381 2511.*

Cellar door: Monday–Friday and holidays 9–5, Saturday 10–4, Sundays 12–4. Picnic areas, electric BBQs, children's playground, parking for sixty cars, buses by appointment.
Winemaker: Richard Rowe.

Owned by the Hardy Wine Company; founded (as Stanley) 1893. Stanley have been slowly putting more emphasis on this winery, just across the river on the New South Wales side of the border, presumably because they can buy cheaper grapes for 2 and 4 litre Leasingham cask production here. Good wines, as you would expect from a major player, covering a broad range of table and fortified products, including the appealing Domaine range of Clare Valley wines. National distribution through Hardys.

North-East Victoria

This is a very special part of the Australian wine world to Victorians, and indeed to the many admirers of the splendid fortified wines produced with the generous assistance of north-east Victorian sunshine.

It is an area stretching from Milawa, within sight of the beautiful Victorian Alps, north to the once-booming gold town of Rutherglen, and a little way up and down the Murray River. I like the area very much for the friendliness of its people, the beauty of the country and the diversity and quality of the wines.

But the area has had its problems. Several wine companies, notably Seppelt and Lindemans, closed their local operations, and the economics of producing the wonderful old muscats, tokays and ports changed together with tastes and profit and interest rate pressures. Perhaps the first to really exploit the changing times were the Brown Brothers of Milawa. Their emphasis on, and success with, varietal table wines has been spectacular.

This is a wine area you can visit if driving between Sydney and Melbourne, to the snowfields, or along the Murray Valley Highway west of Albury/Wodonga.

Eating out

Wangaratta is the largest town in the area, a very pleasant one too, with some good pubs, including the Albion, the Pinsent, the Royal Sydney and the Royal Victoria.

Peter's Cellar 47 (54 Riley Street, Wangaratta [057] 21 6309) has Continental French food. In Milawa the Old Emu (Bright Road [057] 27 3410) has, surprisingly, Swiss food—oh well, the Alps aren't far away! In Rutherglen itself the Shamrock (152 Main Street [060] 32 9439) has a pleasant blackboard menu; the Poacher's Paradise (Main Street [060] 32 9502) is à la carte; in Wahgunyah, near Rutherglen, Tuilleries (Distillery Road [060] 33 2028) has, naturally enough, French-style food in elegant surroundings.

All Saints Vineyard *All Saints Road, Wahgunyah Vic. 3687. (060) 33 1218 or (060) 33 1922.*

Cellar door: Monday–Saturday 9–5, Sunday 11–5. Historic winery. BBQ and picnic areas, museum. Bankcard, Mastercard, Visa.
Winemaker: Andrew Sutherland Smith.

Founded 1864; owned by All Saints Winery Pty Ltd, which was formed on 1 January 1989, the shareholders being George Sutherland Smith, Brian Anders, Robin Sinclair, Ingrid Lehmann and the late Mike Fallon. Distinctive red brick winery, based on a Scottish castle dear to the heart of one of George's forebears. Three lines of wines are available: the Lyre Bird range, which includes chardonnay, cabernet/merlot, port, muscat, tokay, amontillado sherry and madeira; the Swan Crest Range; and the Elm Tree Drive, which is a range of red and white table wines and fortifieds. Distributed nationally and by mail order.

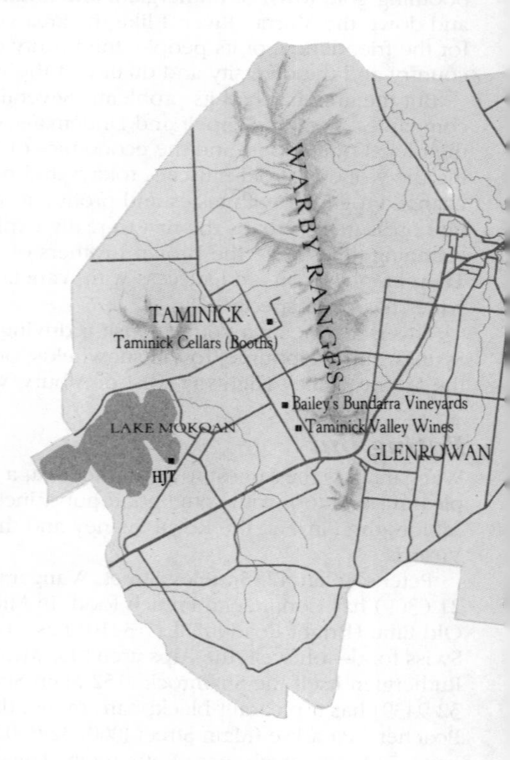

Avalon Wines *RMB 9556, Whitfield Road, Wangaratta Vic. 3678. (057) 29 3629.*

Cellar door: By appointment.
Winemaker: Doug Groom.

Small winery making semillon, chardonnay, pinot noir and cabernet sauvignon. Sells by appointment, local outlets, Richard Farmer in Canberra and mail order.

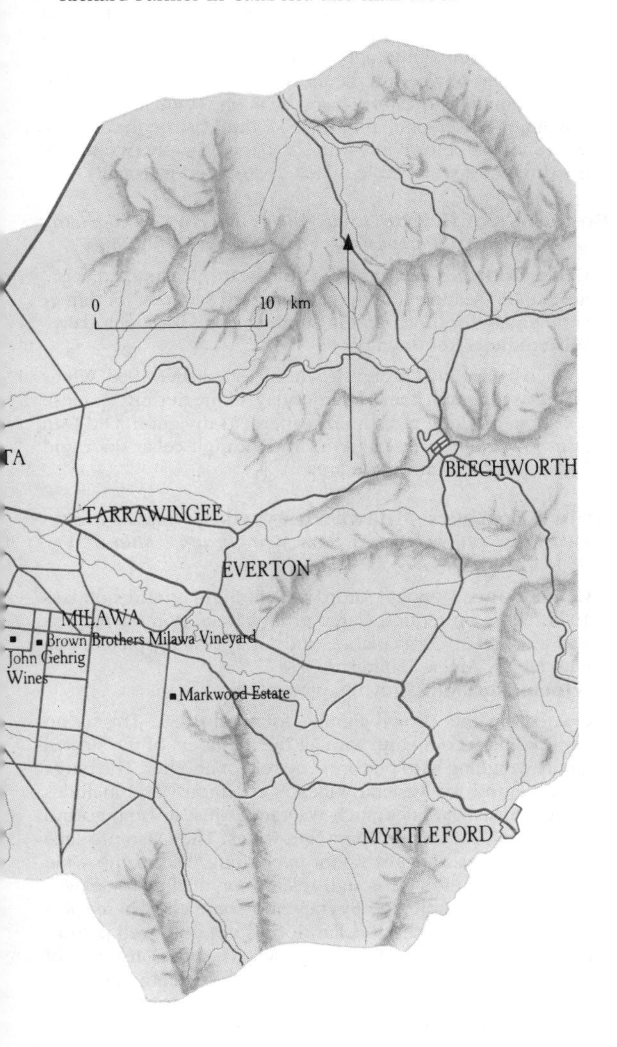

Bailey's of Glenrowan *Corner Taminick Gap Road and Upper Taminick Road, Glenrowan Vic. 3675. (057) 66 2392.*

Cellar door: Monday–Friday 9–5, weekends and holidays 10–5. Historic winery with self-guided tours, museum, large BBQ area. Bankcard, Mastercard, Visa.
Winemaker: Steve Goodwin.

Owned by Davis Consolidated Industries; founded 1870. The Bailey family sold the company to Davis (of Gelatine note) in 1972 and Harry J. Tinson of Davis took over as manager and winemaker, remaining until he left to run his HJT Vineyards in 1986. The power and the glory of the wines made by the Bailey family and later Tinson live on. With Morris, and Chambers Rosewood, they rate as the best of the region. Wines: range of fortifieds—muscats, tokays—plus a range of good red and white table wines. Distributed nationally.

Boynton's of Bright *Ovens Valley Highway (10 kilometres short of Bright), Porepunkah Vic. 3740. (057) 56 2356.*

Cellar door: Seven days 10–5. Bankcard, Mastercard, Visa. Restaurant (seating 100) open Friday and Saturday for dinner and Sunday for lunch and in summer open for lunch daily.
Winemaker: Kel Boynton.

Owned by Kel and Caroline Boynton; established 1988. Wines include sauvignon blanc, chardonnay, Rhine riesling, spätlese lexia, mataro light red, shiraz, cabernet sauvignon, Old Dan port and liqueur muscat. Available through cellar door and licensed restaurants in the area.

Brown Brothers' Milawa Vineyard *Glenrowan–Myrtleford Road (16 kilometres from Wangaratta), Milawa Vic. 3678. (057) 27 3400.*

Cellar door: Monday–Saturday 9–5, Sunday and holidays 10–6. Tours on request (large groups by appointment), gas and electric BBQs available, and an appealing picnic area with tables. Amex, Bankcard, Visa.
Winemaker: John Brown junior.

Owned by the Brown family; founded 1889. This is an extraordinary company, with all the members of the Brown family weighing in to perform one role or another. The range of white and red varietal wines is enormous, and includes some unusual varieties (such as Orange Muscat, Tarango and Mondeuse), producing some fine wines. They also produce fortified wines and just about everything else in the wine world. Distribution is through cellar door, mailing list, extensively in Melbourne and Sydney and some elsewhere, plus export. Brown Brothers' cellar door is not only well patronised (being on the road to the snowfields) but is also one of the best examples of a well-planned and efficiently run cellar door operation in Australia. It is a pleasure to visit Brown Brothers, enjoy their hospitality and taste their wines!

Buller's Calliope Vineyard *Three Chain Road, off Murray Valley Highway, Rutherglen Vic. 3685. (060) 32 9660.*

Cellar door: Monday–Saturday and holidays 9–5, Sunday 10–5.
Winemaker: Andrew Buller.

Family owned; founded 1921. Wines include red and white table wines (see Murray Valley—Buller's), plus excellent fortifieds such as Calliope Vintage Port, Liqueur Muscat and Liqueur Frontignac. Distribution through cellar door and mailing list, plus some Sydney and Melbourne outlets.

Campbell's Wines *Murray Valley Highway, Rutherglen Vic. 3685. (060) 32 9458.*

Cellar door: Monday–Saturday 9–5, Sunday 10–5. Gas BBQs in an 1870 barn with tables and chairs, tours by appointment. All major credit cards.
Winemaker: Colin Campbell.

Family owned; founded 1870. Another progressive winemaker, not unlike the Brown Brothers, with a range of good wines, especially fortifieds, and a well-run cellar door operation. Wines include large range of red and white table wines and fortifieds. National distribution and mailing list (PO Box 44, Rutherglen Vic. 3685).

Chambers' Rosewood *Off Corowa Road, Rutherglen Vic. 3685. (060) 32 9641.*

Cellar door: Monday–Saturday 9–5, Sunday 10.30–5. Swings for children. Bankcard, Mastercard, Visa.
Winemaker: William Chambers.

Family owned; founded 1890s. Bill Chambers is a distinguished national wine judge and here, at his Rosewood winery, in historic surroundings, he makes some outstanding fortified wines. Products include broad range of red and white table wines, but more noted for excellent fortified wines, including sherries, muscats, tokays and some older wines, when on release. Distribution through cellar door and mailing list (PO Box 8, Rutherglen Vic. 3685) and some outlets in Melbourne and Sydney, plus a number of restaurants in Rutherglen itself.

Cofield Anderson Wines *Distillery Road, Wahgunyah Vic. 3687. (060) 33 3798.*

Cellar door: Monday–Saturday 9–5, Sunday 10–5. All major credit cards.
Winemaker: Howard Anderson.

Owned by Max Cofield and Howard Anderson; established 1986. Wines include *méthode champenoise* and sparkling burgundy, plus red and white table wines and fortifieds. Available through cellar door and mail order.

Fairfield Vineyard *Murray Valley Highway, Brown's Plain, via Rutherglen Vic. 3685. (060) 32 9381.*

Cellar door: Monday–Saturday 9–5, Sundays of long weekends and holidays only 1–5. No tours of vineyard, but tours are possible of the old Fairfield Mansion (1889) only on Victorian public holidays and in Victorian and New South Wales school holidays. Tables and chairs for picnics. All major credit cards.

Winemaker: Stephen Morris.

Owned by Mrs Melba Morris-Slamen; founded (in present form) 1972; first vintage 1977. Historic winery, reborn from the ruins of the old winery, using the old winemaking techniques with some success. Owner Mrs Slamen is related to the Morris family. Specialises in 'traditional-style' reds. Distribution through cellar door.

Gehrig Brothers *Murray Valley Highway, Barnawartha Vic. 3688. (060) 26 7296.*

Cellar door: Monday–Saturday 9–6, Sunday and public holidays 10–5. Picnic and BBQ facilities. Bankcard, Mastercard, Visa.

Winemaker: Brian Gehrig.

Family owned; founded 1858. Wines include Rhine riesling, chenin blanc, shiraz, cabernet sauvignon, plus a range of ports and other fortified wines. Distribution mainly through cellar door, some Melbourne outlets.

HJT Vineyards *Keenan Road, Glenrowan Vic. 3675. (057) 66 2252 or (057) 66 2392.*

Cellar door: Open 10–5 Friday and Saturday. Bankcard, Mastercard.

Winemaker: Harry J and Catherine Tinson (owners).

Founded 1979 when HJT himself left Baileys—before that he was an executive with their parent company, Davis, in Sydney. Wines include Rhine riesling, good chardonnays, pinot noir, cabernet sauvignon, port. Available through cellar door only.

John Gehrig Wines *Oxley, via Wangaratta Vic. 3678. (057) 27 3395.*

Cellar door: Monday–Saturday 9–6, Sunday 10–6. Buses by appointment; small tours by arrangement. Nearby picnic area with BBQ on banks of King River. Bankcard, Mastercard, Bankcard.

Winemaker: John Gehrig.

Family owned; founded 1976. Wines include Rhine riesling, chenin blanc, chardonnay, pinot noir, merlot, cabernet/merlot. Distribution through cellar door sales and some Melbourne retail outlets.

Jolimont Wines *Corner Murray Valley Highway and Corowa Road, Rutherglen Vic. 3685. (060) 32 9922 or (03) 654 2300.*

Cellar door: Daily 9.30–5. Bankcard, Mastercard, Visa.
Winemaker: Steve Warne.

Owned by a private company; founded 1984. Wines include red and white table wines, sparkling burgundy and fortified wines. Distributed through cellar door only.

Jones Winery *Jones Road, Rutherglen Vic. 3685. (060) 32 9496.*

Cellar door: Monday–Saturday 9–5, Sunday on public holiday weekends only 10–5. Bankcard, Mastercard, Visa.
Winemaker: Les Jones.

Family owned; founded 1860s; Jones purchased it in 1927. Small but historic (and friendly) winery producing chablis, white frontignac, shiraz and ports. Distribution through cellar door only.

Markwood Estate Vineyard *Morris Lane, Markwood (RMB 84, Markwood, via Milawa Vic. 3678). (057) 27 0361.*

Cellar door: Monday–Saturday and holidays 9–5, closed Sunday. BBQ and picnic facilities.
Winemaker: F. J. (Rick) Morris (owner).

Founded 1971. Rick Morris, a member of the famous Morris family of Rutherglen, decided in 1971 to go his own way with this small winery not far from Brown Brothers. Wines include chardonnay, cabernet sauvignon, shiraz, flor sherry, old tawny port and white port. Distribution through cellar door and mailing list.

Morris' Mia Mia Vineyard *Off Murray Valley Highway (15 kilometres east of Rutherglen), Rutherglen Vic. 3685. (060) 26 7303.*

Cellar door: Monday–Saturday 9–5, Sunday 10–5. Tours by arrangement only. BBQs and seating for 100. Bankcard, Mastercard, Visa.
Winemaker: Mick Morris.

Owned by Pernod Ricard (Orlando Wines); founded 1859. Touring this old winery is an experience, if only to see how little things have changed. Only a modern tasting room designed by architect Robin Boyd indicates that there *have* been changes and progress. Orlando's considerable skills and expertise have obviously help lift the quality of the table wines, notably the whites, and it is surely to them one can look for the source of the Morris cask wines. However Morris' muscats, tokays and ports, especially the older ones (some material is over eighty years old!) are clearly among the great wines of the world, and may even be the greatest dessert wines. They are made by a man whose winemaking skills are equalled only by his generosity of mind and spirit. Other wines include the usual range of table wines including a good chardonnay, several good reds (cabernet and shiraz), also an interesting and powerful red made from the durif variety (incorrectly known to the Americans as petite sirah). Distribution nationally through Orlando.

Mount Prior Vineyard *Howlong Road, Rutherglen Vic. 3685. (060) 26 5591.*

Cellar door: Open seven days 10–5. Bankcard, Mastercard, Visa. The Kitchen In The Cellar restaurant is open Monday–Friday for lunch and Friday and Saturday for dinner. The House at Mount Prior is a guest-house in an old-style homestead and has overnight accommodation, a dining room which seats ten and is open to the general public.
Winemaker: Gary Wall.

Another historic winery; founded 1860; re-established in 1974. Owned by James Henry Sawyer since February 1989. Wines include chardonnay, Rhine riesling/traminer, champagne, chenin blanc, cabernet/merlot shiraz, durif and pinot noir. Under the Ibis Range there is white burgundy and hermitage. There is also Mt Prior port, muscat (a blend of the best of the Rutherglen muscats) and tokay. Available through cellar door and by mail order.

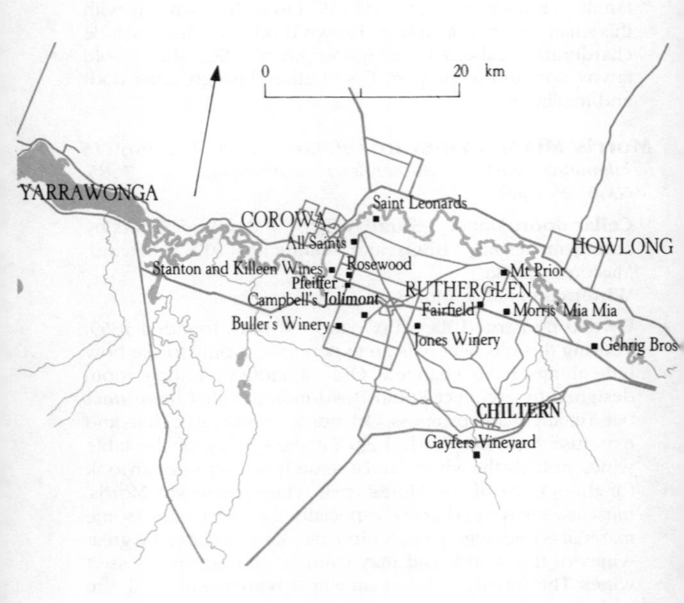

Pfeiffer Wines *Distillery Road, Wahgunyah Vic. 3687. (060) 33 2805.*

Cellar door: Monday–Saturday and holidays 9–5, Sunday 11–4. BBQ and picnic area on banks of Sunday Creek. Bankcard, Mastercard, Visa.
Winemaker: Chris Pfeiffer.

Family owned; founded 1984. Chris Pfeiffer was a local Lindemans winemaker, in itself a recommendation of quality, and when they closed down their nearby winery he bought the old Seppelt distillery (hence the name of the road), and turned it into a winery. Wines include Rhine riesling, chardonnay, spätlese frontignac, pinot noir, cabernet sauvignon, gamay, auslese tokay and local fortifieds. Distribution through cellar door and mailing list (PO Box 35, Wahgunyah Vic. 3687).

Reads *Pound Road, Oxley Vic. 3678. (057) 27 3386.*

Cellar door: Monday–Saturday 9–6, Sunday 10–6.
Winemaker: Kenneth Read.

Small, new maker on the King River near Oxley, making sauvignon blanc, chardonnay, riesling, crouchen, cabernet/shiraz and a vintage port. Distribution limited, mainly through cellar door and by mailing list.

Rosewhite Wines *Happy Valley Road, Happy Valley Vic. 3737. (057) 52 1077.*

Cellar door: Friday 10–9, Saturday–Monday 10–5.
Winemaker: Ron Mullett.

Another small maker, 8 kilometres north-west of Myrtleford, making chardonnay, pinot noir and cabernet sauvignon. Sales through their cellar door.

St Leonards *St Leonards Road, Wahgunyah Vic. 3687. (060) 33 1004.*

Cellar door: Monday–Saturday 9–5, Sunday 11–5. $2 tasting fee, refundable on purchases. BBQs with wood supplied and picnic area on banks of Murray River. Gourmet picnic hampers provided but must be pre-ordered. All major credit cards.
Winemaker: Roland Kaval.

Owned by Brown Brothers; managed by Roland Kaval; founded 1860; re-established 1972. St Leonards is another North-East Victorian winery which has been through varied and troubled times from the days phylloxera arrived in the Rutherglen area. Now operated as an independent subsidiary of the Brown Brothers winery at Milawa, to the south. The quality of the grapes, produced from St Leonards' estate-grown grapes, is high and the winery itself is very attractive.

Wines include chardonnay, semillon, sauvignon blanc,

orange muscat (a dry white wine), an outstanding chenin blanc, gewürztraminer, shiraz and cabernet sauvignon. Distribution through cellar door and by mail order (PO Box 32, Wahgunyah Vic. 2687).

Stanton and Killeen *Murray Valley Highway, Rutherglen Vic. 3685. (060) 32 9457.*

Cellar door: Monday–Saturday 9–5, Sunday 11–4. Groups by appointment only. Bankcard, Mastercard, Visa.
Winemaker: Chris Killeen.

Family owned; founded 1870s. Historic winery and family making Moodemere reds, including cabernet sauvignon, and durif, and a comprehensive portfolio of fortified wines (but no whites). Distribution through cellar door, mailing list (PO Box 15, Rutherglen Vic. 3685) and in Sydney and Melbourne.

Taminick Cellars *Taminick, via Glenrowan Vic. 3675. (057) 66 2282.*

Cellar door: Monday–Saturday 9–5, Sunday 10–5. Bankcard, Mastercard, Visa.
Winemaker: Chris Booth.

Family owned; founded 1900s. Wines include trebbiano/semillon white wine blend, shiraz, cabernet sauvignon and port. Distribution through cellar door and mailing list.

Taminick Valley Wines *RMB 2, Taminick Road, Glenrowan Vic. 3675. (057) 66 2254.*
Not open to the public..
Winemaker: Gerald Baker.

Owned by Gerald and Angela Baker; founded 1979. Wines include shiraz, cabernet sauvignon and cabernet/shiraz. Limited availability in some Melbourne outlets.

Pyrenees

The Pyrenees area of central-western Victoria is not far (some 50 kilometres) from the Great Western area, but produces wines which are substantially different.

The countryside is rugged and beautiful in an Australian context. In fact, if you enjoy this kind of isolated beauty, it is worth detouring through the Pyrenees area just for the scenery, even if the wines are not a sufficient attraction. Heading north-west from Melbourne, drive to Ballarat and then take the Sunraysia Highway to Avoca and on another 18 kilometres to Moonambel for the wine country, before returning to the Pyrenees Highway for Ararat.

The district seems to be well suited to most types of winegrowing, particularly reds and sparkling wines, but no really major maker has found a home there (if one excludes Remy for not being an *Australian* maker; and Taltarni for similar reasons).

The wines coming from most of the wineries are exciting, and the area looks to have a strong place at the quality end of the wine futures market.

Eating out

A limited offering. The Commercial Hotel (Brooke Street, Moonambel [054] 67 2273) has a restaurant and serves spit roasts and counter lunches, as well as local wines. The Victorian Hotel (138 High Street, Avoca [054] 65 3362) has the Pyrenees Cellar Bistro, with counter lunches and à la carte food, plus pit roasts at weekends. One attractive option to the east, in Maryborough, is the Goldfields Restaurant (Ballarat Road [054] 61 3122) which serves sausages, country beef, and venison; licensed.

Bringing your own food might be the answer in warmer weather. While the Pyrenees Ranges might not have the grandeur of their European namesake, they are spectacular viewing.

Chateau Remy *Vinoca Road, Avoca Vic. 3467. (054) 65 3202 or (054) 65 3444.*

Cellar door: Monday–Friday 8.30–4, Saturday 10–4, Sunday 12–4. Bankcard, Mastercard.
Winemaker: Vincent Gere

Owned by Remy Martin of France; established in 1980. Completely *méthode champenoise* and varieties include cuvée brut, vintage brut, rosé brut, chardonnay-pinot and the attractive Blue Pyrenees Estate label which is a blend of cabernet sauvignon, shiraz and merlot. Distributed nationally and through cellar door.

Dalwhinnie Vineyard *Taltarni Road, Moonambel Vic. 3478. (054) 67 2388 or (054) 67 2292.*

Cellar door: Open seven days 10–5. Bankcard, Mastercard, Visa.
All-glass tasting room overlooking the valley and vineyards.
Winemaker: David Jones.

Owned by Ewan Jones; founded 1976. Vineyard established by local architect Ewan Jones; it produces admirable red wines and a good chardonnay. The name is presumably a reference to the Scottish distillery in Dalwhinnie, Scotland. Wines include chardonnay, cabernet sauvignon, cabernet/shiraz and merlot. Available through cellar door, mailing list (RMB 4378, Moonambel Vic. 3478) and in Melbourne and Sydney.

Mount Avoca *Moates Lane, Avoca Vic. 3467. (054) 65 3282 or (03) 419 8586.*

Cellar door: Monday–Saturday 10–5, Sunday 12–5. Bankcard, Mastercard, Visa.
Winemaker: Rodney Morrish.

Owned by John Barry; founded 1970 (vineyard), 1978 (winery). Carefully planned operation by Melbourne stockbroker John Barry; good wines including semillon, trebbiano, chardonnay, sauvignon blanc, cabernet sauvignon and shiraz. Distribution national and mailing list (PO Box 60, Avoca Vic. 3467).

Mountain Creek Vineyard *(03) 592 0267.*

Not open to the public.

Redbank *Sunraysia Highway, Redbank Vic. 3478. (054) 67 7255.*

Cellar door: Open seven days 9–5. BBQ near dam for picnics, etc. Amex, Bankcard, Diner's Club, Mastercard, Visa.
Winemaker: Neill Robb.

Owned by Neill and Sally Robb; founded 1973. Wines include chardonnay, pinot noir, shiraz, cabernet sauvignon, malbec and merlot. Best red is produced from (and under label of) Sally's Paddock. Some vintage port at cellar door only. Distribution nationally, cellar door and mailing list

Summerfield Vineyards *Moonambel–Stawell Road, Moonambel Vic. 3497. (054) 67 2264.*

Cellar door: Monday–Saturday and holidays 9–6, Sunday 10–6. Bankcard, Mastercard, Visa.
Winemaker: Ian Summerfield.

Family owned; founded 1970. Wines include notable reds, shiraz, cabernet sauvignon and cabernet/shiraz and a trebbiano-based champagne. Distribution through local hotels and bottle shops, cellar door and mailing list.

Taltarni Vineyards *Off Moonambel–Stawell Road, Moonambel Vic. 3478. (054) 67 2218.*

Cellar door: Open seven days 10–4. Picnic area. All major credit cards.
Winemakers: Dominique Portet and Greg Gallagher.

Owned by John Goelet of the US; founded 1972. There is an

intriguing story of a French winemaking family behind the labels. Father Portet was technical director of Chateau Lafite for twenty years; elder brother Bernard runs a well-known Napa Valley (California) winery, Clos due Val, and Dominique, after much global searching, produces some excellent, if robust, wines here in central Victoria. Products include *méthode champenoise* sparkling wine, plus a range of dry whites (Rhine riesling, fumé blanc, chablis style) and reds (cabernet sauvignon, cabernet/malbec blend). Distribution in all States and some exports, including U.S.

Warrenmang Vineyard *Mountain Creek Road, Moonambel Vic. 3478. (054) 67 2233.*

Cellar door: Open seven days 9–5. BBQ area and tours possible. Restaurant, accommodation and conference complex. The restaurant holds 100 people and is open for lunch and dinner seven days and there is accommodation for forty-eight people. Bankcard, Mastercard, Diner's Club, Visa.
Winemaker: Luigi Bazzani (owner).

Founded 1974. The wines from Warrenmang, now controlled by Luigi Bazzani alone (he started with partners), are typical, full-flavoured 'minty' central Victorian wines. The wines include chardonnay, traminer, Grande Pyrenees (cabernet/merlot/shiraz/cabernet franc), shiraz and vintage port. Distributed through mailing list and cellar door and some major States.

Yarra Valley

One thing that winegrowing areas close to cities have is a ready market. Hence the Hunter Valley, just a few hours' drive north of Sydney, has such a ready market that the sceptics say—quite rightly—that many Hunter winemakers bring in fruit and even wine from other areas to meet the tourists' demand. But, if anything, the Yarra Valley, on the suburban outskirts of Melbourne, is *too* close. Like some other viticultural areas, winegrowers here are worried that the vines will be lost to houses. That certainly has happened in the past, and may happen again, which would be a pity as this is a district which seems to produce excellent fruit and flavourful, elegant wines.

It is a grape-growing area of ever-changing beauty, to be more appreciated because it is so close to the city. Drive to Lilydale—an hour or so—and you're there. The geographic factors, plus soil and climate, have combined to produce some excellent wines, and hence a proliferating number of wineries—around thirty at the last count.

Eating out

Three of the local wineries have restaurants, and the area is just outside the vast restaurant pool of north-western Melbourne itself. There are also a number of clubs, including golf clubs, around the Valley. Recommended for counter lunches is the Grand Hotel (Bell Street, Yarra Glen [03] 730 1230). Two BYO à la carte restaurants are the Herb Farm (61 Mangans Road, Lilydale [03] 735 0486) and Mt Rael restaurant (Yarra Glen Road, Healesville [059] 62 4107). There is also Olinda Park restaurant on the Maroondah Highway at Lilydale (03) 735 1719, with an à la carte menu and a choice of 107 wines from the Yarra Valley. Further afield (thirty minutes' drive from the Yarra Valley) is Burnham Beaches Country House (Sherbrooke Road, Sherbrooke [03] 755 1903) which has fifty rooms available for accommodation and offers breakfast, lunch and dinner seven days a week.

Bianchet *Lot 3, Victoria Road, Lilydale Vic. 3140. (03) 739 1779 or (03) 739 1776.*

Cellar door: Saturday and Sunday and all holidays 10–6. Every day in January or by appointment. Bankcard, Visa; Mastercard. Groups welcome by appointment.
Winemaker: Lou Bianchet (owner).

Founded 1976. Lou and Teresa Bianchet came to Lilydale from a farming background in the Veneto region of Italy. A warm welcome is offered to interested visitors, and some very enjoyable wines too. Products include chardonnay, gewürztraminer, semillon/tokay, merlot, pinot noir, shiraz, cabernet sauvignon and Verduzzo (Italian-style white wine). Distribution through cellar door, mailing list and some Melbourne retailers.

Coldstream Hills *Lot 6, Maddens Lane, Gruyere, via Coldstream Vic. 3770. (059) 64 9388, fax (059) 64 9389.*

Cellar door: 10–5 Saturday, Sunday and public holidays.
Winemaker: F. James Halliday.

Founded 1985; owned by James and Suzanne Halliday. It takes a brave judge to put himself in the dock—but that is what lawyer-turned-winemaker Halliday did. He is well known as a wine judge and wine critic (for the *Weekend Australian* newspaper, among others), and is a prolific author of authoritative wine books. All this makes the decision to make his own wines a bold one. He has, so to speak, put his

reputation on the wine! It is also interesting to observe where someone with a broad view of the Australian wine industry chose to invest his money. At this spectacular home-cum-vineyard-cum-winery James and Suzanne are growing the premium varieties of chardonnay, semillon, sauvignon blanc, pinot noir, cabernet sauvignon, merlot and cabernet franc. The result is high-quality table wine, understandably at the expensive end of the spectrum.

de Bortoli Winery and Restaurant *Pinnacle Lane, Dixon's Creek, Vic. 3775. (059) 65 2271.*

Cellar door: Weekdays 9–5, weekends and public holidays 10–5.30. Mastercard, Bankcard, Visa. BBQ facilities. Gourmet picnic hampers available (Sundays–Tuesdays) which come with a complimentary bottle of wine. Restaurant, serving northern Italian food, has spectacular views. Open Wednesday–Sunday for lunch and afternoon teas, Saturday for dinner from 7 and Sunday for dinner from 5. Conference facilities, also a private dining room catering for twelve to fourteen.
Winemakers: Stephen Webber and David Ellis.

The de Bortoli family bought this property, Chateau Yarrinya, in 1987. Good wines include the Yarra Valley range (Rhine riesling, gewürztraminer, chardonnay, sauvignon blanc, cabernet sauvignon, shiraz and pinot noir); the Windy Peak range (chardonnay and cabernet/shiraz) and late-bottled vintage port (limited release) from the Yarra Valley. There are also wines from their winery in the Riverina (see New South Wales entry), including the botrytised range, tawny port and liqueur muscat. Distribution nationally and through cellar door.

Diamond Valley Vineyards *2130 Kinglake Road, St Andrews Vic. 3761. (03) 710 1484.*

Cellar door: By appointment only. Bankcard, Mastercard.
Winemaker: Dr David Lance.

Owned by David and Catherine Lance; founded 1976. Small maker of high-quality reds. Wines include Rhine riesling, chardonnay, cabernet and, most notably, the reluctant starter in the quality stakes, pinot noir. Distribution in Victoria, New South Wales, Queensland, Northern Territory and Tasmania and through mailing list from address above

Domaine Chandon *Green Point, Maroondah Highway, Coldstream Vic. 3770. (03) 739 1110.*

Cellar door: Open for visitors from 1990.
Winemaker: Wayne Donaldson.
Viticulturalist: Michael Murtagh.
Managing Director: Dr. A. D. Jordan.

This is the largest winery in the area, and a bold gesture of faith in the Yarra Valley. Domaine Chandon Australia is the second major venture by Moët et Chandon into *méthode champenoise* sparkling wine production outside France. The first, Domaine Chandon, was established in 1973 in the Napa Valley, California, and is now the leading producer of premium sparkling wine in the US. The vineyards in Coldstream are planted to the classic champagne varieties of chardonnay, pinot noir and pinot meunier. Only sparkling wines, including a rosé brut, are made here, under the guidance of a leading

Australian winemaker, Tony Jordan. They are sold through leading restaurants and retail wine outlets around Australia.

Fergusson's *Wills Road (north of town), Yarra Glen Vic. 3775. (059) 65 2237.*

Cellar door: Monday–Friday 10–5, Saturday and Sunday 11–5. Tours by arrangement. Amex, Bankcard, Diner's Club, Visa. Restaurant on premises open Tuesday–Sunday for lunch and Friday and Saturday for dinner. Other functions by arrangement.
Winemaker: Chris Keyes.

Owned by Peter Fergusson; founded 1968 and rebuilt after a fire in 1989. Can be a raucous place for a meal with a like-minded crew! Good red wines from various sources. Products include chardonnay, Rhine riesling, late-harvest lexia, shiraz, cabernet sauvignon, port and 'winter warmer and mulled wine'. Distribution through cellar door and some Melbourne and Sydney outlets.

Halcyon Daze Vineyard *Lot 15, Uplands Road, Chirnside Park Vic. 3116. (03) 726 7111.*

Open by appointment only.
Winemaker: Richard Rackley.

Small winery established in 1982 by Richard and Cheryl Rackley. Plantings comprise cabernet sauvignon, merlot, cabernet franc, pinot noir, chardonnay and riesling. Distribution by mailing list (PO Box 310, Lilydale Vic. 3140) or in selected fine wine stores and restaurants.

Kellybrook *Fulford Road, Wonga Park Vic. 3115. (03) 722 1304.*

Cellar door: Monday–Saturday 9–6, Sunday 11–6. Restaurant for sixty with a fixed price menu, wines included. Open Friday and Saturday nights for dinner at 7.30 and lunch on Sunday at 12.30. Bankcard, Mastercard, Visa.
Wine- and cidermaker: Darren Kelly (owner).

Founded 1960. A different, yet equally rewarding, look at how fruit can be fermented to make other sophisticated alcoholic beverages. Wines include wide range of sparkling and table wines, including the usual varietals, plus a range of ciders, made from many different varieties of apples. Also apple brandy. Distribution through cellar door, mailing list and elsewhere in Victoria.

Lillydale Vineyards *Lot 10, Davross Court, Seville Vic. 3139. (03) 735 3929.*

Cellar door: Open daily 10–5.
Winemaker: Alex White.

Owned by Alex White and Martin Grinbergs; founded 1976.

Wines include chardonnay, traminer, Rhine riesling, cabernet sauvignon. Yarra Dry White, pinot noir and sauvignon blanc. Distributed in Victoria, New South Wales and Queensland and by mailing list to PO Box 313, Lilydale Vic. 3140.

Lirralirra Estate *Paynes Road, Lilydale Vic. 3140. (03) 735 0224.*

Open by appointment only.
Winemaker: David Lloyd.

Established in 1981; owned by Alan and Jocelyn Smith, with vines planted to semillon, sauvignon blanc and muscadelle, with the eventual aim of producing sauternes. Cabernet sauvignon also available using Yarra Valley fruit. Available through a limited number of retail outlets and restaurants or direct from the winery.

Lochvie Wines *28 Lavendar Park Road, Eltham (near Montsalvat) Vic. 3095. (03) 439 9444.*

Cellar door: Saturday 9–5, Sunday 12–5. Other times by appointment.
Winemaker: John Lewis.

Owned by John Lewis; established in 1982. Vines (900) planted to cabernet sauvignon and merlot. This small vineyard, which slopes down to the junction of the Yarra, is run solely by John and Pat Lewis. Wine is sold at 'atypical' Yarra Valley prices, and is available through cellar door and mail order.

Long Gully Estate *Long Gully Road, Healesville Vic. 3777. (03) 807 4246 or (059) 62 3663.*

Cellar door: Weekends and public holidays 12–5 or by appointment; $2 surcharge for tasting five varieties. All major credit cards.
Winemaker: Peter Florance.

Owned by Reiner and Irma Klapp; established in 1982. Wines include chardonnay, sauvignon blanc, riesling, semillon, pinot noir, cabernet sauvignon and merlot. Distributed through cellar door and in Sydney, South Australia and Melbourne, or mailing list from PO Box 1073, Windsor Vic. 3181.

Lovegrove of Cottles Bridge *Heidelberg–Kinglake Road, Cottles Bridge Vic. 3099. (03) 718 2996 or 718 1569.*

Open by appointment only.
Winemaker: Ian Leamon.

Established in 1980 and owned by Malcolm and Hilde Lovegrove with vines planted to cabernet sauvignon, merlot, chardonnay, sauvignon blanc and pinot noir. Wines available through cellar door and mailing list (PO Box 124, Hurstbridge Vic. 3099).

Maddens Lane Winery *Maddens Lane, Gruyere Vic. 3139. (059) 64 9273.*

Not open to the public.
Winemaker: Wines made at Yarra Burn.

Maddens Lane Winery, formerly Prigorje, was purchased in 1988 by Geoffrey and Felicity Norris. Vines planted to semillon, chardonnay and pinot noir. Available through mail order.

Monbulk *Macclesfield Road, Monbulk Vic. 3797. (03) 756 6965.*

Cellar door: Saturday, Sunday and public holidays 12–5.30. Other times by appointment. Tours welcomed. Picnic area in lakeside setting in Dandenongs. Bankcard, Visa.
Winemaker: Paul Jabornik (owner).

Founded 1984. Wines include usual red and white varietal table wines. The Jabornik family specialise in kiwi fruit wine, which is very good.

Mount Mary *Coldstream West Road, Lilydale Vic. 3140. (03) 739 1761.*

No cellar door sales. Mailing list offers small quantities of wine.
Winemaker: Dr John Middleton (owner).

Founded 1971; this doctor of medicine was one of the modern-day pioneers of the Yarra Valley. Planted to bordeaux and burgundy grape varieties, and two red wines and two white wines are made. A blend of cabernet sauvignon, cabernet franc, merlot, malbec and petit verdot produces a wine called Cabernets. The other bordeaux grape varieties are white—sauvignon blanc, semillon and muscadel. There is also pinot noir and chardonnay. Distribution through mailing list and selected restaurants and a few retail outlets.

Oakridge Estate *Aitken Road, Seville Vic. 3191. (059) 64 3379.*

Cellar door: Weekends 10–5. Bankcard, Mastercard, Visa.
Winemaker: Michael Zitzlaff.

Founded 1980; owned by the Zitzlaff family. Wines include cabernet sauvignon, cabernet franc and merlot. Distribution through mailing list (PO Box 13, Seville Vic. 3139) and some in Sydney, Brisbane, Adelaide and Melbourne.

St Hubert's *St Huberts Road, Coldstream Vic. 3770. (03) 739 1421.*

Cellar door: Monday–Friday 9–5, weekends 10.30–5.30, public holidays 10–5.30. Bankcard, Mastercard, Visa.
Winemaker: Brian Fletcher.

Established in 1966, and a maker of some impressive wines.

After some years of trading difficulties, St Hubert's was taken over by Bailey's of Glenrowan in July 1990. Wines include chardonnay, pinot noir, merlot, cabernet sauvignon and the Rowan range, which is a blend of grapes from the Yarra Valley and North-East Victoria. Distributed nationally and by mailing list.

Seville Estate *Linwood Road, Seville Estate Vic. 3139. (059) 64 4556.*

Cellar door: By appointment only.
Winemaker: Dr Peter McMahon (owner).

Founded 1972 by another medico who recognised the potential quality of the area for fine winemaking near the eastern extremities of Melbourne suburbia. Individual and highly praised wines, which are hard to find, especially his excellent sweet whites. Products include chardonnay, Rhine riesling, shiraz, merlot, cabernet franc, pinot noir and cabernet sauvignon. Distribution through mailing list and merchants of fine wines in capital cities, also in a few selected restaurants.

Shantell Vineyard *Off Melba Highway at 60 kilometre signpost, Dixons Creek Vic. 3775. (059) 65 2264 or (03) 819 4563.*

Cellar door: Weekends and public holidays 10–5.
Winemaker: Kathleen Quealy.

Established in 1981 and owned by Shan and Turid Shanmugam, with vines planted to chardonnay, pinot noir, cabernet sauvignon and semillon. Available through cellar and mail order.

Tarrawarra Vineyard *Healesville Road, Yarra Glen Vic. 3775. (059) 62 3311.*

Cellar door: By appointment.
Winemaker: David Wollan.

Vines established 1983. Good wines including chardonnay and pinot noir Also the Tunnell Hill range made from selected Yarra Valley fruit (see below). Available from selected fine wine outlets nationwide and through cellar door.

Tunnel Hill

See Tarrawarra, above. A second, more economic, label for Tarrawarra.

Wantirna Estate *Busby Park Lane, Wantirna South Vic. 3152. (03) 801 2367.*

Not open to the public.
Winemakers: Reg Egan, with assistance from daughter Maryann.

Established in 1963 and owned and run by the Egan family

(Reg Egan has a background in Melbourne law), with vines planted to cabernet sauvignon, merlot, pinot noir, chardonnay and a small amount of cabernet franc. Available through mailing list (PO Box 231, Glen Waverley Vic. 3150), restaurants and wine merchants in Melbourne, Sydney and Noosa Heads.

Warramate Vineyard *Lot 4, Maddens Lane, Gruyere Vic. 3770. (059) 64 9219*

Cellar door: Weekdays by appointment only, Saturday 9–6, Sunday 10–6. Bankcard, Mastercard, Visa.
Winemaker: Jack Church.

Owned by Jack and June Church. Vines planted 1969, first vintage 1974. Wines include Rhine riesling, with excellent shiraz and cabernet sauvignon. Distribution through cellar door and mailing list.

Yarra Burn *Settlement Road, Yarra Junction Vic. 3797. (059) 67 1428.*

Cellar door: Monday–Sunday 10–6. Bankcard, Mastercard, Visa. Restaurant open Saturday nights, Sunday lunches Open any time for group bookings. Guided tours by prior arrangement.
Winemaker: David Fyffe.

Founded 1976; owned by David and Christine Fyffe. Wines include chardonnay, cabernet, pinot noir, shiraz, semillon, merlot and *méthode champenoise*. Available through cellar door, mailing list and a surprising number of capital city outlets. Good wines.

Yarra Ridge Vineyard *Glenview Road, Yarra Glen Vic. 3775. (03) 730 1613.*

Cellar door: Open by appointment only.
Winemaker: Peter Steer with consulting advice from Dr A. D. Jordan.

Louis and Vivienne Bialkower acquired this vineyard in 1982, and quality is generally exceptional. Vines are planted to sauvignon blanc, chardonnay, cabernet sauvignon, pinot noir, merlot and cabernet franc. Available through mail order (PO Box 275, Yarra Glen Vic. 3775) and cellar door.

Yarra Vale Vineyard *Maroonda Highway, Coldstream Vic. 3770. (059) 62 5226.*

Cellar door: Open seven days 10–5. Restaurant planned for late 1990.

Established in 1982 and owned by Don and Lena Bucci. Vines are planted to cabernet sauvignon, merlot, cabernet franc, pinot noir, a small amount of shiraz, chardonnay, sauvignon blanc, Rhine riesling and traminer. Available cellar door.

Yarra Yarra Vineyard *Steels Creek Vic. 3775. (03) 830 4180.*

Not open to the public but visits can be arranged by appointment.
Winemaker: Ian Maclean.

Owned by the Maclean family and purchased in 1978. Vines are planted to bordeaux grape varieties only: cabernet sauvignon, cabernet franc and merlot are blended to produce a complex dry red, and sauvignon blanc and semillon produce a dry white. Available through mail order (PO Box 426, Yarra Glen Vic. 3775) and in selected restaurants.

Yarra Yering Vineyard *Briarty Road, Gruyere Vic. 3770. (059) 64 9267.*

Cellar door: Saturday and holidays 10–5, Sunday 12–5. Bankcard, Mastercard.
Winemaker: Dr Bailey Carrodus (owner).

Founded 1969. Bailey Carrodus is a retired scientist for whom I have great fondness, as his were the first Yarra Valley wines I ever tasted; I liked them very much, though others criticised some of his reds.

They are honestly labelled as Dry Red No. 1 and Dry Red No. 2, with an unpretentiousness that belies their great quality. Perhaps my admiration came from tasting them at his lovely vineyard.

Wines include semillon/sauvignon blanc, chardonnay, pinot noir, cabernet/malbec/merlot and shiraz. Also a straight shiraz under the Underhill label. Available nationally and through cellar door.

Yarrinya Estate

See De Bortoli, this section.

Yeringberg Maroondah *Highway (18 kilometres north-east of Lilydale), Coldsteam Vic. 3770. (03) 739 1453.*

Cellar door: By appointment only.
Winemaker: Guill de Pury (owner).

Founded 1969. Dr de Pury followed the footsteps of his eminent Swiss-born grandfather in planting grapes on the same site—the wines are generally exceptional, and very unprocurable; something like trying to find a doctor in the middle of the night!

The vines are planted to chardonnay, marsanne, rousanne, pinot noir, cabernet sauvignon, cabernet franc, merlot and malbec. The four Yerinberg wines are chardonnay, marsanne, pinot noir and cabernet. In the future the rousanne grapes will probably be blended with the marsanne. Available through mailing list and from selected restaurants and retailers.

Other

Hickinbotham Winemakers *2 Ferguson Street, Williamstown Vic. 3016. (03) 397 2949.*

No cellar door sales.
Winemakers: Andrew and Ian Hickinbotham.

Owned by Hickinbotham Winemakers Pty Ltd; founded 1980. A distinguished family of winemakers, headed by Ian Hickinbotham, who at the turn of the decade struck out on their own with the imaginative venture of Hickinbotham Winemakers at Anakie in the Geelong area. They have since moved, though are still making wine from many areas in small and individual batches.

They show the innovation that marked the life of Ian's son Stephen Hickinbotham, who developed the light, fresh red wine Cab Mac. Stephen was killed in an aircraft crash in 1986, but the Hickinbotham family appears to be a resolute as ever in pursuit of excellence and individuality. Wines include Mornington Peninsula chardonnay, Maffra Rhine riesling, Tasmanian cabernet sauvignon, Anakie shiraz and chardonnay. Distribution through Haviland Wine Company in Sydney (02) 449 7867 and Wayne Leicht in Melbourne (03) 819 5928.

Northern Territory

There is little one can say about the winemaking activities of the Northern Territory, other than to note the fact that the activities of its sole wine concern have ensured that each State and mainland Territory of Australia now produce wine. If the sandy wastes of Israel can produce wine grapes (leading one American visitor to note once that the Israelis had performed the retro-miracle of turning wine into water), why not wine from a town like Alice? While one would not make the trip *just* to taste the wine, the wine is quite drinkable.

Chateau Hornsby *Petrick Road, Alice Springs NT 5750. (089) 55 5133, after hours (089) 52 6704.*
Cellar door: Daily 9-5. Informal tours. Lunches which include scotch fillet steaks, satés, crêpes, salad and beer bread. Lunches can be eaten in brush shelters around the winery. All major credit cards.
Winemaker: Denis Hornsby (owner).

Founded 1974; first vintage 1978. Wines include straight shiraz, straight cabernet sauvignon, early-picked light red and Rhine riesling/semillon blend. A moselle comes from 'down south'. Labelled as Chateau Hornsby and Hornsby Estate. Available through cellar door and within Alice Springs.

Glossary of wine words

This guide to some of the more common terms used in the wine and liquor business excludes specific references to wineries, as these are listed in the main body of the text. A fuller glossary, 'The Last Sip', is contained at the back of *The Great Australian Wine Book*.

Wine, like anything else, has its own language. And, of course, describing flavours and tastes in words is as difficult with wine as it is with food. Still, human communication being what it is, we try to put into words what we also put into our mouths.

Given that communicating tastes is exceptionally difficult, the words that follow are an attempt at trying (a bit like the story about the dog who walked on his hind legs—one was not surprised that it was not done well, one was surprised that it was done at all). And given that you won't understand what some of these terms mean until you actually taste the physical or chemical sensations involved, this is a quick guide to some of the more common terms used in winemaking and wine drinking. A good place to start, however, is to make the decision: I like drinking this/I don't like drinking this!

Some of the terms are obvious (acidic, sweet, dry); some are less obvious, even obscure (full-bodied, corked, volatile). You may never use these if you are, like me, 'just a drinker and enjoyer'. But you *can* be certain that you'll hear a few of them from time to time, over dinner tables, in wine writers' columns, etc. This is how to translate the key terms, names and phrases into English.

Terms in SMALL CAPITALS *have entries elsewhere in the glossary.*

Acetic acid This acid (CH_3COOH) is the component that turns wine into vinegar by oxidation (exposure to air). Obviously, not desirable unless you want to put it on your salad. An excess of it in a wine makes the wine VOLATILE.

Acid Acids of various types are present in wine, and are essential to your enjoyment and to the wine's longevity. Too much can spoil the wine, even turn it into vinegar; too little also affects the wine's quality. It needs to be present in BALANCE with other components of the wine.

Aftertaste The flavour that lingers on in your mouth after tasting or swallowing, and which can be either pleasant or unpleasant—or non-existent, which would indicate a neutral flavoured wine. Harsh or unpleasant aftertaste may indicate the presence of ACETIC ACID in the wine.

Alcohol The substance which makes the difference between grape juice and wine! Alcohol is produced by FERMENTATION and in this context means ethyl alcohol (C_2H_5OH), produced by the action of yeasts on grape sugars during the fermentation. 'Alcoholic' usually means high in alcohol. Its ability to relax and provide enjoyment, or to intoxicate (make drunk) is fairly well appreciated, but alcohol also has an important bearing on the taste of a wine.

Amontillado A wood-matured fino sherry. A dry fortified wine, usually with a rather 'nutty' type of taste. Pronounced 'ay-mon-tee-ard-oh'.

Ampelography The science of classifying different grape varieties. There are thousands, and sometimes the differences are apparently insignificant. One of the ways of telling the differences, when everything looks the same (like chicken sexing, I guess), are the subtle differences in the shapes of the leaves of individual grapevines.

Aperitif French term for an appetiser drink; here means a pre-dinner (or lunch) glass of wine, perhaps a sherry or a sparkling wine.

Appellation A system for guaranteeing the origin (and sometimes the quality) of a wine. From the French-Government-controlled *Appellation d'origine*. *Appellation Controllée* is the way the French choose to control and promote their area wines from, say, the Burgundy, Champagne or Chablis areas. Similar systems are now being used in some wine districts of Australia, and the promise is to provide the consumer with a 'warranty'. So far it doesn't mean much here, and some Europeans are still overcharging for their wines, and cheating people blind on quality.

Aroma The smell of a wine, usually meaning pleasing smells, rather than OFF ODOURS. Young wines often have more obvious odours, normally associated with grape varieties, and wood often comes through your nostrils with oaky reds.

Astringent Tannins produce astringent tastes in wine. You can detect astringency by the involuntary 'puckering' of your mouth, as the tannins hit your taste buds. Tannins come from grape skins, seeds and wood.

Auslese A German term meaning the selection of riper-than-normal grapes for winemaking. Its use on Australian labels usually designates a fruity white with rather more sweetness than normal; Orlando make some good examples. Pronounced 'ows-laser'.

Austere Means different things to different palates, though generally meant to indicate a wine that has recognisably strong flavours, with nothing too dominant.

Balance The assessment that a wine has flavour components in complete harmony, no one being too dominant.

Baumé A measurement of the sugar content of grapes. The Baumé figure roughly translates to the alcohol content in the finished wine (as percentage of alcohol by volume). For example, grapes at 10 Baumé should produce a wine with about 10 per cent alcohol. Pronounced 'bow-may'.

Beerenauslese Another German term one level up the sweetness (sugar) scale from AUSLESE. Very ripe grapes help make such sweet wines. Pronounced 'beer-en-ows-laser'.

Big Powerful in flavours or bouquet.

Bilgy Term evocatively describing unpleasant wine characteristics emanating from slime bacteria caused by waterlogged oak barrels.

Bitterness Unpleasant characteristic in wine, usually detected on the aftertaste. Not to be confused with acidity.

Blanc White, as in sauvignon blanc, the white grape variety. 'Blanc noir' is sometimes used as a term to describe white wine made from red grapes. Pronounced 'blonk'.

Bland Wine tasting term denoting a wine without character, though not necessarily having any wine faults.

Blend Mixing of two or more grape varieties to increase quality or maintain consistency. Can also be a blend of growing areas.

Body Full-bodied means with fullness of flavour in the mouth; conversely 'light-bodied' means lightness of flavour. Some makers (for example Huntington Estate at Mudgee) have labelled their reds FB or MB, for full bodied or medium bodied, a useful guide for potential drinkers. This can help with selection of wines to enhance enjoyment of foods.

Botrytis cinerea A parasitic fungus which, if present in a vineyard, can attack ripe grape berries, removing water and concentrating sugar and flavour constituents. Helps make some of the world's greatest sweet white wines (for example, the wines of Sauternes in France). See also NOBLE ROT.

Bottle age Time spent in the bottle after making and possible wood ageing. 'Will improve with bottle age' means the maker suggests the wine will taste better with several years' proper cellaring.

Bottle Usually means a 750 millilitre glass container, the equivalent of the old 26 fluid ounce bottle. Various shapes are made by glass makers such as ACI, designated for example as champagne, riesling, hock, claret and burgundy bottles. Half bottles (375 millilitres) are becoming popular.

Bottle variation A difference in the taste of a wine from bottle to bottle, of the same wine. These otherwise unexpected differences can be due to storage conditions, cork faults, unclean bottles, poor equipment or other factors which may be beyond the winemaker's control.

Breathing Allowing a wine to come in contact with air before serving. There is little agreement among wine enthusiasts about whether this practice enhances wine enjoyment or not. It may occasionally let an off odour (for example sulphur) dissipate, but there is considerable doubt about whether it 'improves' most wines.

Bright Perfectly clear wine with no suspended particles. Bright colour is an important pointer to wine quality.

Brut Dry; usually the term is applied to sparkling wines. Commercial brut styles now have a small amount of liqueuring added to sweeten the wine somewhat, hence the growth of the term brut-de-brut, suggesting the wine is fully dry. Pronounced 'broot'.

Buff In this context, a wine enthusiast or devotee. Its use is usually perjorative, as in '*That* stuck-up wine buff!'

Burgundy Famous wine-producing area in eastern France. In Australia the term has been rendered almost meaningless as a guide to taste, but can mean a softer style of red wine.

BYO Bring Your Own liquor to a restaurant. Melbourne is Australia's BYO capital, but most other cities have such establishments. At last count Sydney had at least 350, and in some other States—South Australia, for example—the law states that restaurateurs *have* to allow you to bring your own wine or beer, though they can charge a CORKAGE fee per bottle.

Cabernet franc Relative of cabernet sauvignon and a red grape used in the blends of some bordeaux wines. When well done, adds pleasing complexity and fruit flavours.

Cabernet sauvignon Red (or black) grape variety, widely considered to produce the finest red wines in the world. The classic centrepiece of the clarets of Bordeaux, France. Widely grown in most areas of Australia and still gaining popularity. Pronounced 'CAB-ER-NAY SO-VIN-YON'.

Capsule In wine, usually a reference to the cylinder of plastic or lead that is used to wrap the neck of wine bottles, hence 'neck capsule'.

Carbon dioxide (CO_2) This gas is a by-product of fermentation, and with still wines dissipates into the atmosphere. However when a secondary fermentation is induced inside a champagne bottle the CO_2 dissolves in the wine, producing the famous bubbles upon opening. Not desirable in still wine.

Carbonated Sparkling wines made cheaply by the direct injection of CO_2 into the wine. They are both cheaper and coarser on the palate than bottle-fermented wines.

Carignan Red grape variety grown in south-eastern France but not now widely used (or acknowledged) in Australia.

Cassis A liqueur made from blackcurrants. Sometimes used to add a dash to champagne.

Chablis Famous wine area of France produced some excellent dry white wines, mainly using the CHARDONNAY grape variety. Now widely used in Australia to designate a dry white wine of unspecified grape origin. Pronounced 'chab-lee'.

Champagne Another French wine region, this time giving its name to bottle-fermented sparkling wine. In Australia, wines so labelled must be fermented in a bottle, not in a tank, and not carbonated. Standard champagne bottles hold 750 millilitres; magnums 1.3 to 1.5 litres, jeroboams 3.2 litres, rheoboams 4.8 litres, and so on. The biggest is the Nebuchadnezzar of 20 litres or 26 bottles.

Chaptalisation Adding sugar (cane, beet or any other) to fermenting grape juice in order to increase alcohol levels in the finished wine. Illegal in Australia (and usually unnecessary), but widely practised in Europe, where sunlight levels can be low, thereby yielding low natural grape sugar levels.

Chardonnay White grape variety producing some of the world's best white wines, notably in the Burgundy, CHABLIS and Champagne regions in France. Now widely and increasingly grown in other countries, notably the US, Australia, New Zealand and South Africa. Accepts wood maturation gracefully. Pronounced 'shar-donn-ay'.

Charmat Monsieur Eugene Charmat was a Frenchman who developed a method of making sparkling wines in pressure tanks, thereby reducing the cost. Many Charmat-method sparkling wines are produced in Australia, and they are very economical and usually good drinking, though cannot by law be called 'champagne'.

Chasselas White grape variety, grown in parts of France and the United States. Of no great distinction in Australia.

Chenin blanc White grape variety which makes the wines of the Loire area of France. Here in Australia it tends to make rather neutral flavoured white wines, though Houghton in Western Australia make some good ones. Sometimes wood matured.

Cigar box An aroma akin to the smell it describes though, in a red wine, not as unpleasant as it sounds. Combination of the fruit, wood and other constituents of a red wine, notably some of the great CLARETS.

Cinsaut Red grape variety which makes rather ordinary red wines. Sometimes incorrectly called 'oeillade'. Pronounced 'sin-so'.

Claret Originally the English word for the wines of BORDEAUX, and probably derived from *clairette,* meaning 'light red'. Like BURGUNDY it has become somewhat meaningless when applied generically to Australian wines, other than to mean a red wine, perhaps more a more full-bodied example.

Climate The climate (meaning temperature, humidity, rainfall, winds and so on) has a great deal to do with the quality of fruit from grapevines and therefore with the quality of the finished wine. 'Cool climate' is now the vogue word for growing areas of Australia, and elsewhere, which seek to produce higher quality fruit, and this is often associated with altitude. 'Microclimate' refers to the variations in climate within one general vineyard area—for example, between the top and bottom of a sloping vineyard.

Cloudy A cloudy wine has suspended particles in it, obscuring the colour. An indicator of problems.

Cognac Brandy area of western France, the products of which are generally acknowledged to be the best in the world. VSOP is one style, meaning 'very special old pale'. It is a distilled wine aged in wood for lengthy periods. Pronounced 'conn-yac'.

Colour In wine an extremely important indicator of quality and condition. Darker colours usually indicate older wines.

Cooler Mixture of wine and fruit juice. Fashion fad imported from the US several years ago, though there's really nothing new about it—think of hock, lime and lemon, or champagne and orange juice! With 3–6 per cent alcohol content and bubbles and sugar to disguise this, it can be a potent drink for the young.

Coonawarra Australian wine region in the south-east of South Australia, not far from the Victorian border. Cool, produces some of the best red wines in Australia, especially cabernet sauvignon. Top makers include Wynns/Penfolds, Lindeman/Rouge Homme, Hollick, Brand, Mildara, Chateau Reynella and Redman.

Cork The bark of a tree *(Quercus suber),* mainly grown around the Mediterranean end of Europe. Becoming scarcer and therefore more expensive, leading many winemakers to use 'agglomerated' cork—that is, instead of one whole piece of cork to keep the wine away from the outside air, little bits of cork which are glued together to make a cylindrical stopper. Corks can fail, leading to wine which is CORKED.

Corkage Fee charged by a restaurant to allow you to take your own wine, usually a few dollars a bottle (that is, per cork removed).

Corked Usually a wine whose quality is affected by the failure of the cork to keep the air away from the liquid. Unusual, but it can happen.

Corkscrew Device to removed the cork from the bottle's neck. Good ones are a treasure, bad ones frustrating and annoying. The hip pocket 'Waiter's Friend' is good if well designed and soundly made; worth spending a bit more to get a good one.

Crush The free grape juice from the grape berries. Sometimes used to denote the size of a winery, for example 'They have a crush of 10 000 tonnes'. The crusher is the area of a winery where the ripe, picked grapes are dumped for the initial extraction of the juice.

Crust A deposit sometimes found in red wines and ports, particularly vintage ports. Comes from grape solids and, while it may not look terribly inviting, it is harmless and can be removed by straining or decanting. Smaller wineries tend to produce wines with a crust because they may not have the technology to entirely remove these solids before bottling.

Crystals Tiny tartrates which may sometimes be seen in the bottle or on the bottom of the cork. Again, sometimes found in the wines of smaller makers who don't have the wherewithal to remove them. Harmless.

Cuvée Most generally a blend. Often used in relation to champagne, as in 'This cuvée is an outstanding one'. Pronounced 'coov-ay'.

Decant Transfer of wine from the bottle into another container, usually a glass decanter. According to your viewpoint, it achieves one of three purposes: aerates the wine and possibly dissipates any unwanted odours; allows you to leave any CRUST in the bottle; and looks more attractive than putting a bottle on the table (which few people worry about today, anyway!). Any clean strainer (or a specially designed wine strainer) will do the trick if decanting wine or port.

Demi sec French term meaning semi-dry. In Australia usually means 'half sweet'. Often applied to cheaper sparkling wines.

Demijohn No, not a partially complete outdoor toilet! A narrow-necked jug, usually wrapped in wickerwork, which held liquor, often sherry. Used to be quite widely used in Spain and Portugal.

Dessert wine Just what it sounds like—wine designed for consumption with sweeter foods. Usually a sweeter, richer style of wine such as sauternes, port, muscat and tokay.

Distillation Process by which most spirits (in the case of wine, brandy) are made. Heating up an alcoholic beverage vapourises the alcohol at a lower temperature than water, so the alcohol can be captured and concentrated. There are various types of 'stills' to do this, including pot stills and continuous stills.

Dosage Also known as *liqueur d'expedition,* this is a small amount of sugar (usually cane sugar) added to sparkling wines before they are sealed and sold, to give them an extra touch of sweetness.

Drunk (1) A person adversely affected by consumption of too much ALCOHOL. (2) The condition of being under the influence of excessive alcohol consumption.

Dry Absence of RESIDUAL SUGAR in a wine.

Earthy Tasting term meaning that the wine has the flavour or odour of the soil. Hunter wines occasionally have this quality, as do some others. It is not necessarily unpleasant.

Ester Class of organic compounds formed by the reaction of acid with alcohol. This happens in ageing bottles of wine, such as vintage ports and old, dry wines. 'Estery' means strong scents coming from esters derived from bottle maturation.

Ethyl alcohol See ALCOHOL.

Fermentation The process of converting sugars (in this case grape sugars) into ALCOHOL by yeasts.

Filtering Modern winemaking calls for a good deal of filtering as today's drinkers expect clean, bright wines. Various types of filters (such as Micropore) and filtering compounds (such as diatomaceous earth) are used to remove grape solids from wines.

Fining Way of clarifying wine before it is bottled, for example by the use of egg whites; different to FILTERING.

Finish End taste of a wine after it has been swallowed or spat out. High tannin contents might produce a 'firm finish', or lack of flavour might yield a 'poor finish'.

Fino A very dry style of sherry. See also FLOR.

Firm Term referring to taste experience at the back of the palate, caused by tannins.

Flabby Similar to 'fat', meaning the wine has unpleasantly voluptuous flavours on the back palate. High in glycerine in character, soft and broad flavoured.

Flagon Glass container usually holding 2 litres, referred to in the US as a 'wine jug'. The name 'flagon' probably derives from a contraction of the words 'half gallon', as this was the original size. Connotes cheaper wines, though some good, sound, Australian reds can still be found in these containers.

Flat Uninteresting, little flavour. In sparkling wines, of course, little or no bubble left in the wine.

Flavour The taste of wine.

Flinty Term usually applied to dry whites, especially of the CHABLIS type. Traces of gun flint on the palate—steely.

Flor Yeast which grows on the surface of wine, especially sherry, giving a nutty character. Usually applied to flor fino sherry.

Flowery An attractive scent reminiscent of flowers. 'Floral' and 'fragrant' are similar words of approval often applied to pleasing young white wines, especially rieslings.

Fortify To add grape spirit to a wine. Fortification increases alcohol content and helps preserve the wine. Fortified wines include sherries, ports, muscats, tokays and vermouths.

Foxy If you've ever smelt a fox or fox skin, you'll understand! In wines, often applied to the native North American vines of the species *Vitis labrusca* which have it very noticeably in the BOUQUET.

Free run The juice released from the grape berries when first crushed at the winery—before being pressed further. Usually the highest quality juice because it contains fewer or no extractives from the skins, stalks or seeds.

Fumé blanc Dry white wine, usually with wood character. Intended to describe wines from the SAUVIGNON BLANC grape variety, though the words on a label are no guarantee that this is the case. Pronounced 'fume-ay-blonk'.

Gamay Red grape grown in France, where it helps produce beaujolais wines. Probably related to PINOT NOIR, it also produces lighter style reds, though of lesser distinction.

Gewürztraminer See TRAMINER.

Grange Adelaide suburb and vineyard which gave its name to the famous Penfold's hermitage red wine which bears this name. The great vintages were '55, '62 and '65, closely followed by '66, '71, '76, '80 and '87.

Green A wine not ready for drinking, or made from underripe fruit. One which has malic acid content.

Grenache Red grape variety widely grown throughout Australia for use in red and fortified wines, now unfashionable. Can still make some good ports and rosé wines, occasionally good reds.

Grog Slang word for an alcoholic drink. Thought to refer to Royal Navy Admiral E. Vernon (1684–1757) who ordered the watering of rum. He always wore a grogram cloak, and so was called 'Old Grog'.

Hard Term which, with 'harsh' refers to bitter and dry tastes associated with tannins on the finish of some wines.

Heat degree days (HDD) The figure for heat degree days is derived from a viticultural formula which indicates the effect local climate has on the speed of ripening, and hence the quality of the resulting grapes. The lower the HDD number the higher the quality of the resulting wines, as cool climate usually prolongs ripening.

Herbaceous A taste which can be related to herb flavours. Some reds, notably cabernet sauvignon, and some whites (sauvignon blanc for example) are sometimes described as being herbaceous.

Hermitage Synonym used frequently for the red grape variety SHIRAZ.

Hock English name for dry white wine, now little used. Comes from the German town of Hochheim, where Rhine wines are made (using mainly riesling grapes).

Hogshead Wood barrel for storing and usually imparting oak flavours to wine. Contains about 300 litres.

Honeyed Relates to the flavour of honey in some wines. Aged Hunter semillons are often said to taste 'honeyed'.

Hot Refers to slightly burning sensation in the mouth produced by some wines. Usually indicates a high level of alcohol, as with ports.

Hydrogen sulphide (H_2S) Rotten egg smell in wine caused by winemaking or storage fault, usually very obvious even in minute concentrations. Bad wine fault.

Jammy Term usually applied to red wines. Heavily pressed fruit from hot climate vineyards sometimes produce broad, 'jam-like' flavours in these wines. Less common now that temperature control equipment and night grapepicking can help avoid these often coarse, sometimes unpleasant, tastes.

Jeroboam See CHAMPAGNE.

Jimmy Watson Melbourne wine merchant and wine bar owner, now dead, who donated a trophy for the best one-year-old red wine at the Melbourne Wine Show. Much sought-after by winemakers, though there is some dispute about whether such a young wine (the bulk of which is usually still in oak barrels when judged) can be reasonably commercially assessed.

Kerosene Term sometimes applied to aged Australian rieslings. Presumably caused by the similarities of some compound in these wines to petroleum compounds, which is not as silly as it sounds, as both emanate from organic substances.

Lactic An acid character evident on the palate of some wines, resulting from MALOLACTIC FERMENTATION.

Late-bottled vintage (LBV) A Portugese port term meaning a young port wine made in the vintage, given some wood treatment and designed for comparatively (that is, against VINTAGE PORT) early drinking. Some are made in Australia, though it is an unusual type of wine here.

Late-picked Grapes picked when riper than average, hence with higher levels of sugar. Can be used in the production of SPÄTLESE and AUSLESE wines.

Lees Deposits in cask or bottle, notably the residue in champagne bottles from dead yeast cells after the secondary fermentation is complete. 'Lying on lees' is the process which helps lend bottled fermented champagne its yeasty flavour.

Legs Columns of wine, especially fortified wine, which trickle down the side of a glass. Supposed to indicate high alcohol content in a wine.

Luscious A full-flavoured, rich, ripe, fruity and sweet-flavoured wine.

Maderise Wine characteristic named after fortified old wines of Madeira. Supposed to indicate bottle-developed character resulting from the oxidation of the alcohol content to acetaldehyde, producing an oxidised, almond-like flavour in wine and fortified wine. Also gives a brown colour.

Magnum Large bottle containing the equivalent of two ordinary bottles of wine, or 1.5 litres. Magnums should age more slowly than 750 millilitre bottles of the same wine, which is another way of saying they should last longer. Some winemakers (not many, but Redman, Taylors and Leconfield among them) bottle reds in magnums.

Malbec Red grape variety grown in areas of France. Slowly gaining approval in Australia as a blending partner with other reds, notably CABERNET. Used in many good wines, such as Jacob's Creek Claret, to soften and make more enjoyable when young.

Malolactic fermentation A technical problem for winemakers which seldom affects drinkers these days. It is (if you really want to know!) the decomposition of malic acid by bacteria to give lactic acid and carbon dioxide—which means that if it happens in the bottle it can blow the cork out. Malic acid is a complex compound ($COOH.CH_2CH[OH].COOH$). Its arrival is referred to as 'malo' by winemakers, and they like to see it happen to their wines in the barrel rather than in the bottle.

Marc Leftover solid material after the pressing of the grapes. The dry residue of grapeskins and seeds.

Marsanne White grape variety, grown in the Rhône Valley of France but only in a few Australian areas, notably the Goulburn Valley of Victoria, where it makes dry white wines which, with age, develop a HONEYED character.

Mataro Red grape variety producing wines of lacklustre quality.

Mature Usually applied to wines with some age. A mellow flavoured and coloured wine. Usually means an attractive older wine.

Medals Awards from Australian and other WINE SHOWS for well-made wines. Here the capital city wine shows are the most reliable indicators of quality. Gold medals are awarded to wines attaining 18.5 points or more out of 20; silver medals 17.0–18.4; and bronze medals 15.5–16.9. Generally, any wine of recent vintage that has won any medal at a capital city wine show should be worth drinking.

Meniscus The upper part of a liquid column made convex or concave by capillary action. In our context, the shallow part of a wine against the top edge of a glass, where you can more easily assess the colour of the wine.

Mercaptan A chemical which can be formed in wine and which lends its host some very unpleasant characteristics. Derived from H_2S.

Merlot Premium red grape variety, usually blended with other reds, such as CABERNET SAUVIGNON. Widely grown in France and used as a blend in areas such as Bordeaux. Can lend a pleasingly 'velvety' texture and agreeably fruity flavours to a red wine BLEND.

Méthode champenoise The authentic French method of making bottle-fermented CHAMPAGNE. Pronounced 'meth-od champ-en-wahz'.

Mistelle Grape juice (which is of course sweet, as the sugar is still present) used as a sweetening agent. For example in VERMOUTH.

Mondeuse Red grape variety not much used in Australia, but used in BLENDS with others, for example by Brown Brothers with CABERNET and SHIRAZ.

Moselle Australian version of the wines of the River Mosel, in Germany, where riesling is used to make the local wines. Here, it means a light, fruity and pleasantly cheap white wine, but not made from riesling grapes though.

Mousy A description of a wine with an unpleasant taste and smell. Possibly one with some bacterial disease.

Mulled wine Heated wine (usually red) with added herbs, spices, sugar—and Lord knows what else! Use the cheapest wine you can (if you have to do it all all), because it will only get worse. Normally only concocted by frustrated skiers when there is no snow around.

Muscadelle White grape variety linked with the MUSCAT family. Makes some of the great Australian fortified wines. Also grown quite widely in France for inclusion in sweet whites.

Muscat A name (or a prefix) given to a large family of grapes of colours ranging from very white to very black, and quite a few other colours in between. In general, however the muscat families share several characteristics: they are good bearers and have rather broad and obvious flavours. Therefore they are ideal for cask and flagon wines, for which they provide much of the base material. From this widespread family of grapes comes, among others, muscat of Alexandria (occasionally labelled 'lexia' in Australia), muscat blanc à petits grains and muscat de frontignan.

Must Grape juice (usually fresh) which includes the skins and the seeds, after the initial crushing process.

Müller thurgau White grape variety, a cross between riesling and sylvaner, developed in Switzerland, and tolerant of colder ripening climes. Not much grown in Australia because there is little climatic need for it, and also because the resulting wines tend to be a little coarse in flavour. New Zealand grows this variety quite well.

Neutral Little flavour—nothing bad, but not much to commend it, either.

Noble rot A fungal infection *(Botrytis cinerea)* which attacks ripe grape berries and helps make some of the world's greatest sweet wines.

Nose The smell or BOUQUET of a wine. To 'nose' a wine is to smell it.

Nutty Sherries can occasionally smell nutty, as with FLOR sherries.

Oak Various types of wood are used to store wine in, and usually also to impart extra and more complex flavours to them. French, American and German oak barrels are widely used in Australia. They are getting quite expensive as oak trees get scarcer.

Oenology The science of winemaking. A winemaker who goes to wine school is taught by oenologists. Pronounced 'en-ol-o-gee'.

Off odours Unpleasant or unexpectedly displeasing smells in a wine.

Oily Pips and stalks in grapes can inject 'oily' flavours into a wine. Not good.

Olfactory Relating to your sense of smell.

Oloroso Sherry-style—old and sweet to semi-sweet wine. Can be matured in wood and also be quite LUSCIOUS.

Overripe A wine made from grapes which were too ripe when picked. See also JAMMY.

Oxidation Oxygen presence causes decomposition in wine, turning it eventually to vinegar. Try it. Leave an open bottle of wine in the cupboard for a few days—and it'll taste frightful! Higher temperatures speed the process.

Palomino Rather neutral white grape variety, used in sherry making.

Pedro Pedro ximinez (or PX) is another grape variety used in sherry making and in some bland white wines.

Peppery A not entirely unpleasant spicy characteristic sometimes found in young red wines (especially shiraz wines) and ports. Rather raw, biting and with a characteristic reminiscent of black pepper.

Perfumed Similar to some perfume smells—usually the result of a fermentation by-product.

Petillant French word meaning lightly carbonated (sparkling) wine.

pH Winemaking term relating the measure of the acidity or alkalinity of a solution, in this case, a wine.

Phylloxera *Phylloxera vasatrix* is a resilient vine louse, a parasitic plague which swept through Europe's vineyards late last century and almost ruined them, and was carried to Australia. The only known 'cure' is to replant the grapevines whose roots it attacks with vines planted on American rootstock, which is resistant to the louse—maybe explaining its origins.

Pinot noir The red grape of BURGUNDY and one of the varieties which also helps make CHAMPAGNE in France. Generally produces lighter styles of red wines though they can, when well made, have intense and deep flavours. We're still playing around with it in Australia, but getting better by the year. Pronounced 'peen-oh-n'war'.

Port A fortified red wine, the name coming from Oporto, on the River Douro in Portugal. After dinner drinks (in Australia generally, at least) of quite high alcohol content (17–20 per cent). There is considerable confusion about port wines which can be simply summed up: tawny ports are blended wines which have usually been kept in wood barrels by the maker for some years in order to mature them for drinking when sold. Vintage ports (which bear a year of origin on the bottle) are usually sold early by the makers and you, the consumer, are expected to do the cellaring until the wine is ready for drinking. Australia makes excellent examples of both styles. See also LATE-BOTTLED VINTAGE and RUBY PORT.

Pot still Traditional method of BRANDY distillation.

Pressings What you get when you use a bit of mechanical muscle to squeeze extra juice, more highly flavoured (and with more tannins), from the skins, seeds and pulp of the grapes.

Pricked A wine which smells of ethyl acetate, which can be said to be becoming VOLATILE.

Puncheon Larger oak barrel, holding about 500 litres of wine.

Pungent Strong and aromatic, maybe too much so.

Punt Concave base of a bottle, usually a champagne bottle as it helps retain strength—though lots of other table wine bottles seem to be adopting this (expensive) pretension.

Px Abbreviation for pedro ximinez, a neutral white grape variety sometimes used in sherries.

Racking Transferring wine from one cask (barrel) to another for a variety of reasons.

Rancio Oxidised character evident in older sweet wines and some sherries. In this context, not necessarily a fault. A bit like the affectionate comment: 'He's a great old bastard!'

Residual sugar The natural grape sugar left behind (usually by design) after the fermentation has finished. Characteristic of many modern white wines, especially rieslings, usually pleasant though sometimes cloying if overdone, or done in the wrong type of wine.

Rhine riesling Literally, the riesling grape deriving from the Rhine areas of Germany. One of the world's classic grapes, and one which does a different, and magnificent job, in many of the better Australian white wines. A grossly underestimated and misunderstood variety, which still and probably always will make some of the finest Australian white wines.

Rosé Again, a much misunderstood wine style. *Should* be the classic summer red of Australia. Light, fresh and fruity wine made from red grapes, either sweet, medium or dry—but best as a dry, yet flavoursome, young wine. Pronounced 'rose-ay'.

Ruby port A lighter style of vintage port without the tannins or the acid, which is nevertheless bottled early to be enjoyed for its rich fruit and complex spirit characters, while still relatively young. There are minor differences in the definition of this port style, depending on whether you want the Portugese rubies, which tend to spend more time in wood, or Australian, which are fresher.

Sauvignon blanc White variety of grape from BORDEAUX and the Loire areas of France, where it makes superb sweet *and* dry wines. Its grassy/steely and sometimes asparagus-like characters can be attractive (like oysters, with which it is often well matched), or loathed. Do try a good one or two, though, as it is an acquired taste. Pronounced 'so-vin-yon-blonk'. Sometimes blended with semillon.

Semillon Another great French (especially from BORDEAUX) white grape variety, which makes quite different wines in Australia in different regions. Usually makes dry, sometimes wood-matured, full-bodied whites in Australia, notably in the Hunter Valley.

Sharp Acid taste on the palate. Worth thinking about, though not necessarily unpleasant.

Sherry Delightful aperitif drink, originally from southern Spain (Jerez) and widely made in Australia though slowly losing its marketplace popularity. A FORTIFIED wine which can be sweet, medium or dry. Also see FINO and AMONTILLADO, etc.

Shiraz Excellent and very versatile Australian red grape variety, also widely referred to (especially on wine labels) as HERMITAGE. Makes some excellent and often reasonably priced red wines from most areas, and is best noted for its parentage of Penfold's GRANGE Hermitage brand.

Soft Wine-tasting term. No harsh sensation on the palate and after-palate.

Solera Method of producing some fortified wines (sherries and some ports) by rotating wine through casks to blend old with new wine.

Sour Bitter, unpleasant.

Spätlese Late-picked style of fruity and/or sweet white wine. Pronounced 'sh-spayt-laser'.

Spicy Some TRAMINER wines, among others, can have this character.

Spritzig A small amount of CO_2 in a wine, such as a rosé. Leaves a slight fizzing sensation on tongue.

Spumante Italian sparkling wine. Here it usually means sweet, sparkling and cheap. Pronounced 'spew-man-tay'.

Stalky Tasting of grape stalks—rather like OILY.

Sulphur dioxide (SO_2) Chemical used as an anti-oxidant in winemaking, also for sterilisation. The smell of sulphur can be present in a newly opened bottle of wine, but it should dissipate. With today's truth-in-labelling laws, referred to on food and wine labels as 'Preservative (220) added'.

Sultana White, heavy bearing and large-berried grape. One of the most grown in Australia, it has dual purpose, that is, it can also be used for dried fruit and as a table grape. Makes rather coarse white wines, and a lot of it goes into cask and flagon brands.

Supple Favourite word of wine writers, meaning they like it but can't find the right words to describe its pleasant taste.

Sweet More than fruity—pertaining to sugar.

Sylvaner White grape variety making so-so aromatic whites.

Syrah Best red grape variety of the Rhône Valley of France. Similar if not the same variety as SHIRAZ. Also spelt 'sirah', but it is not the same variety known as 'petite sirah' in the US (which is probably the variety properly labelled durif).

Tannin A vital ingredient (and preservative) in wines, especially red wines. It comes from the stalks, skins and pips on grapes. The taste of tannins on the palate when the wine is young give that bitter, puckering taste on the palate. A complex and important constituent of wine.

Tart Tasting of acidity (malic acid) in a noticeable way.

Tartaric acid The main acid in wine. ($COOH.[CH.OH]_2COOH$).

Tawny Blended PORT, often made from wines of several different ages, and ready for drinking when purchased.

Tirage liqueur Sugar solution which is added to a base wine to turn it into champagne. The secondary fermentation converts this into a small amount of extra alcohol and CO_2, which is dissolved in the wine.

Traminer White grape variety, widely grown in various parts of the world, producing wines with abundant fruit flavours, though not necessarily sweet, and often with spicy overtones. 'Gewürztraminer' is often used to designate this spiciness. Pronounced 'tram-een-ah'.

Trebbiano White grape variety from Italy (also known as UGNI BLANC). Added in some parts of Australia to fairly ordinary medium to dry whites; sometimes blended with others.

Ugni blanc Synonym for TREBBIANO white grape.

Ullage The air space between the top of the wine in a bottle and the bottom of the cork. If excessive, the wine is 'ullaged', and may not last as long as it should.

Varietal Wine made from a particular grape variety (for example, Rhine riesling). Opposite to generic wine (for example, chablis).

Verdelho White grape variety used on the island of Madeira. Mainly grown in Western Australia for dry whites, but also used there for excellent fortified wines; used in the Hunter Valley for some dry whites. Occasionally spelt 'verdelhao'.

Vermouth Wine fortified and to which many flavour components are added, for example, herbs, flowers, roots. Pronounced 'ver-muth'. Pleasant summer drink when mixed with soda or lemonade.

Vigneron Grapegrower.

Vigorous In wine, a lively taste or feel. In a grapevine, very fast growing, sometimes a bad thing.

Vin Wine (French). As in *vin ordinaire*, meaning 'ordinary wine'. To vinify is to make grapes into wine. Pronounced 'vann'.

Vinegar Wine spoilt by the vinegar bacteria—deliberately or otherwise. Not pleasant to drink, either way, and a major winemaking fault, easily detected.

Vinosity Wine-tasting term pertaining to alcoholic strength of a wine and the grape character of the wine.

Vintage port See PORT.

Vintage The period of picking the grapes each year, as in 'the vintage'. Also the year a wine was made ('vintaged').

Vintner Winemaker.

Viscous Thick appearance in wine; showing the presence of glycerol.

Viticulture The agricultural skill of growing grapevines.

Vitis The grapevine genus. *Vitis vinifera* is the grape-bearing vine responsible for most of the world's quality wines. *Vitis labrusca* is the North American native vine (see FOXY). There are many thousands of other types of vine.

Volatile A wine spoilt by the presence of ACETIC ACID is said to be volatile, or have volatile acidity (VA).

Wine shows The Royal Agricultural Societies in the various capital cities organise wine judging on a circuit which usually begins in Sydney (the judging is done before the Royal Easter Show) and runs Brisbane–Melbourne–Perth–Adelaide–Hobart–Canberra. The Canberra Show is open to entries which have won medals in the other shows. The experts seem to agree that the wine shows to watch (because standards are highest) are Sydney, Adelaide and Canberra.

Wine The fermented juice of grapes.

Woody Strong bouquet of wood (oak) in wine, not necessarily offensive, but possibly very obvious.

Yeast Single cell organisms responsible for conversion of grape sugar into ethyl alcohol (fermentation).

Youthful Wine showing pleasantly young characteristics—fresh perhaps.

Zinfandel Red grape variety widely grown in California. Little grown in Australia, though some is planted in Western Australia, mainly in the Margaret River region. Does quite well in California, where it roughly equates in importance to SHIRAZ in Australia. Wines made from 'zin' tend to be BIG and high in alcohol.

Wine industry organisations

1990 OFFICE HOLDERS

Australian Wine and Brandy Corporation *Wellington Centre, 2 Portrush Road, Payneham SA 5070. (08) 365 1165, Fax (08) 365 0555, Telex AA 82780.*
George Paciullo (Chairman)
Martin Gilkes (General Manager)
Margaret Mountford (Secretary)
Brenton Roneberg (Manager, Market Services)
Alan Russell (Corporate Affairs Manager)

Australian Winemakers' Federation (FAWA) *(This body changed its name from Federation of Australian Winemaker Associations in late 1990; it incorporates the Australian Wine and Brandy Producers' Association Inc., the Wine and Brandy Co-operative Producers' Association of Australia Inc. and the Australian Winemakers' Forum). Wellington Centre, 2 Portrush Road, Payneham SA 5070. (08) 365 0333, Fax (08) 337 9606.*
Ian G. Mackley (President)
Ian Sutton (Chief Executive)
Tony Crawford (Executive Officer)

Wine and Brandy Producers' Association of SA *Wellington Centre, 2 Portrush Road, Payneham SA 5070. (08) 365 0500*
David Dean (Manager).

Wine Information Bureau (SA) *Wellington Centre, 2 Portrush Road, Payneham SA 5070. (08) 365 0500.*
Simon Tam (Wine Advisory Officer).

Australian Winemakers' Forum *PO Box 33A, Crafers SA 5152. (08) 339 4122.*
Alister Purbrick (President)
Brian Croser (Secretary)
Keith S. Christie-Ling (Administration Secretary).

Victorian Wine Industry Association Inc. *331A Bay Street, Port Melbourne Vic. 3207. (03) 646 3644, Fax. (03) 646 1342.*
V. Thomson (President)
Gordon Broderick (Executive Officer).

The Liquor Merchants' Association of Queensland *QHA House, 40 Thompson Street,*

Bowen Hills Qld 4006. (07) 252 7672.
Alan Cook (Manager).

Wine Industry Association of WA *PO Box 83, Claremont WA 6010. (09) 384 8307.*
E. A. Avery (President)
R. L. Page (Secretary).

Wine Information Bureau of Western Australia *PO Box 83, Claremont WA 6010. (09) 384 8307.*
Joan McGuren (Administrative Secretary).

Winegrape Growers' Council of Australia Inc. *PO Box 503, Nuriootpa SA 5355. (085) 62 2088.*
Robert Taplin (President)
Kerry Ward (Executive Secretary).

Wine & Brandy Co-op. Producers' Assoc. of Australia *PO Box 335, Berri SA 5343. (085) 83 2303.*
I. J. Pendrigh (President)
Philip Mann (Secretary).

Australian Wine Research Institute *Waite Road, Urrbrae SA 5064. (08) 379 1111 Fax (08) 379 0666.*
P. L. Laffer (Chairman)
Dr. T. H. Lee (Director).

Area winemakers' associations 1990

SOUTH AUSTRALIA

Adelaide Plains Winemakers' Association *PO Box 1, Angle Vale SA 5117. (085) 24 3157.*
Jack Minnett (President)
Joe Grilli (Secretary)

Barossa Winemakers' Association *PO Box 321, Nuriootpa SA 5355. (085) 62 1866.*
David Wardlaw (President)

The Clare Valley Winemakers' Association *PO Box 211, Clare SA 5453. (088) 43 4258.*
Jane Mitchell (Chairman)
Chris Proud (Vice-Chairman)

McLaren Vale Winemakers' Inc. *PO Box 169, McLaren Vale SA 5171. (08) 323 8999.*
Anne Pollard (Secretary)

Viticultural Council of South East of South Australia *PO Coonawarra SA 5263.*
Ian Hollick (President)
Gavin Hogg (Secretary) (087) 36 3380

NEW SOUTH WALES

Hilltops Winemakers' Association *Woodonga Hill Winery, Cowra Road, Young NSW 2594.*
Phil Lindsay (President) (063) 82 1555, ah 82 2972
Lorry Doldissen (Secretary) (063) 84 4243

Hunter Valley Vineyard Association *PO Box 550, Maitland NSW 2320.*
David Hammond (President) (049) 98 7666
Barry Shields (Secretary) (049) 98 7520

Wine Grapes Marketing Board *PO Box 385, Griffith NSW 2680.*
John J. Dal Broi (Chairman)
Stuart McGrath-Kerr (Executive Officer) Fax (069) 62 3255

MIA Winemakers' Assoc. *PO Box 488, Griffith 2680.*
Andrew Schulz (President) (069) 62 4133

Mudgee Wine Grape Growers' Association *Montrose Wines, Henry Lawson Drive, Mudgee NSW 2850. (063) 73 3853.*
Robert Paul (Secretary)

Upper Hunter Winemakers' Association *Arrowfield Wines, Jerrys Plains NSW 2330.*
Richard Hilder (President) (065) 47 2467
Jim Grant (Secretary) (065) 76 4041

VICTORIA

Bendigo & District Winemakers' Association *PO Box 167, Kangaroo Flat, Bendigo Vic. 3555.*
Ron Laughton (President) (054) 33 2528
Laurie Norris (Secretary) (054) 43 0799

Geelong District Winegrowers' Association *Idyll Vineyard, Ballan Road, Moorabool Vic. 3221.*
Dr Daryl Sefton (President) (052) 76 1280
Brian Moten (Secretary)
Nini Sefton (Publicity Officer)

Goulburn Valley Viticultural Association *PO Box 194, Shepparton Vic. 3630.*
Geoff Elford (President)
Frank Dawson (Secretary) (058) 29 9486

Victorian & Murray Grape Growers' Council Inc. *1 Kamira Court, Mildura Vic. 3500.*
Brian Ferry (President) (050) 27 4757

North-East Winegrowers' Association *c/- North-East Tourist Authority, PO Box 250, Wangaratta Vic. 3677. (057) 21 5711, Fax (057) 21 9708.*

Yarra Valley Winegrowers' Association *PO Box 826, Lilydale Vic. 3140.*
Dr Tony Jordan (President) (03) 73 91110
Stephen Webber (Secretary) (059) 65 2271

WESTERN AUSTRALIA

Margaret River Grape Growers & Wine Producers' Association *PO Box 204, Margaret River WA 6285.*
Erl Happ (President) (097) 55 3300
Michael Kelly (Secretary) (097) 55 6285

Mount Barker–Frankland Wine Producers' Association *PO Box 891, Albany WA 6330.*
Merven Lange (President) (098) 55 2229
Angelo Diletti (Secretary) (098) 41 1037

Perth Hills Vignerons' Association *6 Robertson Road, Gooseberry Hill WA 6076.*
Peter Fimmel (President) (09) 293 8339
Doris Duncan (Secretary) (09) 45 45748

South West Coastal Wine Producers' Association *PO Box 1058, Bunbury WA 6230.*
Betty Killerby (President/Secretary) (097) 95 7222

Swan Valley & Regional Winemakers' Association *Lot 103, Corona Way, Belhus Estate, Upper Swan WA 6056.*
John Barrett-Lennard (09) 29 64581

TASMANIA

Vineyards' Association of Tasmania *PO Box 214, Launceston Tas. 7250.*
Andrew Pirie (President) (003) 82 7197
Dr R. Richardson (Secretary) (003) 82 7190

QUEENSLAND

Queensland Winemakers' Association *Kominos Wines, New England Highway, Severnlea Qld 4352.*
Tony Comino (President) (076) 83 4311

AUSTRALIAN CAPITAL TERRITORY

Canberra District Vignerons' Association *PO Box E206, Queen Victoria Terrace Canberra ACT 2601.*
Dr John Kirk (President) (062) 46 5212
Dr David Carpenter (Secretary) (062) 38 1393

Index